Contents

☑ Use the tick boxes to check off the topics you've completed.

Module 1 (Development of Practical Skills) is tested in context throughout this book, alongside Modules 2 to 6.

Exam Advice

To pick up every mark you can, you'll need tip-top exam technique as well as your knowledge of chemistry.

Get Familiar with the Exam Structure

For **A-Level Chemistry**, you'll be sitting **three papers**.

Periodic table, elements and physical chemistry (Modules 1, 2, 3 and 5) **2 hours 15 minutes** **100** marks **37%** of your A Level	**15 marks** of **multiple choice** questions. **85 marks** of **short answer** questions and **extended response** questions.
Synthesis and analytical techniques (Modules 1, 2, 4 and 6) **2 hours 15 minutes** **100** marks **37%** of your A Level	**15 marks** of **multiple choice** questions. **85 marks** of **short answer** questions and **extended response** questions.
Unified chemistry (Modules 1 to 6) **1 hour 30 minutes** **70** marks **26%** of your A Level	**Short answer** and **extended response** questions.

1) As you can see, **all three papers** test you on **Module 1**. Module 1 relates to **practical skills**. The Module 1 theory is tested in context throughout this book, alongside Modules 2 to 6.

2) Your **maths skills** will also be tested in all three papers.

3) **Short answer** questions could include **structured** questions, **calculations** and **problem solving**.

4) Some of the **extended response** questions will be marked using a '**Level of Response**' mark scheme. For these questions, you'll be marked based on the **quality** of your responses as well as their chemistry **content**. Your answers will need to be **coherent** and **fully explained**, and have a **logical structure**. Questions marked using a 'Level of Response' mark scheme will be shown with an **asterisk** (*) next to their number.

Manage Your Time Sensibly

1) Use the **number of marks** available to help you decide **how long** to spend on a question.

2) Some questions will require **lots of work** for only a **few** marks but others may be much quicker. **Don't** spend ages struggling with questions that are only worth a couple of marks — move on. You can always **come back** to them later when you've bagged loads of marks elsewhere.

3) **Multiple choice** questions can sometimes be quite **time-consuming**, but they're still only worth **one mark** each. So if you're pressed for time, you might want to focus on the **written answer** questions, where there are **more marks** available.

If you're really stuck on a multiple choice question, making an educated guess is always better than leaving it blank.

Be Careful Drawing Diagrams

1) Draw all your diagrams nice and big, so you can clearly show all the **detail** you need to get the marks.

2) Make sure you include **everything** the question **asks** for in your answer.

3) When you're drawing **mechanisms**, remember to pay close attention to your **curly arrows**. They need to be clearly coming from a **lone pair**, **negative charge** or **bond** for you to get the marks.

4) If you're asked to draw a particular type of **formula**, make sure you give your answer in the format asked for. For example, if you're asked for a **displayed** formula **don't** draw a **skeletal** formula instead.

Remember to Use the Exam Data Sheet

1) In your exams, you'll be given a **data sheet**. It'll contain lots of **useful information**, such as:
   - the characteristic **infrared absorptions** of some bonds in organic molecules,
   - **carbon-13 NMR** and **proton NMR chemical shifts** of some common functional groups;
   - some **constants** and **conversions**,
   - a copy of the **periodic table**.

2) You'll find a **data sheet** containing the above information on **pages 192-194** of this book.

A-Level
Chemistry
Exam Board: OCR A

A-Level Chemistry exams coming up? We don't envy you... but that's mainly because we've been too busy making this brilliant Exam Practice Workbook. It'll help you with your exam prep no end.

Inside, you'll be greeted by page after page of realistic exam-style questions covering both years of the OCR A course — perfect for making sure you've mastered it all.

And if that's not enough to bring a smile to your face, the fully worked answers and top exam tips should do the trick. There's no better way to prepare for the real exams!

A-Level revision? It has to be CGP!

Published by CGP

Editors:
Alex Billings, Katie Burton, Mary Falkner, Paul Jordin, Caroline Purvis, Emily Sheraton.

Contributors:
Sarah Binns, Mike Dagless, David Paterson, Megan Pollard, Andy Rankin, Sarah Rich, Louise Watkins.

IR spectrum on page 66 — Source: NIST Chemistry WebBook (http://webbook.nist.gov/chemistry).
IR spectrum on page 70 — Adapted from NIST Chemistry WebBook (http://webbook.nist.gov/chemistry).
Mass spectrum on page 69 — Adapted from NIST Chemistry WebBook (http://webbook.nist.gov/chemistry).

ISBN: 978 1 78294 922 0

With thanks to Emma Clayton, Barrie Crowther, Glenn Rogers, Helen Ronan, Hayley Thompson and
Karen Wells for the proofreading.

With thanks to Ana Pungartnik for the copyright research.

Printed by Elanders Ltd, Newcastle upon Tyne

Based on the classic CGP style created by Richard Parsons.

Atoms, Compounds and Equations

Got to start somewhere, so how about a nice recap of basic atomic structure, relative masses and ionic formulae? Of course it's not all *quite* that simple, there are a couple of tricky equations to balance, but overall it's not too bad.

For each of questions 1-4, give your answer by writing the correct letter in the box.

1   How many neutrons would you find in the nucleus of a copper-64 atom?

29

A   29   B   34

C   35   D   64

Your answer   C

(1 mark)

2   What is the formula of caesium selenide?

A Cs_2Se B $CsSe$

C $CsSe_2$ D $CsSe_4$

Your answer   A

(1 mark)

3   Which row shows the atomic structure of $^{109}Ag^+$?

	Protons	Neutrons	Electrons
A	47	62	47
B	47	62	46
C	46	63	47
D	47	60	46

Your answer

(1 mark)

4   A sample of neon has a relative atomic mass of 20.187. The relative abundances of all the isotopes present in the sample are given in the table below. Which isotope of neon is isotope **X**?

Isotope	Neon-21	Neon-20	X
Relative abundance / %	0.3	90.5	9.2

A   Neon-19   B   Neon-22

C   Neon-24   D   Neon-23

Your answer

$21(6.3 + 9.2x$

$\dfrac{21 \times 0.3 + 20 \times 90.5 + x9.2}{100} = 20.187$

$=$

(1 mark)

4

5   The diagram below shows an isotope of oxygen.

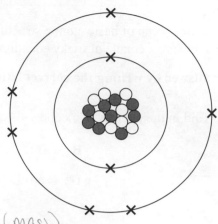

(a) (i)   State the meaning of the term isotopes. (mass)

same atomic number but different #relative
atomic mass number = which gives a different
number of neutron

(1 mark)

     (ii) Give the mass number and the atomic number of the isotope shown.

     mass number: ....   atomic number: ....

(1 mark)

(b) Oxygen typically forms ions with a 2– charge. Give the number of electrons in an O^{2-} ion.

     ....

(1 mark)

(c) The diagram is based on a model of the atom that is widely used today.
     Suggest why this model is still used by scientists when more accurate models have since been developed.

     Because the nucleus is neutral.

     ....

     Electrons are placed in shells

(2 marks)

6   Copper(II) sulfate solution reacts with aqueous sodium hydroxide to form a precipitate
     of copper(II) hydroxide. $CuSO_4 + 2NaOH \rightarrow Cu(OH)_2 + Na_2SO_4$

(a) (i)   Give the formula of the soluble salt also produced in the reaction.

     $Cu(OH)_2$

(1 mark)

     (ii) Write the simplest ionic equation for the reaction occurring. Include state symbols.

     $Cu^{2+} + SO_4^{2-} + 2Na^+ + 2OH^- \rightarrow Cu(OH)_2 + 2Na^+ + SO_4^{2-}$

     $Cu^{2+} + 2OH^- \rightarrow Cu(OH)_2$

(1 mark)

(b) (i)   Sodium hydroxide also reacts with sulfuric acid to form a salt and water.
           Write a balanced symbol equation for this reaction.

     ....

(1 mark)

(ii) By considering the ions reacting and the species being formed, show that your equation in **(b) (i)** can be simplified to the ionic equation for neutralisation ($H^+ + OH^- \rightarrow H_2O$).

$$2OH^+ + 2H^+ \rightarrow 2H_2O_{(l)}$$

$$2NaOH + H_2SO_4 \rightarrow Na_2SO_{4(s)} + 2H_2O$$

(2 marks)

7 Mass spectrometry is a technique used by scientists to help identify elements and compounds.

The mass spectrum of a sample of an element, **J**, is shown below.

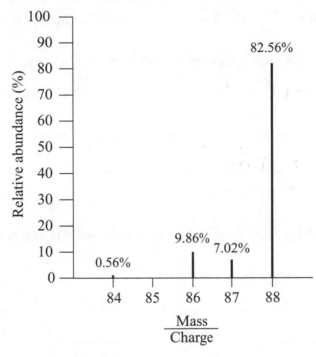

(a) Calculate the relative atomic mass of element **J**.
Give your answer to **one** decimal place.

A_r of element **J** = ...
(2 marks)

(b) Use your answer to **(a)** and the Periodic Table to identify element **J**.

....
(1 mark)

8 Nitric oxide, NO, is a colourless gas at room temperature and pressure.

(a) Nitric oxide reacts with carbon monoxide, CO, to give nitrogen and one other gaseous product.
Suggest a balanced symbol equation for this reaction.

$$2NO + 2CO \rightarrow N_2 + CO_2$$

(2 marks)

$$2NO + 2CO \rightarrow N_2 + 2CO_2$$

$$O_2 \quad CO$$

Module 2 — Foundations in Chemistry

6   N^{3-} O^{2-}

(b) Nitric oxide reacts with propanone to produce CH_3COOCH_3.
Give the relative molecular mass of CH_3COOCH_3.

~~N_2O_3~~   NO

30₆

M_r = ...
(1 mark)

(c) (i) Nitric oxide is produced in the oxidation of ammonia and the reaction of copper with dilute nitric
acid. Unbalanced equations for these reactions are shown below. Balance these equations.

..2.. NH_3 + ..2.5.. O_2 → ..2.. NO + ..3.. H_2O

$3Cu$ + ..8.. HNO_3 → ..3.. $Cu(NO_3)_2$ + ..2.. NO + ..4.. H_2O

3 18+2

(2 marks)

(ii) Give the name of the ionic compound with the formula $Cu(NO_3)_2$.

Copper(II)nitrate
....
(1 mark)

(iii) State the formulae, including charges, of the two ions which make up $Cu(NO_3)_2$.

Cu^{2+} $(NO_3^-)_2$
....
(1 mark)

9   One of the key identifying features of elements and compounds is their relative mass.

(a) State the meaning of the term relative atomic mass.

....

....
(2 marks)

(b) Describe how relative isotopic mass differs from relative atomic mass.

....

....
(1 mark)

(c) Calculate the M_r of the copper-containing complex $[Cu(NH_3)_4(H_2O)_2]^{2+}$.

M_r = ...
(1 mark)

(d) Potassium manganate(VII), $KMnO_4$, reacts with hydrochloric acid to produce three chlorine-containing
species. Two of these species have M_r values of 71.0 and 125.9. Suggest the formulae of these two species.

.... and ....
(2 marks)

Amount of Substance, Acids and Redox — 1

Maths skills are super-important in chemistry, and this section's crammed with questions to help you practise using them. There's a bit on acid-base reactions and redox reactions too, to keep things exciting

For each of questions 1-4, give your answer by writing the correct letter in the box.

1 How many chlorine atoms are present in one mole of PCl_5?

    A 6.02×10^{23}

    B 3.01×10^{24}

    C 6.02×10^{24}

    D 3.01×10^{23}

Your answer   B

> Remember, you can find any constants you need on the data sheet on pages 192-194.

(1 mark)

2 Vanadyl sulfate has the chemical formula $VOSO_4$.
What is the oxidation number of vanadium in vanadyl sulfate?

    A   +2   **B**   +3

    C   +4   **D**   +6

Your answer   C

(1 mark)

3 A scientist burned 1.86 g of phosphorus in oxygen. 4.26 g of an oxide of phosphorus was produced. What is the empirical formula of this oxide?

    A PO_2 **B** P_2O_4

    C P_2O_5 **D** P_4O_{10}

Your answer

(1 mark)

4 Excess barium chloride solution can react with copper sulfate solution to form a precipitate of barium sulfate: $BaCl_{2(aq)} + CuSO_{4(aq)} \rightarrow CuCl_{2(aq)} + BaSO_{4(s)}$

What volume of 0.650 mol dm^{-3} copper sulfate solution is needed to form 3.16 g of barium sulfate ($M_r = 233.4$)?

    A   87.8 cm^3

    B   0.0208 cm^3

    C   20.8 cm^3

    D   8.80 cm^3

Your answer   C

(1 mark)

8

5 Ascorbic acid is more commonly known as vitamin C. It has the following composition by mass: 40.9% carbon, 4.5% hydrogen and 54.6% oxygen.

(a) Determine the empirical formula of ascorbic acid.

$C - 40.9 = 3.40$
$H = 4.5 = 4.5$
$O = 54.6 = 3.4125$ ✓
CHO

empirical formula = ... CHO ....

(2 marks)

(b) The relative molecular mass (M_r) of ascorbic acid is 176.0.
Determine the molecular formula of ascorbic acid.

molecular formula = ...

(1 mark)

(c) A vitamin C tablet contains 300 mg of ascorbic acid.
Calculate the number of moles of ascorbic acid in one tablet.

number of moles = ...

(1 mark)

6 Limewater is an aqueous solution of calcium hydroxide.

Calcium hydroxide solution reacts with dilute hydrochloric acid according to the equation:

$$2HCl_{(aq)} + Ca(OH)_{2(aq)} \rightarrow CaCl_{2(aq)} + 2H_2O_{(l)}$$

A student has a 25.0 cm³ sample of limewater of unknown concentration. She adds the sample to a volumetric flask and makes it up to 250 cm³ with distilled water. She then carries out a titration to determine the volume of 0.100 mol dm⁻³ hydrochloric acid needed to neutralise 25.0 cm³ of the diluted limewater solution.

(a) State the dependent variable in this experiment.

...... Volume of HCL ....

(1 mark)

The student's results are shown in the table below.

	Titre			
	Rough	1	2	3
Initial reading / cm³	11.10	28.50	11.25	27.60
Final reading / cm³	28.50	45.15	27.60	44.30
Volume of HCl added / cm³	17.4	16.65	16.35	16.7

(b) (i) Complete the table by filling in the volume of hydrochloric acid added for each titre.

(2 marks)

(ii) Calculate the mean titre using the results shown in the table.

mean titre = ...16.675.......... cm³

(2 marks)

(iii) Determine the concentration of calcium hydroxide in mol dm⁻³ in the original limewater sample. Give your answer to an appropriate number of significant figures.

$\text{mol of HCl} = 0.016675 \times 0.1 = 1.6675 \times 10^{-3}$

concentration = ... mol dm⁻³

(4 marks)

7   Butane gas (C_4H_{10}, $M_r = 58.0$) is used in camping stoves. A cylinder of volume 750 cm³ contains 2.50 g of the butane gas.

Remember, any constants you might need are on the data sheet on pages 192-194.

(a) Calculate the pressure, in kPa, exerted by the gas on the inside of the container at a temperature of 10.0 °C. Give your answer to an appropriate number of significant figures.

pressure = ... kPa

(4 marks)

Butane burns in oxygen to produce carbon dioxide and water: $C_4H_{10} + 6.5O_2 \rightarrow 4CO_2 + 5H_2O$

(b) Calculate the mass of butane burned during complete combustion with 3.84 g of oxygen gas.

mass = ... g

(3 marks)

EXAM TIP

If a question asks you to give your answer to an appropriate number of significant figures, it just means you need to round your final answer to the lowest number of significant figures that's in the data you're given. You'll get a whole mark just for doing that. Don't be tempted to round too soon though — always use the full, unrounded answers from any intermediate calculations.

Score

24

Amount of Substance, Acids and Redox — 2

1   A student is preparing 250 cm³ of a standard solution of sodium hydrogencarbonate ($NaHCO_3$).

She uses the following method:

1. Weigh out the required mass of sodium hydrogencarbonate into a weighing boat.
2. Tip the solid into a 250 cm³ volumetric flask.
3. Add distilled water to the flask until the bottom of the meniscus touches the line.
4. Stopper the flask and turn it upside down a few times to mix the contents.

(a)   State **two** ways in which the student's method could be improved.

1. ....

   ....

2. ....

   ....

(2 marks)

The student fixes the mistakes in her method and repeats the procedure.
She makes a standard solution with a concentration of 0.30 mol dm⁻³.

(b)   (i)   Calculate the mass of sodium hydrogencarbonate that would be required to make a
250 cm³ solution with a concentration of 0.30 mol dm⁻³.

mass = ... g

(2 marks)

(ii)   The student pours 100 cm³ of the solution into a beaker containing 150 cm³ of distilled water.
Calculate the concentration of the solution in the beaker in mol dm⁻³.

concentration = ... mol dm⁻³

(2 marks)

The student then carries out a titration of a standard solution of sodium hydroxide against 25 cm³ of hydrochloric acid. She adds the hydrochloric acid and indicator to a conical flask. The standard solution of sodium hydroxide is then slowly added from a burette.

The student makes the following errors when preparing the standard solution of sodium hydroxide:

1. She didn't notice that the mass balance was showing a negative reading before the solid sodium hydroxide was weighed out.
2. Some of the sodium hydroxide was spilt on the bench when the student transferred it from the weighing boat to the volumetric flask.

(c)   State and explain how each of these errors would affect the mean titre volume.

....

....

....

(2 marks)

2   Metals can be extracted from their ores using chemical reactions.

(a)   Galena (PbS) is a common ore of lead. The extraction of lead from galena is a two-step process.

$$\textbf{Step 1:}\ 2PbS + 3O_2 \rightarrow 2PbO + 2SO_2 \qquad \textbf{Step 2:}\ 2PbO + C \rightarrow 2Pb + CO_2$$

(i)   Calculate the mass of oxygen needed to react with 4.50 tonnes of PbS in **Step 1**.
(1 tonne = 1000 kg)

mass = ... kg
(3 marks)

(ii)   Calculate the mass of lead that can be produced from 4.50 tonnes of PbS.

mass = ... kg
(2 marks)

(b)   The Kroll process is used to extract titanium from its ore. The final step in the Kroll process involves the reaction of titanium(IV) chloride, $TiCl_4$, with a more reactive metal, usually magnesium or sodium.

Calculate the atom economies of reactions A and B shown below.

$$\textbf{Reaction A:}\ TiCl_4 + 2Mg \rightarrow Ti + 2MgCl_2 \qquad \textbf{Reaction B:}\ TiCl_4 + 4Na \rightarrow Ti + 4NaCl$$

atom economy of **reaction A** = ... %

atom economy of **reaction B** = ... %
(2 marks)

Other important metal ores include pyrolusite and hematite.

(c)   (i)   The chemical name for pyrolusite is manganese(IV) oxide.
Write the formula of manganese(IV) oxide.

....
(1 mark)

(ii)   Hematite has the formula Fe_2O_3. Give the chemical name of hematite.

....
(1 mark)

Module 2 — Foundations in Chemistry

3 This question is about the reactions of copper and copper compounds.

(a) When copper metal reacts with cold, dilute nitric acid, Cu^{2+} ions and NO form according to the equation:

$$2HNO_3 + 3Cu + 6H^+ \rightarrow 3Cu^{2+} + 2NO + 4H_2O$$

(i) Explain, with reference to oxidation numbers, why this is a redox reaction.

....

....

....

....

(4 marks)

(ii) Explain in terms of electron transfer what happens when a species is reduced

....

(1 mark)

(b) Copper metal may be extracted from sulfide ores by reaction with oxygen.
The overall equation for the reduction of copper(I) sulfide, Cu_2S, to copper by oxygen is:

$$Cu_2S + O_2 \rightarrow 2Cu + SO_2$$

(i) A sample of Cu_2S reacts to form 3.60 g of Cu. The percentage yield for this reaction is 92.4%.
Calculate the mass of the Cu_2S sample.
Give your answer to an appropriate number of significant figures.

mass = ... g

(4 marks)

(ii) Determine the atom economy of this reaction.

atom economy = ... %

(1 mark)

(iii) Give **two** benefits for sustainability of choosing reactions with high atom
economies over reactions with low atom economies for use in industry.

....

....

....

(2 marks)

4 Ammonia is produced in the Haber Process.

Any constants you might need are on the data sheet on pages 192-194.

(a) (i) 0.0820 moles of ammonia gas was trapped in a gas jar at a temperature of 298 K and pressure of 101 kPa. Use the ideal gas equation to calculate the volume of the gas jar used to trap the ammonia.

volume = ... dm^3

(3 marks)

(ii) Calculate the number of ammonia molecules in this sample.

....

(1 mark)

(b) Gaseous ammonia can react with water to form ammonium hydroxide.
A scientist is analysing a sample of ammonium hydroxide which contains 40.0% nitrogen and 14.3% hydrogen by mass. The rest of the mass is oxygen.

Use this data to show that the empirical formula of ammonium hydroxide is NH_5O.

(3 marks)

(c) A scientist bubbles gaseous ammonia through water, producing an alkaline solution.

(i) Write an equation to show how ammonia reacts with water to produce an alkaline solution.

....

(1 mark)

The scientist then neutralises this solution using nitric acid.

(ii) Write the formula of the salt formed in this neutralisation reaction.

....

(1 mark)

EXAM TIP

The good news is you'll be given the values of any constants you need in your exam on the data sheet. The bad news is you still need to know all the formulae and equations for calculations (e.g. mole calculations and atom economy) off by heart. Formula triangles can help, but the best way to make them stick is generally just to get plenty of practice using them.

Score

38

Amount of Substance, Acids and Redox — 3

1 HClO is a weak acid commonly known as hypochlorous acid.

(a) Write an equation for the dissociation of HClO in solution.

....

(1 mark)

(b) Deduce the oxidation number of Cl in HClO.

....

(1 mark)

(c) HClO reacts with the alkali NaOH in an acid-base reaction.

$$HClO_{(aq)} + NaOH_{(aq)} \rightarrow NaClO_{(aq)} + H_2O_{(l)}$$

(i) Explain what is meant by the term alkali.

....

....

(2 marks)

(ii) Give the full chemical name of NaClO, using a Roman numeral to indicate the oxidation number.

....

(1 mark)

(iii) Write the simplest ionic equation for this reaction. Include state symbols.

....

(1 mark)

2 Hydrated barium chloride crystals have the formula $BaCl_2.nH_2O$. A student carried out an experiment to find the value of n in the formula. They used a 2 decimal place balance to measure the mass of an empty crucible, then placed a sample of the crystals in the crucible and measured the mass again. They heated the sample for 5 minutes, then measured the mass of the crucible and crystals once more.

The table below shows the results of the student's experiment.

Mass of crucible / g	32.2
Mass of crucible and hydrated barium chloride crystals / g	34.64
Mass of crucible and anhydrous barium chloride / g	34.28

(a) State what is meant by the term hydrated in relation to crystalline substances.

....

(1 mark)

(b) One of the results in the table has not been recorded correctly.
Identify this result and explain what is incorrect about the way it has been recorded.

Result: ....

Explanation: ....

(2 marks)

(c) (i) Calculate the mass of water given off during the heating of the hydrated salt.

mass of water = ... g

(1 mark)

(ii) Suggest how the student could have ensured that all of the water had been driven off.

....

(1 mark)

(d) Calculate the value of n in the formula $BaCl_2.nH_2O$.

n = ...

(3 marks)

(e) Another student carries out the same experiment but loses some of the crystals from their crucible during heating. State whether this would make their value of n too high or too low. Explain your answer.

....

....

(1 mark)

3   A student carried out an experiment to identify an unknown Group 2 metal, **X**, by measuring the volume of hydrogen gas given off during the reaction of 0.14 g of **X** with excess hydrochloric acid. The equation for this reaction is: $X_{(s)} + 2HCl_{(aq)} \rightarrow XCl_{2(aq)} + H_{2(g)}$

The student set up the equipment as shown below, added the sample of metal **X** to the acid and replaced the bung on the conical flask.

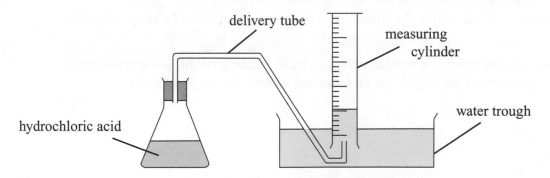

(a) The student carried out their experiment at room temperature and pressure.
The hydrogen gas given off was collected and found to have a volume of 138 cm³.
Use this information to help you identify metal **X**.

identity of metal **X** = ...

(3 marks)

(b) A second student used a similar method to identify a different metal, **Y**.
They reacted 0.0784 g of **Y** with excess sulfuric acid, according to the equation:

$$Y_{(s)} + H_2SO_{4(aq)} \rightarrow YSO_{4(aq)} + H_{2(g)}$$

The student used the same equipment to measure the volume of hydrogen
produced by the reaction. They determined that at a temperature
of 293 K and a pressure of 101 kPa, 28.9 cm³ of hydrogen was formed.

You can find any constants you need on the data sheet on pages 192-194.

Identify metal **Y**.

identity of metal **Y** = ...
(5 marks)

(c) Identify the major source of error in the method used by both students
and suggest an improvement to the method described.

Source of error: ....

Improvement: ....

....
(2 marks)

(d) This method can also be used to identify Group 1 metals by monitoring their
reaction with water. For the Group 1 metal lithium, the equation for this reaction is:

$$2Li_{(s)} + 2H_2O_{(l)} \rightarrow 2LiOH_{(aq)} + H_{2(g)}$$

Calculate the maximum volume of H_2 gas that would be given off at room temperature
and pressure if 0.0245 g of lithium metal was added to an excess of water.

volume of H_2 = ...cm³
(3 marks)

EXAM TIP

There will definitely be some questions to do with practical work in your exams. Conveniently,
you can practise for these every time you do an experiment in class. Remember to think
about what apparatus is most suitable for your experiments, how to control any variables that
might affect your results and how to present your results as clearly and neatly as possible.

Score

28

Amount of Substance, Acids and Redox — 4

1 Solutions of two different acids, sulfuric acid (H_2SO_4) and hydrochloric acid (HCl), are made up and put in unlabelled bottles. Both acids have the same unknown concentration.

(a) Explain how the identity of each acid could be determined by titration using a standard solution of 0.1 mol dm^{-3} sodium hydroxide (NaOH). Include in your answer the procedures involved, equations for any reactions taking place and the expected results.

....

....

....

....

....

....

....

....

....

....

....

....

....

....

....

....

....

....

(6 marks)

(b) Sulfuric acid reacts with magnesium metal to produce magnesium sulfate and hydrogen.

$$Mg_{(s)} + H_2SO_{4(aq)} \rightarrow MgSO_{4(aq)} + H_{2(g)}$$

(i) Explain, in terms of electron transfer, what is meant by the term oxidation.

....

(1 mark)

(ii) Use oxidation numbers to show which element in this reaction has been oxidised.

....

(1 mark)

(iii) Suggest what you would observe during this reaction.

....

....

....

(2 marks)

2 Limestone is an ore of calcium that contains a high proportion of calcium carbonate ($CaCO_3$).

Calcium carbonate reacts with hydrochloric acid according to the equation:

$$CaCO_3 + 2HCl \rightarrow CaCl_2 + CO_2 + H_2O$$

A 1.75 g sample of limestone is added to an excess of hydrochloric acid at a pressure of 101 kPa. 280 cm^3 of carbon dioxide gas is formed at a temperature of 22.0 °C. It was assumed that all of the CO_2 gas produced was formed during the reaction between $CaCO_3$ and HCl.

(a) Calculate the percentage of $CaCO_3$ in the limestone sample.

Any constants you might need are on the data sheet on pages 192-194.

.... %

(5 marks)

(b) Calcium carbonate also reacts with ethanoic acid. Ethanoic acid is a weak acid.

(i) Explain what is meant by the term weak acid.

....

(1 mark)

(ii) Write a chemical equation for the reaction of calcium carbonate with ethanoic acid.

....

(1 mark)

(iii) Explain why calcium carbonate reacts more quickly with a 1 mol dm^{-3} solution of hydrochloric acid than with the same volume of 1 mol dm^{-3} ethanoic acid solution.

....

....

....

(2 marks)

(c) Calcium oxide is another calcium compound that will react with hydrochloric acid.

   (i) Write an equation for this reaction.

   ....
   (1 mark)

   (ii) Identify the type of reaction occurring.

   ....
   (1 mark)

   (iii) Explain, with reference to the oxidation numbers of the species
        involved, whether or not this is classed as a redox reaction.

   ....

   ....

   ....
   (1 mark)

3   Compound **C** is an example of a hydrated salt.

(a) Hydrated salts such as compound **C** contain water of crystallisation.
    Explain what is meant by the term water of crystallisation.

   ....

   ....
   (1 mark)

(b) Analysis of a 2.42 g sample of compound **C** found it to have the following composition by mass:

   Mn, 0.668 g; Cl, 0.861 g; H, 0.097 g; O, 0.776 g

   Deduce the formula of compound **C**. In your answer you should clearly show the water of crystallisation.

   Formula of compound **C** = ...
   (3 marks)

Score

26

Electrons, Bonding and Structure — 1

Chemistry without electrons is like... Well there wouldn't *be* any chemistry without electrons. The shapes of molecules, the types of bonds that form where — all to do with electrons. Like this section, funnily enough.

For each of questions 1-5, give your answer by writing the correct letter in the box.

1   What is the electron configuration of titanium?

    A $1s^2\ 2s^2\ 2p^6\ 3s^2\ 3p^6\ 3d^4$ **B** $1s^2\ 2s^2\ 2p^6\ 3s^2\ 3p^6\ 3d^3\ 4s^1$

    C $1s^2\ 2s^2\ 2p^6\ 3s^2\ 3p^6\ 3d^2\ 4s^2$ **D** $1s^2\ 2s^2\ 2p^6\ 3s^2\ 3p^6\ 3d^3\ 4s^2$

Your answer ☐

(1 mark)

2   Which of these molecules is polar?

    A F_2 **B** CBr_4

    C CO_2 **D** PF_3

Your answer D

(1 mark)

3   Which of these molecules has a pyramidal shape?

    A CF_4 **B** BH_3

    C NCl_3 1 – lone pair   **D** SF_4

Your answer C

(1 mark)

4   Which row in the table below is correct?

	Maximum number of electrons contained		
	3p sub-shell	3d orbital	3rd electron shell
A	2 ✓	10	18
B	6	10	18
C	6	2	18
D	6	2	8

Your answer C

18

(1 mark)

5   Which of the following ions have the electron configuration $1s^2\ 2s^2\ 2p^6\ 3s^2\ 3p^6$?

    A O^{2-} and Cl^- **B** Cl^- and Ca^{2+}

    C O^{2-} and Ca^{2+} **D** Cl^- and Na^+

Your answer A̶ B

(1 mark)

6 A chloride with the formula $\underline{XCl_2}$ can be made by heating element X in chlorine gas. The chloride has a high melting point and dissolves readily in water. The chloride can conduct electricity when molten or in solution, but not when solid.

(a) State the type of structure you would expect XCl_2 to have.

Giant Ionic Lattice structure

(1 mark)

(b) Explain why XCl_2 has a high melting point.

Strong electrostatic force between the atoms, that need breaking

(1 mark)

(c) Explain how melting or dissolving XCl_2 enables it to conduct electricity.

= Ions a electron is not held in a localized positive, free to move around, can carry charge

(1 mark)

7 Ice is a crystalline substance.

(a) Explain how hydrogen bonding arises between water molecules.
Include a diagram to show hydrogen bonding between two water molecules in your answer.

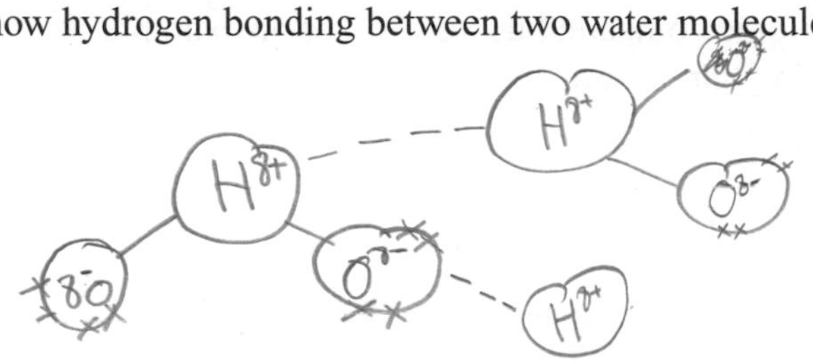

(4 marks)

(b) Describe what happens to the molecules in ice when it is heated to its melting point.

It changes it's state of matter to liquid

(1 mark)

(c) Explain why ice has a lower density than water.

Because when ice freezes, it forms a lattice shape, so the hydrogen bonds are held further apart, causing them to float

↳ water molecules are held further apart from each other in ice as water molecules form 4 hydrogen bonds to other water molecules = making a lattice shape = ice floats.

(2 marks)

8   Sodium chloride, NaCl, and calcium chloride, CaCl$_2$, are examples of compounds with ionic bonding.

(a)   Explain what is meant by the term ionic bond.

Electrostatic forces between oppositely charged ions

(1 mark)

(b)   Draw a dot and cross diagram to show the bonding in solid calcium chloride, showing outer shell electrons only.

(3 marks)

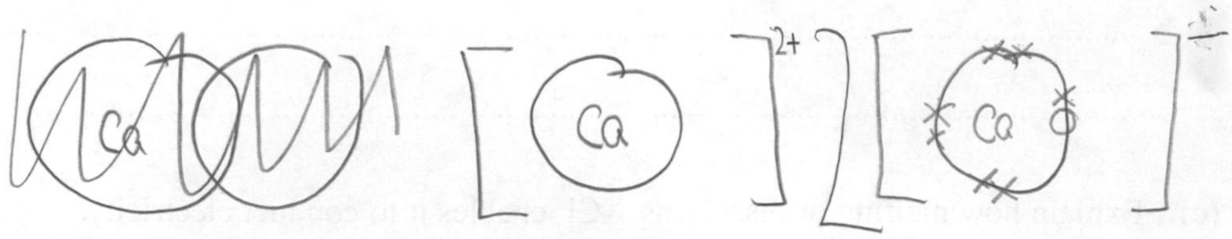

(c)   Write the electron configuration, in terms of sub-shells, of the sodium ion in NaCl.

$1s^2 2s^2 2p^6$

(1 mark)

(d)   Describe the structure of an ionic compound using NaCl as an example.
You may include a diagram in your answer.

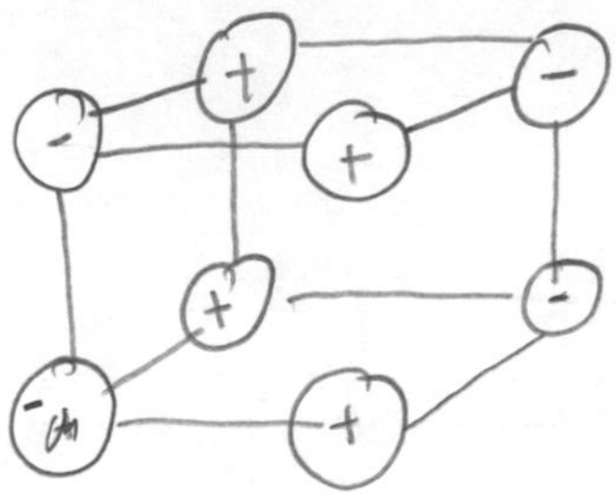

Giant Ionic Compound

(4 marks)

(e)   The Pauling electronegativities of Na, Cl and H are given in the table below.

Element	Pauling electronegativity
Na	0.9
Cl	3.0
H	2.1

Using the information given, explain why NaCl has an ionic structure while HCl has a molecular structure.

Because Na is less electronegative compared to Cl = so bond is more polarized, stronger the ionic bond, difference between H, Cl in electronegativity is small, bond is less polarized, weaker so it is covalent

~~(2 marks)~~

...Br$_2$, CCl$_4$ and CHCl$_3$.

Q1 $CHCl_3$ - Polar

H is less electronegative than Cl, C-Cl are polar, so all the negative charge is pulled towards Cl atoms, making them slightly negative, so Carbon & Hydrogen become slightly positive. creating a permanent dipole

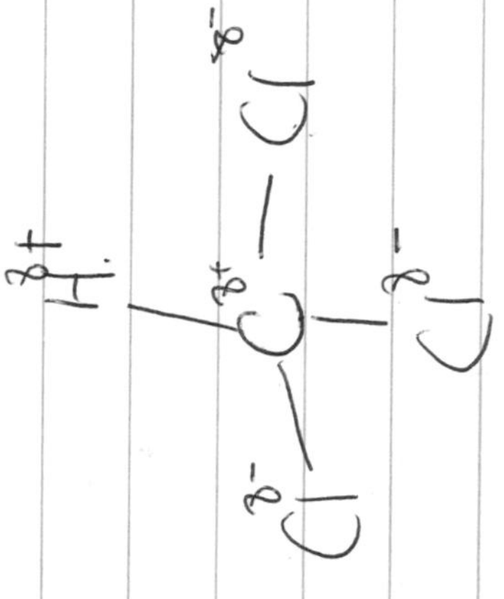

· Charges cancel out.
· No permanent dipole
· Symetrical!

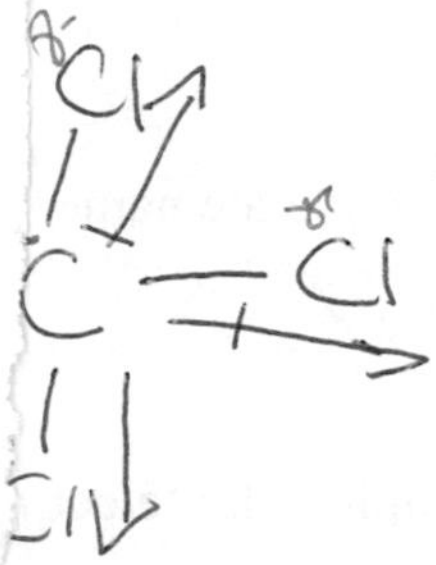

...shared electrons
...the ~~bond~~ atoms
...no overall dipole
...as large electronegative
...become polarized, a dipole
...each other ~~out~~ out, as
...direction, so it becomes non-polar
...a big electronegative difference, so
...more attracted to Cl atom, which will make
...results in dipole between atom = Cl-C, bond
...way, they don't cancel = Polar

(6 marks) 3

EXAM TIP

It's really easy to slip up and put too many electrons in your electron configurations. Make a note of how many you should have before you start writing (you'll need to think about how many electrons have been added or taken away from the atomic number for ions), then add them all up at the end and check they match. Another good check (for atoms) is to see if the number of electrons the outermost shell matches the Group number of the element.

Score

32

Electrons, Bonding and Structure — 2

1 In the atomic orbital model of the atom, electrons exist within fixed sub-shells. These sub-shells contain atomic orbitals.

(a) (i) Explain the meaning of the term atomic orbital.

high fixed energies , where only 2 electrons
can fit

(2 marks)

The diagram below shows the shapes of two different types of atomic orbital.

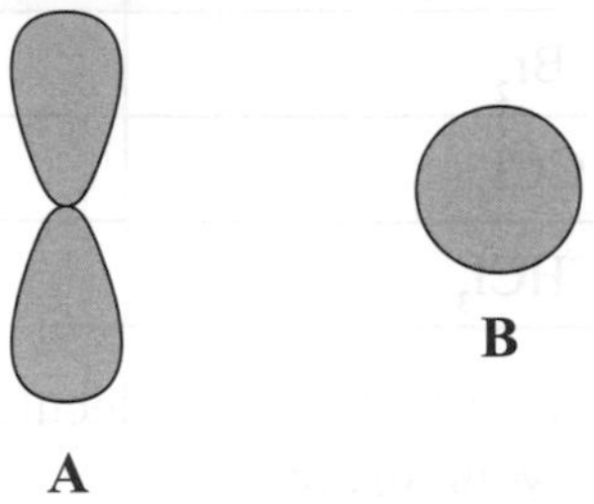

A

B

(ii) Give the names of the type of orbital labelled **A** and the type of orbital labelled **B**.

A: _dumbell_ B: _spherical_

(1 mark)

(b) Complete the 'electrons in box' diagram below for the sulfur atom, including the missing sub-shell labels.

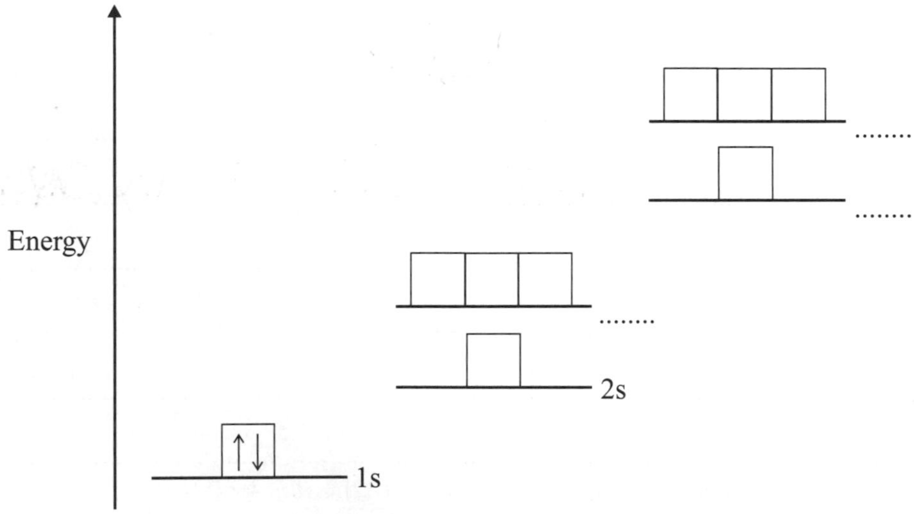

Energy

1s

2s

(3 marks)

(c) Sulfur forms ions with a charge of –2.

(i) Write the full electron configuration of an S²⁻ ion.

$1s^2 2s^2 3s^2 2s^2 2p^6$

(1 mark)

(ii) Which element found in Group 0 of the periodic table has the same electron configuration as an S²⁻ ion?

Argon

(1 mark)

2   The graph below shows the boiling points of some of the Group 6 hydrides.

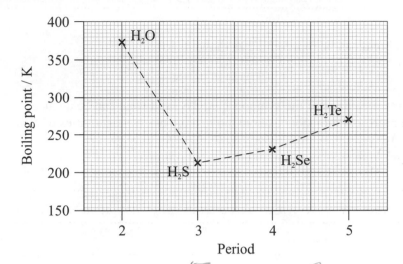

(a)   Describe and explain the trend in the boiling points of H$_2$S, H$_2$Se and H$_2$Te.

H2O has the highest boiling point because of hydrogen bonding, but other hydries don't, they have vans de waals forces, they increase, as number of electrons increase, more VDW more energy needed

(1 mark)

(b)   Explain why the boiling point of H$_2$O is higher than expected.

Because has hydrogen bonding, which is the strongest bond as oxygen being more electronegative than H$^+$, creates a dipole, as negative charge is pulled toward, making it δ$^-$ δH δ$^+$. polar, more energy is needed to break them then vans de waals ⟶ Bond polarized (O-H)

(3 marks)

3   Ammonium carbonate, (NH$_4$)$_2$CO$_3$, is made up of NH$_4^+$ and CO$_3^{2-}$ ions. It was used as an early form of baking powder and commonly known as 'baker's ammonia'.

(a)   In the NH$_4^+$ ion, the nitrogen atom is bonded to each of the four hydrogens. Three of the bonds are single covalent and one is dative covalent.

(i)   State what is meant by the term dative covalent bond.

both the shared electrons come from same atom

(1 mark)

(ii)   Draw a diagram to illustrate the 3-D shape of the NH$_4^+$ ion, showing the different types of bond appropriately.

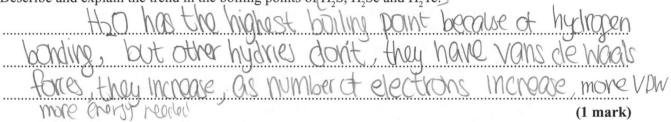

(2 marks)

Module 2 — Foundations in Chemistry

26

(b) (i) State the meaning of the term electronegativity.

....

(1 mark)

(ii) The N–H bond can be represented as shown below.

$$N^{\delta-}\!\!\!-\!\!\!H^{\delta+}$$

Explain the meanings of the symbols $\delta+$ and $\delta-$, and what can be deduced
from the representation above about the relative electronegativities of N and H.

*The bond is polarized, so permanent dipole has result,
N is more electronegative than H, so the negative
charge is pulled towards N, making it δ^-, making H δ^+*

(2 marks)

(c) The carbonate ion, CO_3^{2-}, also has covalent bonds. The carbon atom bonds to one oxygen atom with a double covalent bond and to the other two oxygen atoms with single covalent bonds.
Draw a dot and cross diagram for the carbonate ion.
Show outer shell electrons only, using a different symbol for the two extra electrons.

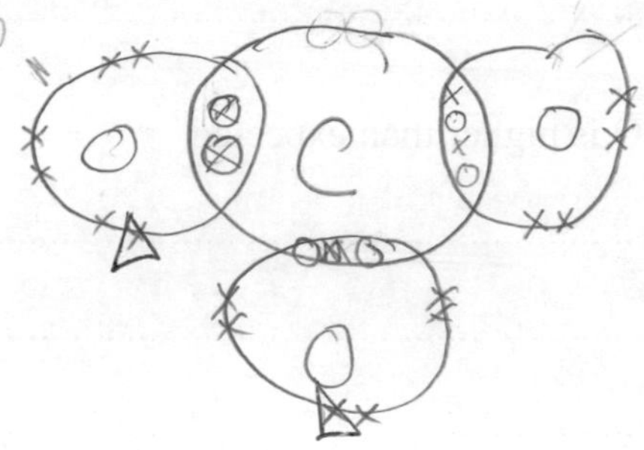

(2 marks)

(d) Modern baking powder contains tartaric acid, the structure of which is shown in the diagram below.

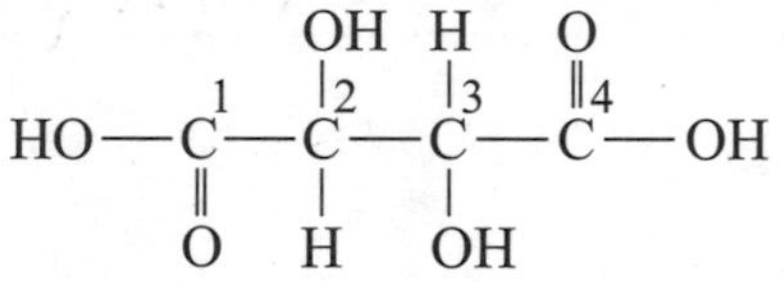

Use electron pair repulsion theory to explain the differences between the shape shown in this diagram and the actual 3-D shape of a tartaric acid molecule. You may refer to the numbered carbon atoms in your answer.

*4, 1 - Trigonal planar = 3 Bonding pair 109.5
2,3 - Tethra hedral = 4 Bonding par
Pet repel each other equalling
= Means it is not straight chain, don't
lie in same plane*

(4 marks)

Module 2 — Foundations in Chemistry

4 SF₂ and SF₆ are the formulae of two sulfur fluorides.

(a) (i) Draw a diagram to show the shape of each molecule. Include any lone pairs around the central atoms and indicate the values of the bond angles. Name the shapes you have drawn.

6 SF₂: SF₆:

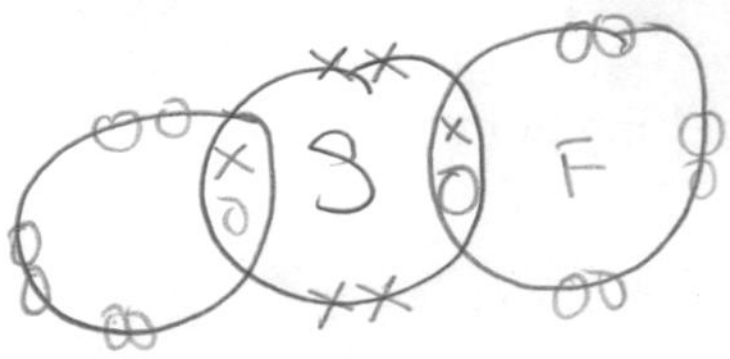

Shape of SF₂: *Non-Linear*

Shape of SF₆: *Octahedral*

(4 marks)

(ii) Explain the shape that you gave for SF₂.

= 6 bonding pair, no lone pair, each angle is at 90°c

(3 marks)

(b) The Pauling scale is a measure of electronegativity. On the Pauling scale, fluorine has an electronegativity of 4.0 and sulfur has an electronegativity of 2.6. Explain why SF₆ is non-polar, but SF₂ is polar.

SF₆ is structured asymetrically, so all the charges cancel out, so permanent dipole is formed, at each SF₂, Fluorine is very electronegative than sulfur, S−F is polarized negative charge is pulled to F making it δ⁻ (slightly negative) H δ⁺ slightly positive) so a permanent dipole is formed, as the bond S−F is polarized.

pull the negative charge in the same direction, creating an uneven distribution of charge in molecule.

(4 marks)

(c) Explain why it is difficult to predict which of the two fluorides has the higher melting point.

SF₆ = It has 6 Fluorides, held together by covalent bond, needs a lot of energy to break

SF₂ = is polar 2F is very electronegative,

(3 marks)

(EXAM TIP) You won't need to know any exact values for electronegativity for your exams, but it's helpful to have an understanding of the overall trends in electronegativity moving around the periodic table. Remember, electronegativity increases across periods and decreases down groups (ignoring the noble gases), so the most electronegative elements (like fluorine and oxygen) are found at the top right.

Score

38

The Periodic Table — 1

The periodic table isn't just a creative way of listing the elements — you can use it to help you describe and explain all kinds of trends in their properties. Better get scrutinising it to answer the questions coming up...

For each of questions 1-4, give your answer by writing the correct letter in the box.

1   Which of these statements explains why metals have high melting points?

    A   The atoms are closely packed.

    B   There is a strong electrostatic attraction between the metal ions and the free electrons.

    C   The atoms have a regular arrangement.

    D   The positive metal ions repel each other.

Your answer ☐

(1 mark)

2   Which of the following halogens is the least reactive?

    A F_2 **B** Cl_2

    C Br_2 **D** I_2

Your answer D

(1 mark)

3   Which of the following electron configurations is that of a d-block element?

    A $1s^2\ 2s^2\ 2p^6\ 3s^2\ 3p^6\ 3d^{10}\ 4s^2\ 4p^5$

    B $1s^2\ 2s^2\ 2p^6\ 3s^2\ 3p^6\ 3d^8\ 4s^2$

    C $1s^2\ 2s^2\ 2p^6\ 3s^2\ 3p^6$

    D $1s^2\ 2s^2\ 2p^6\ 3s^2\ 3p^6\ 3d^{10}\ 4s^2\ 4p^6\ 5s^1$

Your answer B

(1 mark)

4   Which of the following statements about Group 2 elements is correct?

    A   The first ionisation energy of the Group 2 elements increases going down the group.

    B   The second ionisation energy is less than the first ionisation energy.

    C   The first ionisation energy of a Group 2 element is greater than that of the Group 1 element in the same period.

    D   The first ionisation energy of a Group 2 element is less than that of the Group 3 element in the same period.

Your answer C

(1 mark)

5 Graphite and graphene are both forms of carbon.

(a) (i) Describe the structure of graphite. Include a diagram to illustrate your answer.

Diagram:

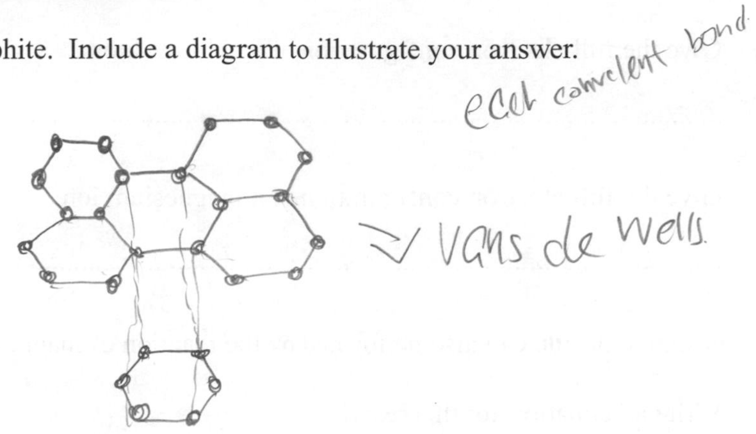

[Handwritten annotations on diagram: "e cov covalent bond", "✓ vans de wells"]

Description: arranged in flat sheets of hexagon, covalently 3 carbon atom convalently bonded, 4th outer electron delocelized

(4 marks)

(ii) Explain how the structures of graphite and graphene are related.

....

....

(1 mark)

(b) (i) Explain why graphite has a very high melting point.

....

....

(2 marks)

(ii) Describe and explain the following properties of graphite.

Electrical conductivity:

....

....

Solubility:

....

....

(2 marks)

(c) In the future, materials containing graphene could be used to make aircraft parts, because it is very light but extremely strong.
Explain why the structure of graphene makes it such a strong material.

....

....

....

(2 marks)

6   Magnesium reacts with chlorine to form the ionic compound magnesium chloride, $MgCl_2$.

(a) (i) Give the full electron configuration of a chlorine atom.

....

(1 mark)

(ii) Give the full electron configuration of a magnesium ion.

....

(1 mark)

(b) Magnesium chloride can also be formed by the reaction of magnesium metal with hydrochloric acid.

(i) Write an equation for this reaction.

....

(1 mark)

(ii) Use oxidation numbers to show that this is a redox reaction.

....

....

....

(2 marks)

(iii) Strontium is below magnesium in Group 2 of the Periodic Table, and reacts more vigorously with hydrochloric acid than magnesium. Explain why strontium is more reactive than magnesium.

....

....

....

....

....

....

(4 marks)

(c) Magnesium metal will react with water to produce magnesium hydroxide.

(i) Give one use of magnesium hydroxide.

....

(1 mark)

(ii) Suggest why magnesium hydroxide is **not** made industrially using the reaction of magnesium and water.

....

....

(1 mark)

The Periodic Table — 2

1   Elements in the same groups or periods of the periodic table display patterns in their ionisation energies.

(a)   State the meaning of the term first ionisation energy.

....

....

(1 mark)

The graph shows the first ionisation energies of the elements in Period 3.

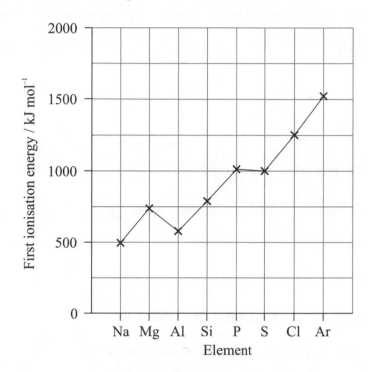

(b)   State and explain **one** similarity and **one** difference between the graph shown above and a graph of the first ionisation energies of the Period 2 elements drawn on the same scale.

....

....

....

....

....

....

(4 marks)

(c)   The table below shows the successive ionisation energies of an element, **X**, in Period 2 of the Periodic Table.

Ionisation energies / kJ mol⁻¹						
1st	2nd	3rd	4th	5th	6th	7th
1402	2856	4578	7475	9445	53268	64362

(i) Write an equation to represent the 2nd ionisation energy of element **X**.
Use **X** as the chemical symbol for the element and include state symbols.

....
(1 mark)

(ii) Suggest why the difference between the 5th and 6th ionisation energies of element **X** is so much larger than that between the 4th and 5th ionisation energies. Explain your answer.

....

....

....

....
(3 marks)

(iii) Identify element **X**.

....
(1 mark)

2 There are trends in the properties of the halogens.

(a) Explain why chlorine has a lower boiling point than iodine.

....

....
(2 marks)

(b) State and explain the trend in the reactivity of the halide ions.

....

....

....
(4 marks)

(c) A more reactive halogen can displace a less reactive halogen from a solution of halide ions.
A student investigates this by adding an excess of chlorine water to a solution of potassium bromide.

(i) Write an ionic equation for the reaction that takes place.

....
(1 mark)

(ii) Identify which species is oxidised in the reaction.

....
(1 mark)

(iii) The student is given a pure solution of the potassium salt formed by the reaction.
When the student adds an aqueous solution containing silver ions to this solution, a precipitate forms.
State what colour you would expect the precipitate to be.

....
(1 mark)

3   The trend in the melting points across Period 3 is shown on the graph below.

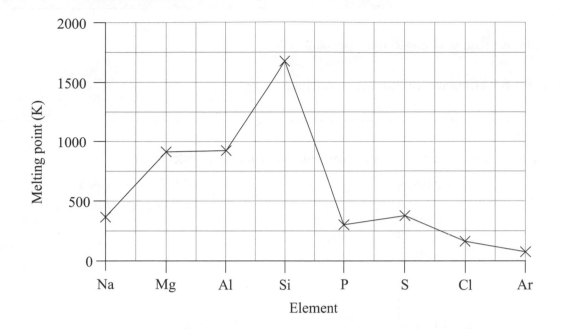

Describe and explain the patterns and variations in the melting points of the Period 3 elements shown on the graph. In your answer include ideas about the structure and bonding of the elements.

....

....

....

....

....

....

....

....

....

....

....

....

....

....

(6 marks)

Score

25

The Periodic Table — 3

1 Calcium is found in Group 2 of the periodic table.

(a) State the full electron configuration of calcium.

....

(1 mark)

The graph shows the first 11 successive ionisation energies of calcium.

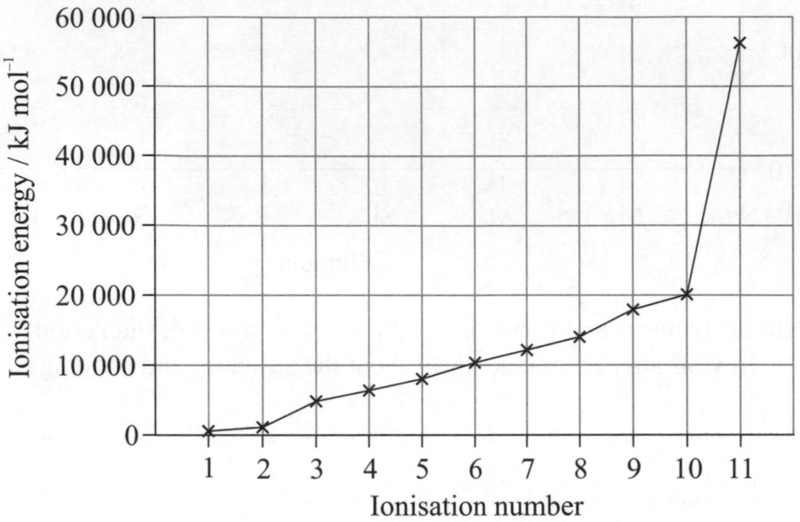

(b) Suggest why the second ionisation energy of calcium is greater than the first ionisation energy.

....

....

....

(2 marks)

(c) Explain how the graph shown provides evidence of the electron structure of a calcium atom.

....

....

....

....

....

....

(4 marks)

2 Group 2 metals are in the s-block of the periodic table.

(a) Explain, with reference to their electron configurations, why Group 2 metals are classified as s-block elements.

....

(1 mark)

(b) (i) State and explain the trend in the reactivity of the Group 2 metals.

....

....
(1 mark)

(ii) Describe **one** similarity and **one** difference in the observations that you would expect to make when pieces of calcium and barium are added to water.

Similarity: ....

Difference: ....
(2 marks)

(c) The oxides of Group 2 metals also react with water.

(i) Write an equation, including state symbols, for the reaction of calcium oxide with water.

....
(2 marks)

(ii) Equal molar amounts of barium oxide and calcium oxide were added to two test tubes containing water. Which of the resulting solutions would have the highest pH? Explain your answer.

....

....

....
(3 marks)

3 Compounds containing chlorine are often used to disinfect water. Reactions **1**, **2** and **3**, all involving chlorine compounds, are shown in the diagram below.

$$Cl_{2(g)} \xrightarrow[\mathbf{2}]{NaOH_{(aq)}} NaClO_{(aq)} + NaCl_{(aq)} + \mathbf{A}$$

$$\Bigg\updownarrow \begin{array}{l} H_2O_{(l)} \\ \mathbf{1} \end{array} \qquad\qquad \Bigg\updownarrow \begin{array}{l} H_2O_{(l)} \\ \mathbf{3} \end{array}$$

$$HClO_{(aq)} \qquad\qquad\qquad HClO_{(aq)}$$
$$+ \qquad\qquad\qquad\qquad +$$
$$HCl_{(aq)} \qquad\qquad\qquad\quad \mathbf{B}$$

(a) (i) Write equations for reactions **2** and **3**, identifying the products A and B.

Reaction **2**: ....

Reaction **3**: ....
(2 marks)

(ii) Write an ionic equation for reaction **1**.

....
(1 mark)

(iii) Identify which of reactions **1-3** form a mixture of products containing chlorine in more than one oxidation state.

....
(1 mark)

Module 3 — Periodic Table and Energy

(b) Describe **two** potential risks associated with using chlorine to treat public drinking water supplies.

1. ....

....

2. ....

....

(2 marks)

4   A student carried out some test tube reactions to investigate the reactions of the halogens with solutions of halide ions.

In experiment **1**, the student placed a sample of chlorine solution in a test tube and added the same volume of potassium bromide solution. She then repeated the procedure with a fresh sample of chlorine solution, this time adding potassium iodide solution.

The student then carried out experiments **2** and **3**, repeating the method used above using the combinations of halogen and halide solutions shown in the table below, and noting her observations.

	Experiment **1** $Cl_{2(aq)}$	Experiment **2** $Br_{2(aq)}$	Experiment **3** $I_{2(aq)}$
$KCl_{(aq)}$			
$KBr_{(aq)}$	Yellow solution forms		
$KI_{(aq)}$	Orange-brown solution forms		

(a) Complete the table to show the observations the student should have made for experiments **2** and **3**.

(2 marks)

(b) Identify the yellow solution formed in the reaction between chlorine solution and potassium bromide solution.

....

(1 mark)

(c) To make the colour changes easier to distinguish, the student shakes the reaction mixtures produced in experiment **1** with cyclohexane, an organic solvent. State and explain what would be observed in each case.

....

....

....

....

....

(4 marks)

(d) Write an ionic equation for the reaction between Cl_2 and KI and identify the oxidising agent in this reaction.

equation: ....

oxidising agent: ....

(2 marks)

(e) Sodium fluoride dissolves in water to form a colourless solution.
Suggest what you would observe if sodium fluoride solution and bromine solution were mixed.
Explain your answer.

....

....

(2 marks)

5 A student has a bottle labelled "sodium sulfate solution" and another labelled "sodium carbonate solution".
The student tests the solutions in both bottles to check that they contain the anions shown on the labels.

(a) (i) For the sulfate ion test, the student removed 5 cm³ of solution from the first bottle,
put it in a clean test tube and added a few drops of barium chloride solution.

Identify **one** additional step the student should have included when carrying out this test.
Explain why this may affect the result of the test.

....

....

....

(2 marks)

(ii) Describe a test that the student could have used to confirm the presence of
carbonate ions in the bottle labelled "sodium carbonate solution".

....

....

....

(3 marks)

(b) The student was given a third bottle which they were told contained either sodium bromide solution or
sodium iodide solution. They carried out a test to confirm which solution they had. The first part of the
test involved the formation of a silver halide. The second part involved trying to dissolve the silver halide.

Describe the test that the student used. Your answer should include a description of the results
that the student would have seen for each solution.

....

....

....

....

....

....

(5 marks)

Physical Chemistry — 1

Bit of a mathsy section this, so better dust off your calculator, sharpen your pencil and find a ruler for those graphs...

For each of questions 1-4, give your answer by writing the correct letter in the box.

1   Consider this reaction: $2SO_{2(g)} + O_{2(g)} \rightleftharpoons 2SO_{3(g)}$ $\Delta H = -197$ kJ mol^{-1}
Which of the following would shift the equilibrium in favour of the product the most?

   A   Decreasing the temperature and increasing the pressure.

   B   Decreasing the temperature and decreasing the pressure.

   C   Increasing the temperature and decreasing the pressure.

   D   Increasing the temperature and increasing the pressure.

   Your answer [ ]

(1 mark)

2   Chloroethane can be produced by the reaction of ethene with hydrogen chloride gas.
$$C_2H_{4(g)} + HCl_{(g)} \rightarrow C_2H_5Cl_{(g)}$$
Some bond enthalpy data for this reaction is shown below.

Bond	C=C	C–H	H–Cl	C–C	C–Cl
Bond enthalpy / kJ mol^{-1}	612	413	432	347	346

What is the value of ΔH for the reaction?

A   +85 kJ mol^{-1} **B**   −494 kJ mol^{-1}

C   +351 kJ mol^{-1} **D**   −62 kJ mol^{-1}

   Your answer [ ]

(1 mark)

3   250 cm^3 of 0.50 mol dm^{-3} sodium hydroxide solution was neutralised by an excess of hydrochloric acid. The total volume of the reaction mixture was 500 cm^3. The maximum temperature change was +3.5 °C. Calculate the molar enthalpy change of the reaction with respect to sodium hydroxide. You should assume that $c = 4.18$ J K^{-1}g^{-1}.

A   −29 kJ mol^{-1} **B**   −59 kJ mol^{-1}

C   +29 kJ mol^{-1} **D**   +59 kJ mol^{-1}

   Your answer [ ]

(1 mark)

4   Which of the following statements about catalysts is true?

   A   Adding a catalyst will increase the yield from a reversible reaction.

   B   Catalysts increase the rate of reaction by offering an alternative reaction pathway with a higher energy.

   C   A catalyst is chemically unchanged at the end of a reaction.

   D   Adding a catalyst will decrease the value of K_c for a reversible reaction.

   Your answer [ ]

(1 mark)

5   A student is investigating the energetics of the reaction shown in the following equation.
$$CuSO_{4(aq)} + Mg_{(s)} \rightarrow MgSO_{4(aq)} + Cu_{(s)}$$

(a)   This reaction is exothermic.
   •   Explain what is meant by this.
   •   Illustrate your answer with a fully labelled enthalpy profile diagram to represent the enthalpy change for this reaction. You do not need to show the activation energy for the reaction.

....

....

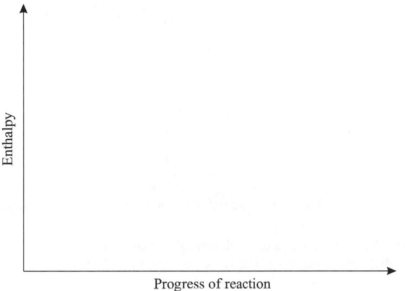

(4 marks)

(b)   The student investigated the reaction experimentally by adding an excess of magnesium ribbon to 20 cm³ of 0.50 mol dm⁻³ copper(II) sulfate solution, $CuSO_{4(aq)}$, in a beaker and monitoring the temperature of the reaction mixture.

(i)   The student used a measuring cylinder with an uncertainty of 0.1 cm³ to measure out the $CuSO_{4(aq)}$. Calculate the percentage uncertainty in their measurement.

percentage uncertainty = ... %
(1 mark)

(ii)   Copper(II) sulfate solution is an irritant and is toxic to aquatic plants and animals. The student wore safety glasses and a lab coat when carrying out the experiment. Suggest **one** other precaution that the student should have taken to minimise the risk of using $CuSO_{4(aq)}$.

....

....

(1 mark)

(c) The student recorded a maximum temperature change of +55 °C over the course of the reaction.

Calculate a value for the enthalpy change of the reaction with respect to $CuSO_{4(aq)}$.
Assume the specific heat capacity of the mixture is 4.18 $J K^{-1}g^{-1}$.
Give your answer to an appropriate number of significant figures. Include units in your answer.

Enthalpy change of reaction = ...

(4 marks)

(d) The experimentally determined value for the enthalpy change of
the reaction is different to the theoretical value under these conditions.

(i) Suggest why this is the case.

....

(1 mark)

(ii) Suggest **one** change the student could make to the experiment to make their result more accurate.

....

(1 mark)

6 Methanol has a number of important uses in the chemical industry.
It can be produced from carbon monoxide and hydrogen using the reaction shown below.

$$CO_{(g)} + 2H_{2(g)} \rightleftharpoons CH_3OH_{(g)} \qquad \Delta H = -90 \text{ kJ mol}^{-1}$$

This reaction is performed at high pressure and at a temperature of 250 °C.

(a) This reaction can be described as a homogeneous reaction.
State what is meant by the term homogeneous reaction.

....

(1 mark)

(b) Write the expression for the equilibrium constant, K_c, for this reaction.

....

(1 mark)

(c) Use le Chatelier's principle to explain why a high pressure is used for this reaction in industry.

....

....

....

....

(3 marks)

(d) (i) Increasing the temperature would increase the rate of the reaction.
Give **two** reasons why using a higher temperature would increase the rate of reaction.

....

....

....

(2 marks)

(ii) A catalyst is typically used for this reaction. This is so that the reaction can be carried
out at a relatively low temperature, but will still proceed at a reasonable rate.
In terms of the effect on the equilibrium position, explain why using a catalyst is
a better option than increasing the temperature to increase the rate of this reaction.

....

....

....

....

....

(3 marks)

(e) One of the main uses of methanol in industry is in the production of methanal (CH_2O).

$$2CH_3OH_{(l)} + O_{2(g)} \rightarrow 2CH_2O_{(l)} + 2H_2O_{(l)}$$

The table below shows the standard enthalpy changes of formation for the compounds in this reaction.

Compound	$CH_3OH_{(l)}$	$CH_2O_{(l)}$	$H_2O_{(l)}$
ΔH_f / kJ mol^{-1}	−239.1	−108.7	−285.8

Use the data provided to calculate the enthalpy change of the reaction under standard conditions.

Enthalpy change of reaction = ...kJ mol^{-1}

(2 marks)

EXAM TIP — If you're calculating an enthalpy of reaction from enthalpy of formation data, you might find that drawing a Hess cycle diagram to illustrate Hess's law helps you to work out what calculation you need to do. But if you'd prefer to stick with just using the formula, that's fine too — both methods should get you the marks in an exam, so just use whichever one works best for you.

Score

28

Physical Chemistry — 2

1 Cobalt(II) acetate is used as a homogeneous catalyst in the industrial production of the plastic PET.

(a) (i) State the meaning of the term homogeneous catalyst.

....
(1 mark)

(ii) Explain the advantages in terms of environmental sustainability of using catalysts.

....

....

....

....

....
(3 marks)

(b) Cobalt(II) ions in water form a pink solution. The addition of chloride ions to cobalt(II) solutions results in the formation of a blue cobalt(II) chloride complex. An equilibrium is set up in a test tube where both cobalt species are present, as shown by the equation below.

$$Co^{2+}_{(aq)} + 4Cl^-_{(aq)} \rightleftharpoons [CoCl_4]^{2-}_{(aq)}$$
pink   blue

The colour of the equilibrium mixture is violet.

(i) Predict and explain the effect on the colour of the solution of increasing the concentration of chloride ions.

....

....

....

....
(2 marks)

(ii) Outline a qualitative method of investigating the effect of decreasing the temperature on the position of equilibrium.

....

....
(1 mark)

(iii) Describe and explain the observations you would expect to make during this investigation if the forwards reaction is endothermic.

....

....

....
(2 marks)

2 Magnesium reacts with hydrochloric acid to give magnesium chloride and hydrogen, as shown by the equation below.

$$Mg_{(s)} + 2HCl_{(aq)} \rightarrow MgCl_{2(aq)} + H_{2(g)}$$

Some students are investigating how the rate of the reaction changes with temperature. To do this, they add magnesium ribbon to 1 mol dm^{-3} hydrochloric acid and measure the volume of hydrogen produced by the reaction over time. Then they repeat this procedure at different temperatures.

(a) The results for the experiment performed at 30 °C are shown below.

Time / s	Volume of gas produced / cm^3
0	0
10	15
20	25
30	30
40	28
50	35
60	35
70	35

(i) On the grid below, draw a graph to represent the data provided. Include a line of best fit.

(3 marks)

(ii) On your graph, circle any outliers in the data. Suggest **one** possible reason for any outliers.

....

....

(2 marks)

(iii) Using your graph, calculate the initial rate of reaction, in $cm^3 \, s^{-1}$, for the reaction performed at 30 °C. Show your working on the graph.

rate of reaction = ... $cm^3 \, s^{-1}$

(2 marks)

(iv) Explain how collision theory can be used to predict how the rate of this reaction changes over time.

....

....

....

....

(2 marks)

(b) (i) Use your knowledge of the Boltzmann distribution to explain how increasing the temperature would affect the initial rate of reaction.

....

....

....

(2 marks)

(ii) Describe and explain how the initial rate of reaction would be different if the students repeated their experiment using 2 mol dm^{-3} HCl instead of 1 mol dm^{-3} HCl.

....

....

....

....

(2 marks)

(c) (i) Suggest **one** way the students could have measured the volume of gas produced by the reaction.

....

(1 mark)

(ii) State **two** factors they needed to consider when selecting suitable apparatus to take this measurement.

....

....

....

(2 marks)

Score

25

Physical Chemistry — 3

1 Enthalpy changes during combustion can be investigated using theoretical and experimental methods.

(a) A student is studying the complete combustion of propane, C_3H_8.
The equation for this reaction is shown below.

$$C_3H_{8(g)} + 5O_{2(g)} \rightarrow 3CO_{2(g)} + 4H_2O_{(g)}$$

(i) The table below shows mean bond enthalpies for the bonds involved in this reaction.

Bond	C–C	C–H	C=O	O–H	O=O
Bond enthalpy / kJ mol⁻¹	347	413	805	464	498

Use the data provided to calculate the enthalpy of complete combustion of propane.

Enthalpy change of complete combustion = ...kJ mol⁻¹

(3 marks)

(ii) The table below shows the enthalpies of formation of the compounds involved in the reaction.

Compound	$\Delta_f H$ / kJ mol⁻¹
$C_3H_{8(g)}$	−104.5
$CO_{2(g)}$	−393.5
$H_2O_{(g)}$	−241.8

Use this data to calculate the enthalpy of complete combustion of propane.

Enthalpy change of complete combustion = ...kJ mol⁻¹

(3 marks)

(iii) Explain why the value for the enthalpy of combustion of propane calculated using enthalpies of formation is not the same as the value calculated from mean bond enthalpies.

....

....

....

(2 marks)

(b) Another student decided to use calorimetry to investigate the complete combustion of propan-2-ol. They burned propan-2-ol in a spirit burner and recorded the change in the mass of the burner and the change in temperature of the water in the calorimeter. Their results are shown below.

Mass of burner before	75.2 g
Mass of burner after	74.8 g
Volume of water in calorimeter	50.0 cm^3
Initial temperature of water	21.5 °C
Final temperature of water	74.0 °C

Calculate the enthalpy of complete combustion of propan-2-ol in kJ mol^{-1}.
The specific heat capacity of water is 4.18 J K^{-1} g^{-1}.

Enthalpy change of complete combustion = ... kJ mol^{-1}

(5 marks)

2   When heated in air, potassium can react with oxygen to produce potassium peroxide, K_2O_2. The overall equation for this reaction is:

$$2K_{(s)} + O_{2(g)} \rightarrow K_2O_{2(s)}$$

(a) Predict the effect of increasing the pressure on the rate of this reaction.
Explain your answer.

....

....

....

....

....

(4 marks)

(b) The Boltzmann distribution of the energies of the oxygen molecules in the reaction mixture at a given temperature is shown in the diagram below.

(i) Shade in the area on the distribution curve that corresponds to the number of oxygen molecules that are able to react with the potassium.

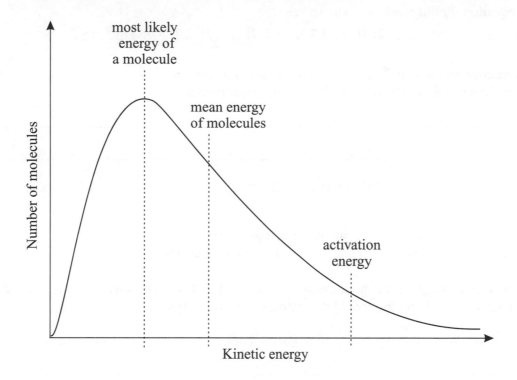

(1 mark)

(ii) Describe and explain how adding a catalyst to the reaction mixture would change the number of oxygen molecules that are able to react.

....

....

....

(2 marks)

(iii) On the diagram, sketch a curve to show how the distribution of the energies of the oxygen molecules would be different at a lower temperature.

(2 marks)

(c) Potassium peroxide reacts with water according to the equation

$$2K_2O_{2(s)} + 2H_2O_{(l)} \rightarrow 4KOH_{(aq)} + O_{2(g)}$$

Give **two** ways in which the rate of this reaction could be monitored.

....

....

....

(2 marks)

Physical Chemistry — 4

1   Under certain conditions, methane can react to give acetylene (C_2H_2) and hydrogen gas.
The equation for this reaction is shown below.

$$2CH_{4(g)} \rightleftharpoons 3H_{2(g)} + C_2H_{2(g)} \qquad \Delta H = +377 \text{ kJ mol}^{-1}$$

(a)   This reaction reaches an equilibrium. Give **two** conditions which must
be met for a reaction to be described as being at equilibrium.

....

....

....

(2 marks)

(b)   A chemical company is considering whether it would be feasible to
use this reaction to produce large amounts of acetylene industrially.

(i)   A scientist suggests that performing the reaction at high pressure would increase the rate of the reaction.
Explain why doing this would decrease the yield of acetylene.

....

....

....

(2 marks)

(ii)   Describe and explain the factors that the company would need to consider when
choosing an appropriate temperature for this reaction in an industrial setting.

....

....

....

....

....

....

....

....

....

....

....

....

(6 marks)

(c) (i) Write the expression for the equilibrium constant, K_c, for this reaction.

....

(1 mark)

(ii) A scientist performed a test experiment. They placed 1.00 moles of methane in a heatproof reaction vessel with a total volume of 3.00 dm^3. The reaction vessel was then placed in a furnace at a very high temperature. The equilibrium mixture contained 0.372 moles of acetylene.

Calculate the value of K_c for this reaction using the information given above.
Give your answer to an appropriate number of significant figures.
Show **all** your working.

K_c = ... $mol^2\ dm^{-6}$

(7 marks)

(iii) The scientist carried out a second test experiment, under different reaction conditions, and found that the value of K_c increased. Explain what this indicates about the position of equilibrium under these new reaction conditions, and what this means for the yield of acetylene.

....

....

(2 marks)

EXAM TIP

Remember, the rate of reaction and the position of equilibrium are separate. Exam questions often ask about the effect of increasing temperature, pressure and concentration, but their effect on rate is different to their effect on the position of equilibrium. So make sure you're clear which one you're being asked about.

Score

20

Basic Concepts and Hydrocarbons — 1

Organic chemistry is pretty tricky, but fear not — this section covers all the basics. Have a go at these questions, and you'll be a master of organic chemistry faster than you can say "smashed avocado with a side of chia seeds".

For each of questions 1-4, give your answer by writing the correct letter in the box.

1   What is the molecular formula of an alkane that contains 16 hydrogen atoms per molecule?

   A C_4H_8 **B** C_6H_{16}

   C C_7H_{16} **D** C_8H_{16}

   Your answer   B

   (1 mark)

2   The structures of four alkenes are shown below.

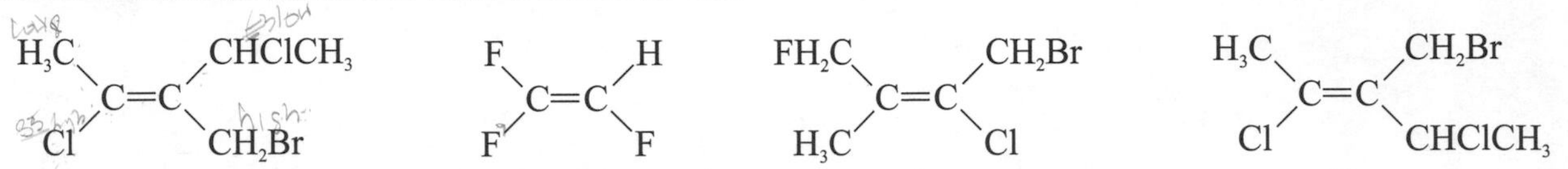

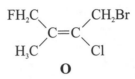

   M   **N**   **O**   **P**

   Which of the alkenes above is a Z isomer?

   A   M   ‑same   **B**   N

   C   O   **D**   P

   Your answer   A

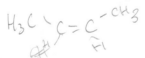

   (1 mark)

3   Which of the following molecules does **not** exhibit E/Z stereoisomerism?

   A   3-methylpent-2-ene   **B**   2-methylbut-2-ene

   C   3-methylhex-2-ene   **D**   3-methylhex-3-ene

   Your answer   B

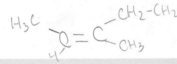

   (1 mark)

4   The molecule shown below is reacted with hydrogen bromide.

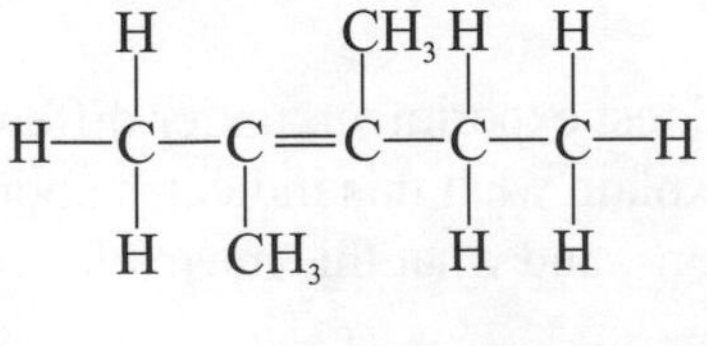

$$H-\underset{H}{\overset{H}{C}}-\underset{CH_3}{\overset{CH_3}{C}}=\underset{H}{\overset{H}{C}}-\underset{H}{\overset{H}{C}}-\underset{H}{\overset{H}{C}}-H$$

   Which of the following are the products of this reaction?

   A   4-bromo-3,4-dimethylpentane and 3-bromo-3,4-dimethylpentane.

   B   3-bromo-2,3-dimethylpentane and 2-bromo-2,3-dimethylpentane.

   C   3-bromo-2-methylpentane and 2-bromo-2-methylpentane.

   D   2-bromo-3,4-dimethylpentane and 3-bromo-2,3-dimethylpentane.

   Your answer

   (1 mark)

5 Hex-1-ene is a hydrocarbon with the molecular formula C_6H_{12}.
Four isomers of hex-1-ene are shown in the table.

Isomer	Displayed formula	Systematic name
A	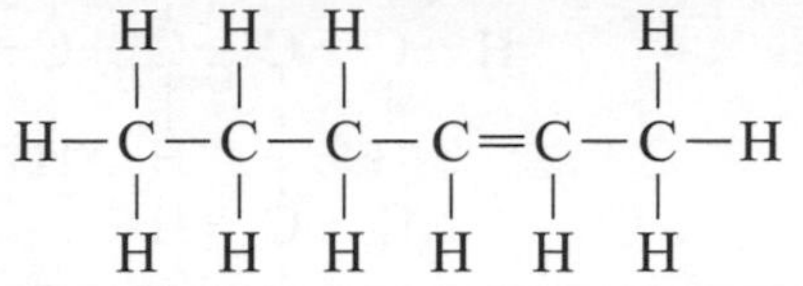	hex-2-ene
B	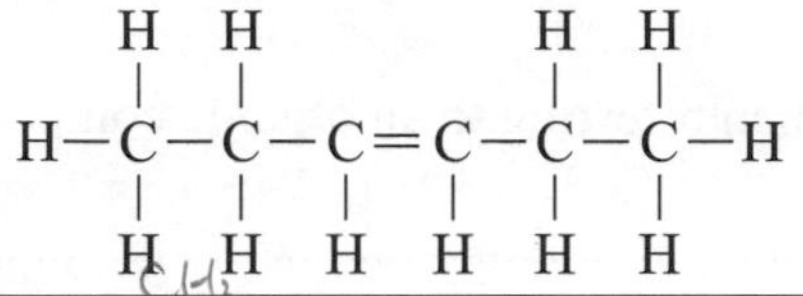	hex-3-ene
C	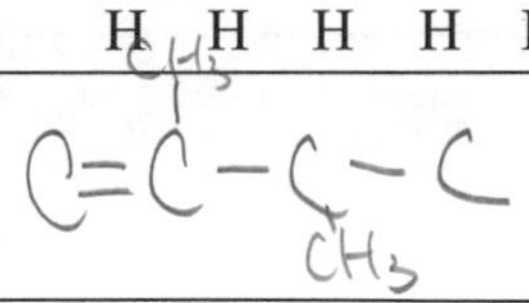	2,3-dimethylbut-1-ene
D	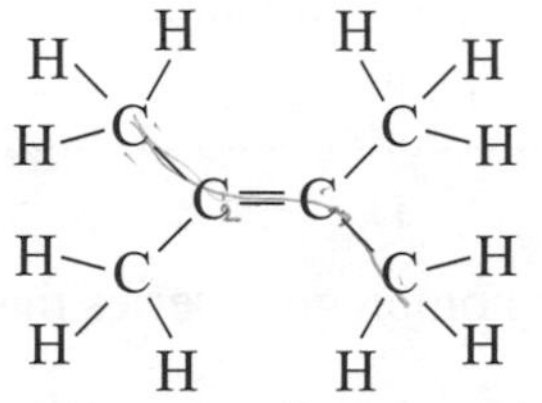	2,3 dimethyl but-2ene

(a) Write the letter of an isomer in the table that reacts with hydrogen to produce hexane.

....
(1 mark)

(b) Draw the displayed formula of isomer **C**.

(1 mark)

(c) State the systematic name of isomer **D**.

....
(1 mark)

(d) Draw the skeletal formula of a structural isomer of hex-1-ene
that does not contain the alkene functional group.

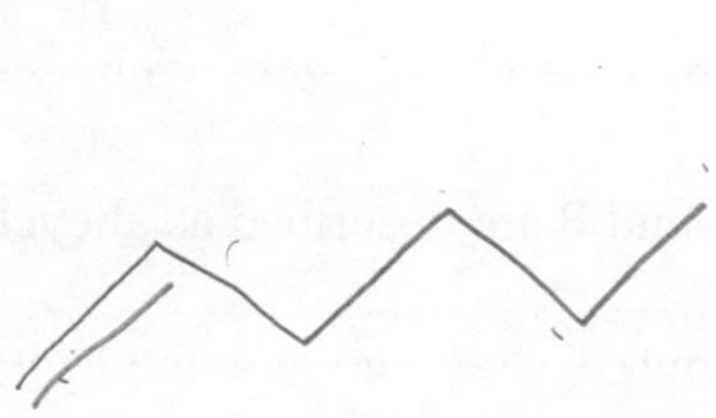

(1 mark)

6 The saturated organic compounds shown below are part of the same homologous series.

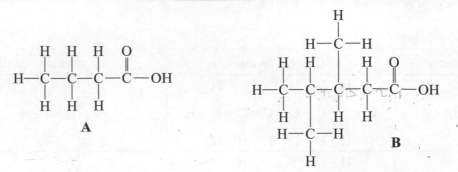

           A   **B**

(a) State what is meant by the term 'saturated' when referring to an organic compound.

Single bond

(1 mark)

(b) State **two** features of a homologous series.

Same

(2 marks)

(c) Write the structural formula of the member of this homologous series that contains 2 carbon atoms.

CH₂ CH₂

(1 mark)

(d) State the systematic name of compound **B**.

3,4 dimethyl pentanoic acid

(1 mark)

7 This question is about alicyclic hydrocarbons and haloalkanes.

Molecules **A** and **B** shown in the diagram below are both alicyclic.

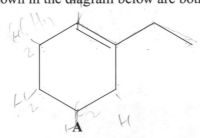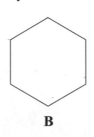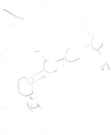

         A   **B**

(a) (i) How many σ-bonds does molecule **A** have?

(1 mark)

(ii) Give the molecular formula of molecule **A**.

(1 mark)

(iii) Explain why molecules **A** and **B** are described as alicyclic.

(1 mark)

(b) Draw the displayed formula of a branched chain aliphatic saturated hydrocarbon that has the same number of carbon atoms as molecule **A**.

[handwritten displayed structure of branched alkane with CH3 groups]

(1 mark)

(c) (i) Give the structural formula of an unsaturated structural isomer of molecule **B** that does not exhibit E/Z isomerism.

[handwritten: Restricted rotation of the C=C double bond]

[handwritten: $CH_3C(CH_3)_2CH_2$]

(1 mark)

(ii) Draw the skeletal formulae of **two** alicyclic saturated isomers of molecule **B**.

[handwritten skeletal structures: triangle labelled "Cyclopropine", pentagon, and "C"]

(2 marks)

(iii) Write the equation for the complete combustion of molecule **B**.
Use molecular formulae for all of the reactants and products.

(1 mark)

(d) The skeletal formulae of four haloalkanes, **C**, **D**, **E** and **F**, are shown below.

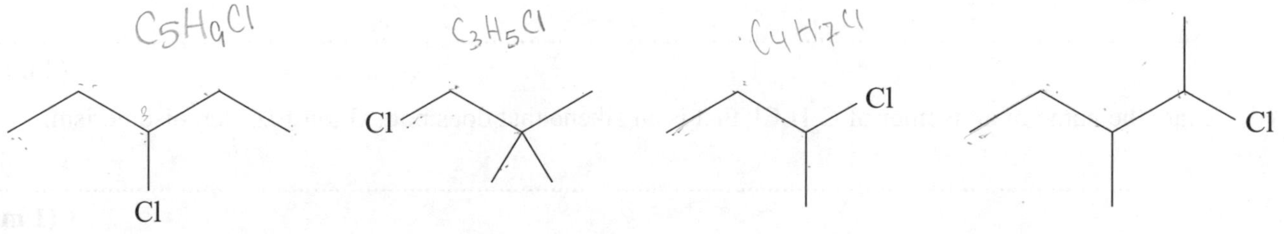

[skeletal structures with handwritten molecular formulae: C labelled C_5H_9Cl with Cl; D labelled C_3H_5Cl with Cl; E labelled C_4H_7Cl with Cl; F labelled (C_5H_9) ... (C_nH_{2n}) with Cl]

| C | D | E | F |

(i) Deduce the general formula of haloalkanes **C**–**F**.

[handwritten: $C_nH_{2n+1}Cl$]

(1 mark)

(ii) Which **two** of the haloalkanes are structural isomers?

[handwritten: C, F]

(1 mark)

(iii) Give the systematic name of haloalkane **C**.

[handwritten: 3-Chloro pentane]

(1 mark)

Score

There are quite a few definitions to learn in chemistry, but it's definitely worth memorising them. If you know your stuff, you'll be able to answer any questions that ask you for definitions quickly and easily in your exams. That will give you more time to answer the trickier questions.

24

Basic Concepts and Hydrocarbons — 2

1 1,2-dichlorobut-1-ene ($C_4H_6Cl_2$) exists as a pair of stereoisomers.

-sene

(a) Draw the Z isomer of 1,2-dichlorobut-1-ene.

[handwritten structures]
H   CH₂–CH₃
C=C
Cl   Cl his

Cl
C=C–C–C
Cl

(1 mark)

(b) Explain why 1,2-dichlorobut-1-ene can exhibit E/Z stereoisomerism.

each carbon atom of a bo double bond is attached 2 different group.
-Restricted rotation around the double bd

(2 marks)

(c) Draw and name an isomer of $C_4H_6Cl_2$ other than 1,2-dichlorobut-1-ene, which exhibits E/Z stereoisomerism. Your answer only needs to show the structure of **one** of the possible stereoisomers.

[handwritten structures]
H₃C   CH₃
C=C
CH₃

H   H   H   H
Cl–C–C–C–C–H
H   Cl   Cl   H

Name: ....

(2 marks)

(d) State the name of an isomer of $C_4H_6Cl_2$ that is an alkene that does not exhibit E/Z stereoisomerism.

....

(1 mark)

2 This question is about polymers.

(a) A section of an addition polymer is shown below.

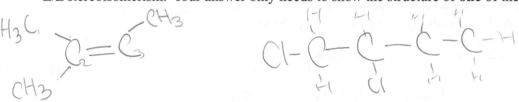

Draw and name the monomer used to form this polymer.

Monomer:

Name: ....

(2 marks)

Styrene acrylonitrile resin (SAN) is a copolymer, used in place of polystyrene where a greater thermal resistance is required. A copolymer is a polymer made from more than one type of monomer. The repeating unit of SAN is shown below.

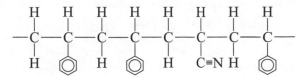

(b) (i) Draw the displayed formulae of the **two** monomers from which SAN is made.

(2 marks)

(ii) One of the monomers of SAN is an aromatic compound.
What is meant by the term aromatic compound?
...... Which contains a Benzene ring. ......
(1 mark)

3 The diagram below shows the structure of ethene, the simplest alkene.

sigma bond

(a) (i) Identify the type of bond labelled **x**, and explain how this type of bond arises.

Type of bond: ...... π bond. ......

Explanation: ...... above & below the bonded atom, sideways overlap ...... p orbits .....
(2 marks)

(ii) Predict the value of the bond angle marked **z**, and explain how this arises.

Bond angle: ...... 120° ......

Explanation: ...... Trigonal planer, 3 bond pair ......

(2 marks)

The diagram below shows the structure of another alkene, **A**.

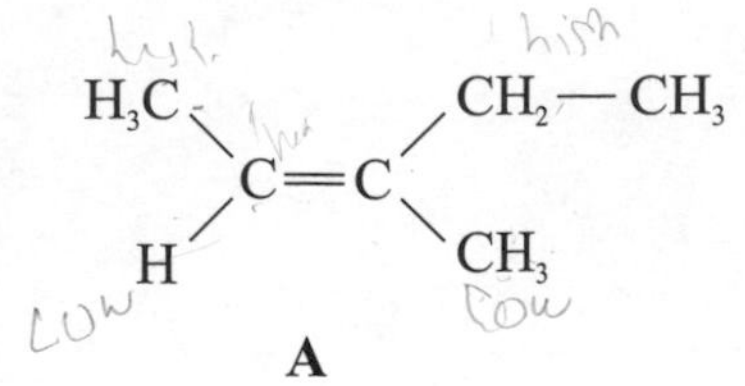

H$_3$C high
CH$_2$—CH$_3$ high
low
C=C
H CH$_3$
low low
A

(b) Alkene **A** shows E/Z isomerism. Explain how Cahn-Ingold-Prelog priority rules can be used to deduce whether **A** is the E or Z isomer of the alkene. Include the full systematic name of alkene **A** in your answer.

....

....

....

....

....

....

....

....

(5 marks)

(c) (i) Explain why alkene **A** exhibits cis/trans isomerism.

....

....

(1 mark)

(ii) Alkene **B** is a structural isomer of alkene **A** that does **not** exhibit cis/trans isomerism. Draw **one** possible structure for alkene **B**.

(1 mark)

(d) Alkene **A** can be reacted with hydrogen in the presence of a nickel catalyst.
(i) Draw the skeletal formula of the product formed in this reaction.

(1 mark)

(ii) Explain why the product of the reaction in (i) is less reactive than alkene **A**.

....

....

(1 mark)

(e) Alkenes can also react with water to form alcohols. Two different alcohols can be formed from alkene **A**. Write an equation to show the formation of the major alcohol product from alkene **A**, showing the structures of any organic reactants and organic products. State the necessary reaction conditions.

Reaction conditions: ....

(2 marks)

4   Excess 1-methylcyclohexene reacts with bromine water in the reaction shown below.

[diagram: 1-methylcyclohexene + Br₂(aq) → dibromo product] $+ \ Br_{2\,(aq)} \longrightarrow$

(a)   Describe the change you would expect to see in the bromine water during the reaction.

....

(1 mark)

(b)   Explain why alkenes are attacked by electrophiles.

....

(1 mark)

      The mechanism involves the formation of a carbocation intermediate.
There are two possible carbocations, **A** and **B**, that can be formed.

(c)   Draw curly arrows on the diagram below to show how the carbocation intermediates are formed.

[diagram: Br—Br reacting with 1-methylcyclohexene, forming Carbocation **A** and Carbocation **B**]

Carbocation **A**

Carbocation **B**

(2 marks)

(d)   State and explain which of the carbocations, **A** or **B**, is most likely to be formed.

....

....

(1 mark)

(e)   1-methylcyclohexene also reacts with hydrogen bromide.
Draw the skeletal formulae of the **two** products formed in this reaction.

(2 marks)

EXAM TIP   If you get a question that asks you for the formula of a molecule, make sure you read the question really carefully. Don't rush in and write or draw the first type of formula that pops into your head — the exam questions often specify a particular type (e.g. molecular, structural, skeletal, displayed), so you can lose marks if you give your answer in the wrong format.

Score

33

Basic Concepts and Hydrocarbons — 3

1   The structures of four saturated organic compounds, **A**, **B**, **C** and **D**, are shown below.

$CH_3(CH_2)_2CH_3$

$H_3C - \overset{\displaystyle CH_3}{\underset{\displaystyle CH_3}{\overset{|}{\underset{|}{C}}}} - H$

$H_3C - \overset{\displaystyle CH_3}{\underset{\displaystyle CH_3}{\overset{|}{\underset{|}{C}}}} - Cl$

A   **B**    **C** 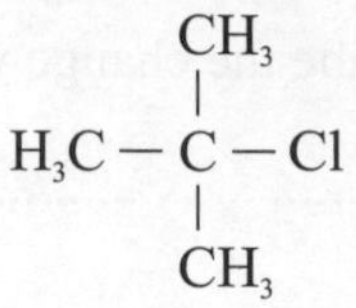   **D**

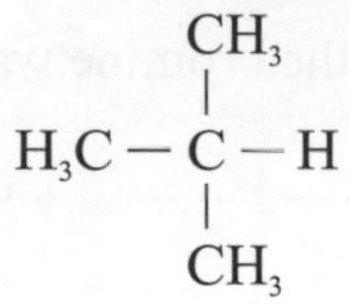

(a)   (i)   Use electron pair repulsion theory to predict the bond angle and
the shape of the bonds around the central carbon atom in compound **B**.

Bond angle: ....

Shape: ....

(2 marks)

(ii)   Draw the skeletal formula of compound **B**.

(1 mark)

(b)* Describe the factors that affect the boiling points of hydrocarbons. By considering these factors, arrange
compounds **A-C** in order of increasing boiling point. Give full reasoning for the order you have chosen.

....

....

....

....

....

....

....

....

....

....

....

....

....

(6 marks)

The enthalpies of some of the bonds and the electronegativities of
the atoms found in compounds **A-D** are shown in the tables below.

Bond	Enthalpy / kJmol^{-1}
C – Cl	346
C – H	413

Atom	Electronegativity
C	2.5
Cl	3.0
H	2.1

(c) Using the information given in the tables, state and explain which compound, **B** or **D**, is more reactive.

....

....

....

....

....

....

(3 marks)

The electronegativity of the atoms in a bond determines
whether it breaks by homolytic fission or heterolytic fission.

(d) (i) Describe the difference between homolytic and heterolytic fission.

....

....

....

(2 marks)

(ii) Give the structural formulae of the **two** species formed when
the C–Cl bond in molecule **D** breaks by heterolytic fission.

....

(1 mark)

2 Synthetic polymers produced from alkenes are non-biodegradable and
therefore need to be disposed of carefully at the end of their lifetime.

(a) (i) PVC is made from the monomer chloroethene. One of the synthetic routes to chloroethene involves
the formation of 1,2-dichloroethane from chlorine and ethane in a photochemical reaction.
Using structural formulae, write equations to show a possible mechanism for this reaction
that involves **one** initiation step, **three** propagation steps and **one** termination step.

Initiation: ....

Propagation step 1: ....

Propagation step 2: ....

Propagation step 3: ....

Termination: ....

(5 marks)

(ii) Give **two** reasons why 1,2-dichloroethane is not the only organic product of this reaction.

....

....

....

....

(2 marks)

(b) Waste PVC can be processed in an incinerator using a combustion reaction.

(i) Describe **two** benefits for sustainability of disposing of PVC in this way.

....

....

....

....

(2 marks)

(ii) Waste PVC can also be used as an organic feedstock to produce new polymers.
Suggest **one** benefit for sustainability of processing PVC in this way, rather than using combustion.

....

....

(1 mark)

Scientists are trying to develop biodegradable and photodegradable polymers in order to reduce plastic waste.

(c) (i) Describe and explain **two** benefits to the environment of
biodegradable plastics, compared to plastics such as PVC.

....

....

....

....

....

(4 marks)

(ii) State and explain what is needed in the environment to break down biodegradable
and photodegradable polymers.

....

....

....

(2 marks)

You might have to draw on ideas from lots of different parts of the course (like shapes of molecules, intermolecular bonding and electronegativity) to answer some of the questions in this section, but you'll need to make sure you understand how these ideas apply specifically to organic molecules, so that you can tailor your answers and keep them nice and focused.

Score

31

Alcohols, Haloalkanes and Analysis — 1

Alcohols and haloalkanes have already put in guest appearances in some of the reactions that have come up earlier in this module. Now they're ready to take centre stage.

For each of questions 1-4, give your answer by writing the correct letter in the box.

1   A student measured the time taken for a precipitate to form when a solution of silver nitrate was added to test tubes containing equal volumes and concentrations of one of 1-chlorobutane, 1-iodobutane and 1-bromobutane dissolved in ethanol. Her results are shown below.

Haloalkane	Time taken for precipitate to form / s
1-chlorobutane	588
1-iodobutane	
1-bromobutane	88

Predict how long it took for a precipitate to form in the test tube containing 1-iodobutane.

A   330 seconds   **B**   50 seconds

C   120 seconds   **D**   810 seconds

Your answer [　]

(1 mark)

2   Which of the following compounds could be distinguished from the other three using molecular ion data from mass spectrometry?

A $NH_2CH_2CH_2NH_2$ **B** $CH_3CH_2CH_2OH$

C CH_3COCH_3 **D** CH_3COOH

Your answer [　]

(1 mark)

3   Which of the following shows an alcohol which can undergo oxidation but not elimination of water?

A
```
      H   CH₃ H
      |   |   |
  H — C — C — C — OH
      |   |   |
      H   CH₃ H
```

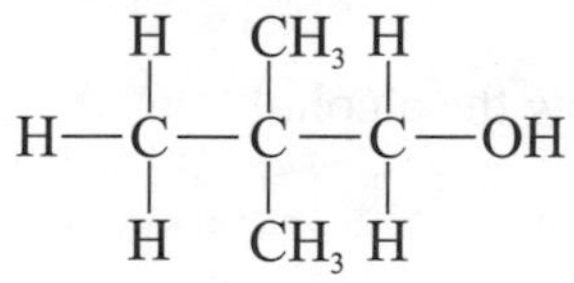

B
```
      H   CH₃ H   H
      |   |   |   |
  H — C — C — C — C — H
      |   |   |   |
      H   CH₃ OH  H
```

C
```
      H   OH  H
      |   |   |
  H — C — C — C — H
      |   |   |
      H   CH₃ H
```

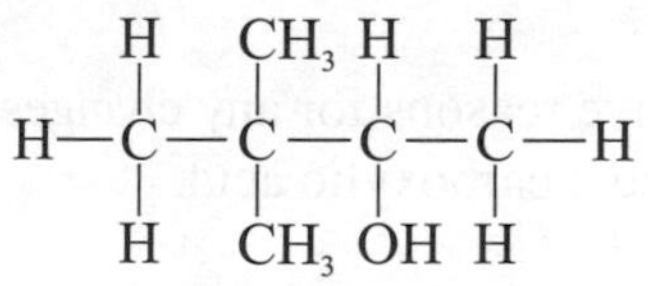

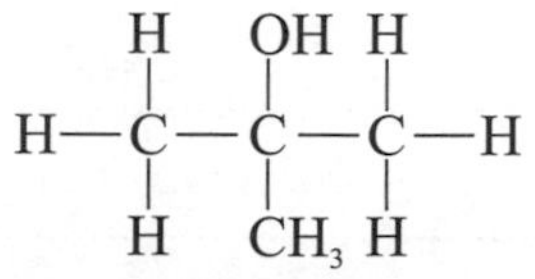

D
```
      H   H   H   H
      |   |   |   |
  H — C — C — C — C — H
      |   |   |   |
      H   H   OH  H
```

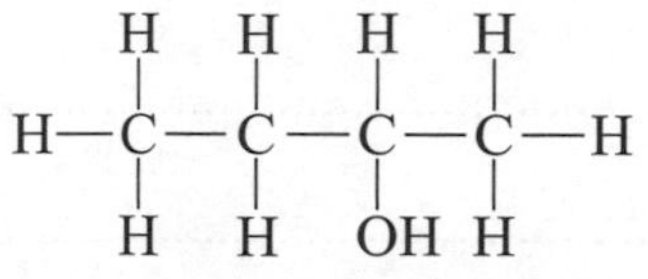

Your answer [　]

(1 mark)

4   The infrared spectrum of compound **X** shows a peak at wavenumber 1700-1725 cm^{-1} and a broad peak at wavenumber 3240-3280 cm^{-1}. Use the data sheet on pages 192-194 to help you determine which of the following functional groups could have caused these peaks.

A   C–C and C=O   **B**   COOH

C   C–O and O–H   **D**   C=C and C=O

Your answer [　]

(1 mark)

5 The apparatus shown below can be used to oxidise an alcohol to an aldehyde.

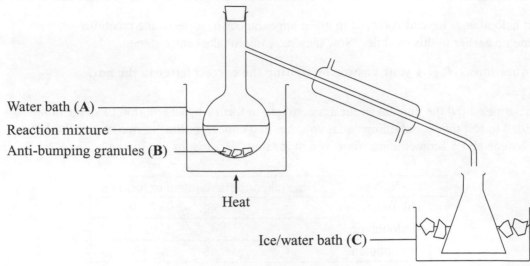

(a) The reaction mixture contains ethanol, sulfuric acid and an excess of an oxidising agent.
Name a suitable oxidising agent for this reaction.

....

(1 mark)

(b) Identify the method shown in the diagram and explain how it allows a pure sample of an aldehyde
to be prepared from an alcohol.

....

....

(2 marks)

(c) Suggest the purpose of the parts of the practical set-up labelled **A** to **C**.

A: ....

B: ....

C: ....

(3 marks)

(d) Describe and give reasons for any changes in the set-up that would allow the alcohol
to be oxidised to a carboxylic acid.

....

....

....

....

(3 marks)

(e) Write an equation to show how ethanol is oxidised to ethanoic acid.
You should represent the oxidising agent as [O] in your answer.

....

(1 mark)

6 Alcohols can be classified as primary, secondary or tertiary.

(a) Draw the displayed formula for each of the following compounds.
Classify each of the compounds as a primary, secondary or tertiary alcohol.
(i) 2-methylbutan-2-ol

Class of alcohol: ....

(2 marks)

(ii) 2-methylpentan-3-ol

Class of alcohol: ....

(2 marks)

Alcohols can be useful as fuels, because they undergo combustion reactions.

(b) Write an equation for the complete combustion of pentan-1-ol.

....

(1 mark)

(c) The boiling points and solubilities for ethane and ethanol are shown in the table below:

	Boiling point / °C	Solubility in water
Ethane	−89	Insoluble
Ethanol	78	Very soluble

(i) Identify the types of intermolecular force present for each compound, and use them to explain the differences between the boiling points of ethane and ethanol.

....

....

....

....

(3 marks)

(ii) Suggest and explain what happens to the solubility of alcohols as the carbon chain increases in length.

....

....

....

(1 mark)

(d) Under acidic conditions, 3-methylbutan-2-ol reacts with sodium chloride to produce an organic product and an inorganic product.

Draw the displayed formula of the organic product formed, and give its name.

Name: ....

(2 marks)

7   Haloalkanes can undergo nucleophilic substitution reactions with a variety of nucleophiles.

(a) Give the meaning of the term nucleophile.

....

(1 mark)

When a warm aqueous solution of potassium hydroxide is added to iodoethane, a nucleophilic substitution reaction occurs producing ethanol and an iodide ion.

(b) (i) Identify the nucleophile in this reaction.

....

(1 mark)

(ii) Draw the mechanism for this nucleophilic substitution reaction.
Include curly arrows and indicate any relevant dipoles.

(3 marks)

(iii) Explain why ethane does not react with potassium hydroxide.

....

....

(1 mark)

Haloalkanes containing multiple halogen atoms can also undergo nucleophilic substitution reactions.

(c) Name the organic compound formed when 2,3-dichlorohexane undergoes a nucleophilic substitution reaction with excess aqueous sodium hydroxide.

....

(1 mark)

EXAM TIP — When you're drawing mechanisms, make sure you're really careful with those curly arrows. To get the marks, the arrows need to go from a bond, a lone pair of electrons or a negative charge. Make sure you show all the relevant positive and negative charges and dipoles correctly.

Score

32

Alcohols, Haloalkanes and Analysis — 2

1 The displayed formula for compound **B** is shown below.

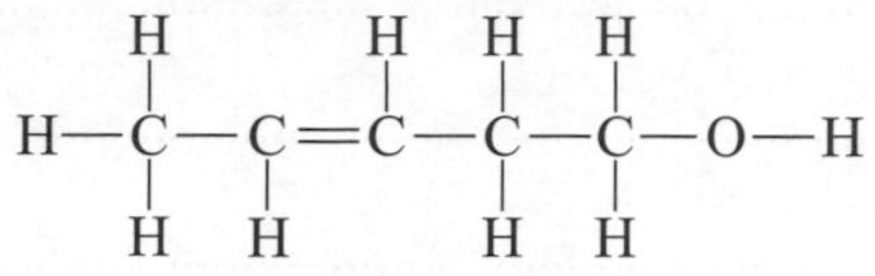

$$H-\underset{\underset{H}{|}}{\overset{\overset{H}{|}}{C}}-\underset{\underset{H}{|}}{\overset{\overset{H}{|}}{C}}=\underset{\underset{H}{|}}{\overset{\overset{H}{|}}{C}}-\underset{\underset{H}{|}}{\overset{\overset{H}{|}}{C}}-\underset{\underset{H}{|}}{\overset{\overset{H}{|}}{C}}-O-H$$

Compound **B**

(a) Name the functional groups present in compound **B**.

....

....

(1 mark)

(b) Identify and explain the types of reaction that occur, along with the expected observations made, when each of the following reagents are added to a sample of compound **B**:

(i) Bromine water at room temperature

....

....

(2 marks)

(ii) Acidified potassium dichromate(VI) whilst heating under reflux

....

....

(2 marks)

(c) Alcohols can be converted into alkanes via a two-stage synthesis.
An example using propan-2-ol is shown below.

$$\text{propan-2-ol} \xrightarrow{\text{Stage 1}} \text{propene} \xrightarrow{\text{Stage 2}} \text{propane}$$

Name the type of reaction, the reagents and the conditions required for each stage of the synthesis.

(i) Stage 1:

Type of reaction: ....

Reagents and conditions: ....

....

(2 marks)

(ii) Stage 2:

Type of reaction: ....

Reagents and conditions: ....

....

(3 marks)

66

2 Infrared spectroscopy is a commonly used method of analysing compounds.

(a) Explain how the infrared spectra for water vapour, carbon dioxide and methane could be used to provide evidence for the fact that these compounds act as greenhouse gases.

....

....

....

....

....

(3 marks)

(b) Infrared spectroscopy is used to test for ethanol in the breath of drivers suspected of drink-driving. Suggest why this test focuses on the C–H bond in the ethanol molecules instead of the OH group.

....

....

(1 mark)

Compound **I** is one of butanol, butanal or but-2-ene. It was analysed using infrared spectroscopy to determine its identity. The spectrum produced is shown below.

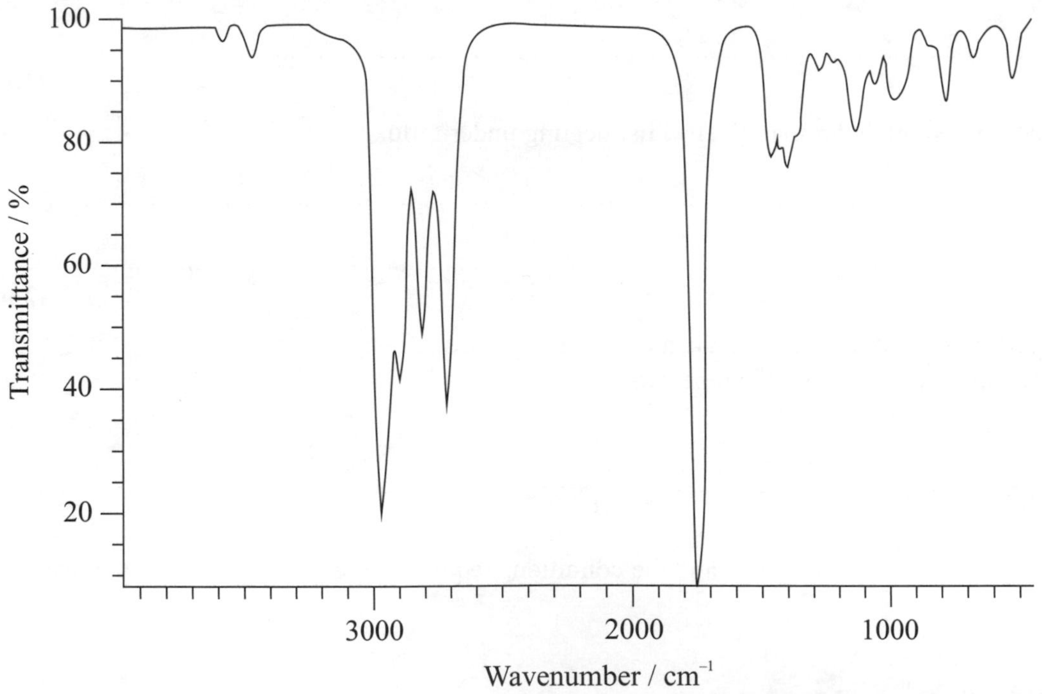

(c) Use the spectrum and the infrared absorption data given on the data sheet on pages 192-194 to identify compound **I** as either butanol, butanal or but-2-ene. Give full reasoning for your answer.

....

....

....

....

(4 marks)

3 In the presence of water, haloalkanes undergo nucleophilic substitution reactions to form an alcohol and a halide ion. These types of reactions are also known as hydrolysis reactions.

(a) Suggest why the reaction with water is slower than other nucleophilic substitution reactions of haloalkanes.

....

(1 mark)

The bond enthalpies of the carbon-halogen bonds are shown below:

Bond	C–F	C–Cl	C–Br	C–I
Bond enthalpy / kJ mol^{-1}	467	346	290	228

(b) Use the data to predict and explain the trend in the rates of hydrolysis of the carbon-halogen bonds.

....

....

....

(2 marks)

The rate of hydrolysis of different carbon-halogen bonds can be compared experimentally using water in the presence of silver nitrate and ethanol.

(c)* Describe the method used to investigate the trend in the rate of hydrolysis of 1-chlorobutane, 1-bromobutane and 1-iodobutane. Your answer should include:
- an explanation of what steps are taken to ensure that the experiment is a fair comparison of the carbon-halogen bonds present,
- general equations for the reactions that take place, using X to represent a halogen.

....

....

....

....

....

....

....

....

....

....

(6 marks)

EXAM TIP

There are lots of reactions in the organic section of this course — and you might well get a question that asks you to put two of them together in an unfamiliar way. If you need to find a route from one compound to another and you haven't a clue how to get there, just keep calm and start by thinking what you do know about the reactions of the initial compound.

Score

27

Alcohols, Haloalkanes and Analysis — 3

1   A student plans to prepare a pure sample of 1-bromobutane from butan-1-ol and potassium bromide.

In the first stage of the experiment the reaction mixture is shaken in a sealed flask.
The mixture contains butan-1-ol, aqueous potassium bromide solution and a third reagent.

(a)   Suggest the identity of the third reagent.

....

(1 mark)

After shaking, the reaction mixture contains 1-bromobutane, and may also contain unreacted reagents.
1-bromobutane is insoluble in water. It is also more dense than water.

(b)   Name a piece of equipment that can be used to remove any water-soluble impurities from the reaction
mixture, and describe how it is used.

....

....

....

....

....

(4 marks)

The impure 1-bromobutane removed from the reaction mixture may still contain traces of water, which must
be removed using a drying agent. At the end of the drying process, the drying agent must also be removed.

(c)   Name a suitable drying agent and suggest how it can be removed from the 1-bromobutane.

....

....

(2 marks)

Once the drying agent has been removed from the 1-bromobutane, there may still be impurities remaining.

(d)   Name and describe a technique that could be used to remove any liquid impurities remaining and allow
pure 1-bromobutane to be collected.

....

....

....

....

....

....

....

(6 marks)

e) Suggest **two** reasons why the percentage yield for this preparation is not 100%.

....

....

(2 marks)

2   Organic compound **X** is a liquid with an unknown identity. The identity and structure of compound **X** can be determined by combining information gathered from different methods of analysis.

The mass spectrum of compound **X** is shown below.

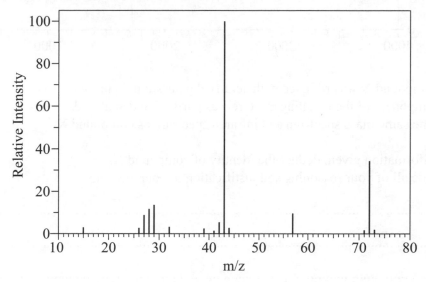

The molecular ion peak on the mass spectrum of compound **X** has a mass/charge (m/z) value of 72. There is also a smaller peak, the M+1 peak, at a mass/charge value of 73.

(a) Explain why this M+1 peak is present.

....

(1 mark)

(b) State what information about organic compound **X** is given by the value of the molecular ion peak.

....

(1 mark)

Combustion analysis showed that the composition by mass of compound **X** is 66.7% carbon, 11.1% hydrogen and 22.2% oxygen.

(c) Use this data to deduce the empirical formula of compound **X**.

(2 marks)

An infrared spectrum for compound **X** was also produced. This spectrum is shown below.

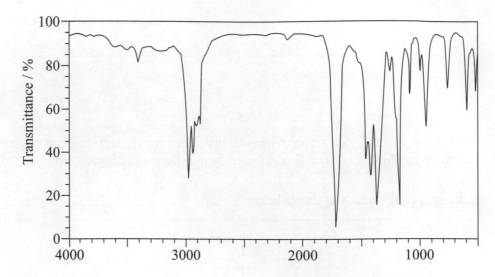

A sample of compound **X** was refluxed with acidified potassium dichromate(VI). The organic component of the resulting mixture was purified and analysed, and produced the same mass spectrum and infrared spectrum as compound **X**.

(d)* Using all the information given, deduce the identity of compound **X**. You must include all of your reasoning and justification in your answer.

....

....

....

....

....

....

....

....

....

....

....

....

....

(6 marks)

Score

25

Rates and Equilibrium — 1

Best pop back to Module 3 to refresh your memory of your Year 1 work on this topic before getting started here.

For each of questions 1-4, give your answer by writing the correct letter in the box.

1   The rate equation for the reaction between two compounds, A and B, is: Rate = $k[A]^2[B]$.
What would happen to the rate of reaction if the concentrations of both A and B were tripled?

A	It would increase by a factor of 3.	**B**	It would increase by a factor of 27.
C	It would increase by a factor of 18.	**D**	It would increase by a factor of 9.

Your answer ☐

(1 mark)

2   Four concentration-time graphs for chemical reactions are shown below.

Graph 1	**Graph 2**	**Graph 3**	**Graph 4**
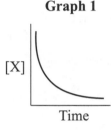	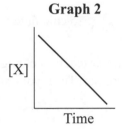	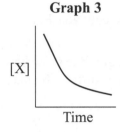	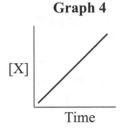

Which graph correctly shows a reaction in which increasing the
concentration of reactant X would **not** affect the rate of the reaction?

A	Graph 1	**B**	Graph 2
C	Graph 3	**D**	Graph 4

Your answer ☐

(1 mark)

3   The equilibrium constant for the reversible dissociation of N_2O_4 into two molecules of NO_2
is 6.03×10^3 atm at 550 K. The partial pressure of N_2O_4 in a sealed container held at 550 K
is found to be 1.78×10^3 atm. What is the partial pressure of NO_2 in the container?

A	4.25×10^3 atm	**B**	3.56×10^3 atm
C	3.39×10^3 atm	**D**	3.28×10^3 atm

Your answer ☐

(1 mark)

4   A scientist heats a sample of gaseous chloroethane. At a certain temperature, chloroethane molecules
start to decompose, forming ethane and hydrogen chloride. The activation energy for the reaction is
254.4 kJ mol^{-1}, the rate constant is 1.37×10^{-4} s^{-1} and the pre-exponential factor is 4.00×10^{14} s^{-1}.

Use the Arrhenius equation to calculate the temperature at which the decomposition reaction happens.

A	330 K	**B**	1250 K
C	720 K	**D**	500 K

*There's a data sheet showing
useful equations and
constants on pages 192-194.*

Your answer ☐

(1 mark)

5 Sodium thiosulfate ($Na_2S_2O_3$) reacts with hydrochloric acid to produce a mixture of products. The equation for the reaction is:

$$Na_2S_2O_{3(aq)} + 2HCl_{(aq)} \rightarrow 2NaCl_{(aq)} + S_{(s)} + SO_{2(g)} + H_2O_{(l)}$$

A student measured the time taken for a fixed amount of solid sulfur to form at different concentrations of sodium thiosulfate. The results of the experiment are given in the table below.

Concentration of $Na_2S_2O_{3(aq)}$ / mol dm^{-3}	Time taken / s	Rate of reaction / $\times 10^{-3}$ s^{-1}
0	0	0
0.200	404	
0.400	199	
0.600	137	
0.800	103	

(a) Complete the table by using the equation $Rate = \dfrac{1}{Time\ taken}$ to calculate the missing rates of reaction.

(2 marks)

(b) (i) On the grid below, draw a graph to show how the rate of reaction changes with increasing concentration of sodium thiosulfate. Include a line of best fit in your answer.

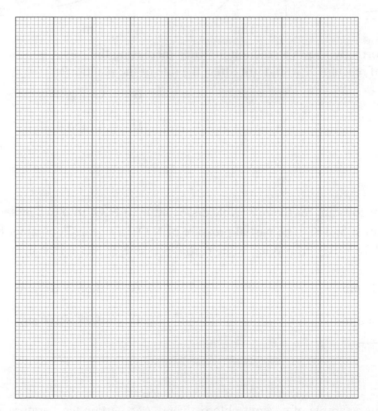

(3 marks)

(ii) Use the graph you drew in **(b)(i)** to determine the order of reaction with respect to sodium thiosulfate. Justify your answer.

....

....

....

(2 marks)

(c)   A series of similar experiments showed that the reaction is zero order with respect to hydrochloric acid. Use this information, along with your answer to **(b)(ii)**, to write the rate equation for this reaction.

....

(1 mark)

6   In a clock reaction the time taken for a set amount of product to form for an initial concentration of a given reactant is measured. This measurement is then used to estimate the initial rate of the reaction.

A student is investigating the iodine clock reaction between hydrogen peroxide and an acidified solution of iodide ions. They vary the concentration of the iodide solution and use the method outlined above to estimate the initial rate at each concentration. The table shows their results.

$[I^-]$ / mol dm^{-3}	Initial rate of reaction / $\times 10^{-8}$ mol dm^{-3} s^{-1}
0	0.0
0.1	1.1
0.2	2.3
0.3	3.6
0.4	4.7
0.5	5.9

(a)   Plot a graph using these results. Include a line of best fit.

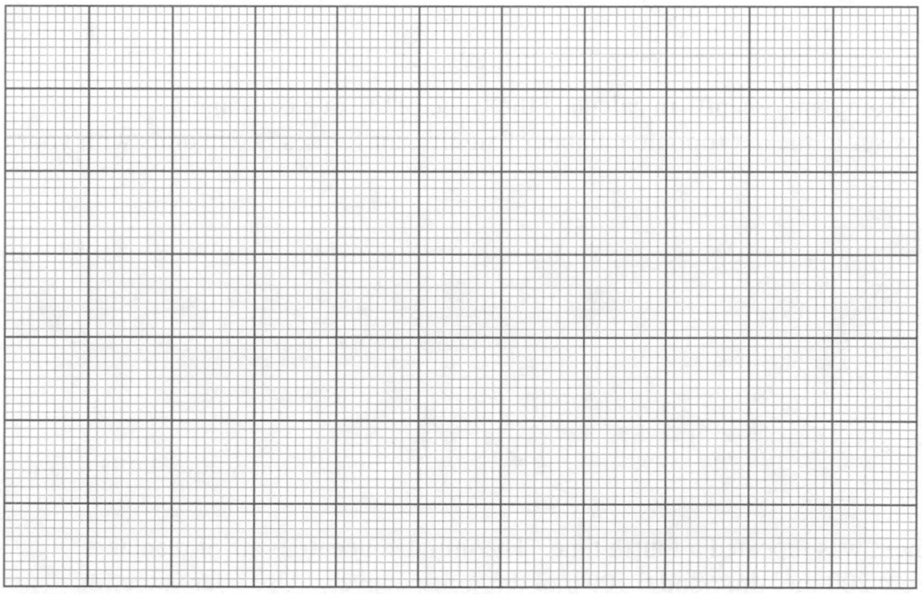

(3 marks)

(b)   Use your graph to determine the rate constant, k, for this reaction. Include units in your answer.

$k = $ .... units = ...

(2 marks)

7 A student carried out a series of experiments to measure the initial rate of reaction between two reactants, **E** and **F**, at various concentrations.

The table shows the results of the experiments.

Experiment	[E] / mol dm^{-3}	[F] / mol dm^{-3}	Initial rate of reaction / mol dm^{-3} s^{-1}
1	0.0800	0.0600	8.00×10^{-4}
2	0.0800	0.0900	12.0×10^{-4}
3	0.120	0.0900	18.0×10^{-4}

(a) Use the data provided to determine the order of reaction with respect to each of the reactants E and F. Justify your answer.

....

....

....

....

(2 marks)

(b) Write the rate equation for the reaction.

....

(1 mark)

(c) Deduce the overall order of the reaction.

....

(1 mark)

(d) Use the data from experiment 1 to calculate the value of the rate constant, k.
Give your answer to the appropriate number of significant figures. Give units with your answer.

$k =$ .... units ....

(4 marks)

(e) The experiment was repeated a fourth time. The initial concentrations of reactants E and F were 0.200 mol dm^{-3} and 0.500 mol dm^{-3}, respectively. Use your value for the rate constant from **(d)** to calculate the initial rate of the reaction for this repeat.

Initial rate of reaction = ... mol dm^{-3} s^{-1}

(1 mark)

EXAM TIP	Make sure you check the units of any data you're given in the exam — sometimes for very small (or very large) quantities you might be given the units in standard form, e.g. $\times 10^{-3}$ s^{-1}. It's important that you remember to take this into account if you're using the data in any calculations, such as calculating the rate of reaction or determining the gradient of a graph.

Score

26

Rates and Equilibrium — 2

1 When steam is passed over carbon the following equilibrium reaction occurs:
$$C_{(s)} + H_2O_{(g)} \rightleftharpoons H_{2(g)} + CO_{(g)}$$

(a) Write the expression for K_p for this reaction.

....

(1 mark)

(b) A scientist is monitoring this reaction. At equilibrium, they find that the partial pressure of the water in the equilibrium mixture is 71.6 kPa. The total pressure of the mixture is 111 kPa. Calculate the partial pressure of the hydrogen in the reaction mixture.

Partial pressure of hydrogen = ... kPa

(2 marks)

(c) Calculate a value for K_p for this reaction.
Give your answer to an appropriate number of significant figures.
Give units with your answer.

K_p = ... units ....

(3 marks)

2 Calcium carbonate reacts with hydrochloric acid to produce calcium chloride, water and carbon dioxide gas.
$$CaCO_{3(s)} + 2HCl_{(aq)} \rightarrow CaCl_{2(aq)} + H_2O_{(l)} + CO_{2(g)}$$

In an experiment to monitor the rate of this reaction at 298 K, an excess of calcium carbonate was added to dilute hydrochloric acid. The volume of carbon dioxide produced by the reaction over time was measured.

(a) Draw a labelled diagram to show an experimental set-up that could be used to collect and measure the volume of carbon dioxide gas produced over time.

(3 marks)

The measurements of carbon dioxide gas were used to calculate how the concentration of HCl changed over the course of the reaction. The results of the experiment are shown on the graph below.

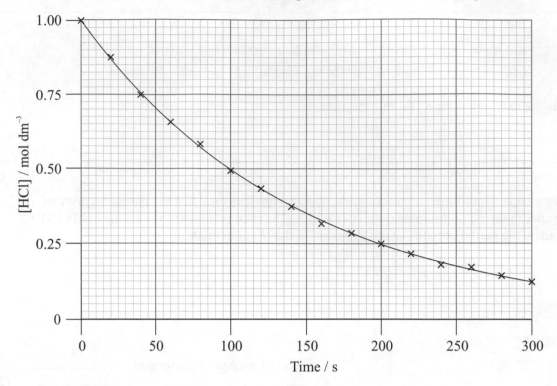

(b) (i) Using the graph, determine the initial rate of the reaction.
Show your working.

Initial rate of reaction = ... mol dm^{-3} s^{-1}

(2 marks)

(ii) State and explain how the rate of reaction changes as the reaction proceeds.

....

....

(2 marks)

(c) Concentration-time graphs can also be used to determine the half-life of a reaction.
(i) Explain what is meant by the half-life of a chemical reaction.

....

....

(1 mark)

(ii) Using the graph, determine the half-life of this reaction and
hence deduce the order of the reaction with respect to HCl.

half-life = ... s

order of reaction = ...

(3 marks)

(iii) Calculate a value for the rate constant, k, for this reaction at a temperature of 298 K. Include units in your answer.

$k =$ .... units = ...

(3 marks)

3 The Haber process and the Contact process are important methods for the production of industrial chemicals.

(a) The Haber process is a reversible reaction used to manufacture ammonia gas. The equation for the reaction is:

$$N_{2(g)} + 3H_{2(g)} \rightleftharpoons 2NH_{3(g)} \qquad \Delta H = -92.4 \text{ kJ mol}^{-1}$$

(i) Write an expression for K_p for this reaction.

....

(1 mark)

(ii) An equilibrium mixture at a pressure of 200 atm is found to contain 15.0 moles of nitrogen, 30.0 moles of hydrogen and 22.0 moles of ammonia.

Use this information to calculate a value for K_p for the reaction under these conditions. Give your answer to an appropriate number of significant figures. Give units with your answer.

$K_p =$ .... units = ...

(6 marks)

(iii) Predict how increases in the pressure and temperature, and the addition of a catalyst, would affect the position of equilibrium and the value of K_p for this reaction. Justify your predictions.

....

....

....

....

....

....

....

....

....

....

....

....

(6 marks)

(b) The Contact process is used in the manufacture of sulfuric acid.
The second step involves the reversible reaction shown in the equation below.

$$2SO_{2(g)} + O_{2(g)} \rightleftharpoons 2SO_{3(g)}$$

A mixture of sulfur dioxide and oxygen was sealed in a container and allowed to reach equilibrium at a constant temperature. The partial pressure of SO_3 was found to be 96 kPa and the partial pressure of O_2 was found to be 40 kPa. The value for K_p under these conditions is 0.056 kPa^{-1}.

(i) Use this information to calculate the partial pressure of sulfur dioxide in the equilibrium mixture.

Partial pressure of SO_2 = ... kPa

(3 marks)

(ii) Calculate the total pressure of the reaction mixture.

Total pressure = ... kPa

(1 mark)

Score

37

Rates and Equilibrium — 3

1   A student is using an initial rate method to determine the rate of the following reaction:

$$CH_3COCH_{3(aq)} + I_{2(aq)} \xrightarrow{\text{HCl catalyst}} CH_3COCH_2I_{(aq)} + HI_{(aq)}$$

The student varies the concentration of each reagent in separate experiments and measures the time taken for the iodine colour to just disappear. The table below shows the results of experiment 1. Water was added to allow the total volume to be kept constant in subsequent experiments.

Expt.	Volume of 1.0 mol dm^{-3} CH$_3$COCH$_3$ / cm^3	Volume of 0.004 mol dm^{-3} I$_2$ / cm^3	Volume of 1.0 mol dm^{-3} HCl / cm^3	Volume of H$_2$O / cm^3	Time / s
1	10	4	10	26	210
2					

The reaction is first order with respect to both CH$_3$COCH$_3$ and HCl and zero order with respect to I$_2$.

(a) (i)   Complete the table by suggesting volumes of reagents that the student could use to show that the reaction is first order with respect to propanone, CH$_3$COCH$_3$. Include the expected result of the experiment in your answer.

(3 marks)

(ii) Write the rate equation for this reaction.

....

(1 mark)

(iii) The initial rate for experiment 1 was found to be 1.5×10^{-6} mol dm^{-3} s^{-1}.
Calculate a value for the rate constant, k, using the data provided in the table.
Give your answer to an appropriate number of significant figures.
Give units with your answer.

$k = $ .... units = ...

(5 marks)

(iv) A proposed rate-determining step for the reaction is shown below.

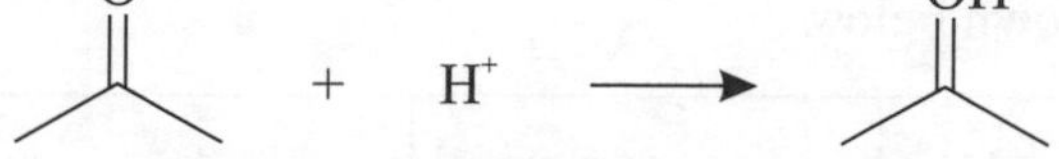

Explain how the rate equation for the reaction provides evidence that this is the rate-determining step.

....

....

....

(2 marks)

Module 5 : Physical Chemistry and Transition Elements

(b) Another student decides to use colorimetry to confirm that this reaction is not first order with respect to iodine. They produce the calibration curve shown below by measuring the absorbances of iodine solutions of known concentration.

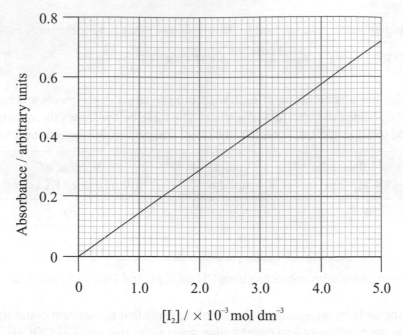

The student takes samples of the reaction mixture at regular intervals and measures their absorbances using the colorimeter. Their results are shown in the table below.

Time / s	0	20	40	60	80
Absorbance / arbitrary units	0.58	0.46	0.36	0.25	0.14
$[I_2] / \times 10^{-3}$ mol dm^{-3}	4.0				

(i) Use the calibration curve to complete the table with the concentrations of iodine present at each time.

(2 marks)

(ii) The student wants to use their results to plot a concentration-time graph for iodine over the course of the reaction. Describe the shape you would expect this graph to have. Explain your answer.

....

....

(2 marks)

2 Iodide ions can be oxidised by iodate(V) ions in acidic solution. The equation for the reaction is:
$$IO_3^-{}_{(aq)} + 5I^-{}_{(aq)} + 6H^+{}_{(aq)} \rightarrow 3I_{2(aq)} + 3H_2O_{(l)}$$

An experiment to determine the activation energy for this reaction was carried out. The processed results are shown below.

Temperature / K	$\frac{1}{T} / (\times 10^{-3}\,K^{-1})$	k / s^{-1}	$\ln k$
673	1.49	1.01×10^{-4}	−9.20
704	1.42	5.00×10^{-4}	−7.60
740	1.35	3.08×10^{-3}	−5.78
775	1.29	1.50×10^{-2}	−4.20

The Arrhenius equation can be used to determine the activation energy for any chemical reaction as long as the values of the temperature and rate constant, k, are known.

(a) (i) Describe how the Arrhenius equation can be used with the data given in the table to calculate the activation energy for this reaction.

....

....

....

....

(3 marks)

(ii) Use your knowledge of collision theory to explain how the value of the rate constant, k, would be affected by an increase in temperature.

....

....

....

....

....

(4 marks)

(b) Iodide ions can also be oxidised by peroxydisulfate ions, $S_2O_8^{2-}$.
The activation energy for this reaction is 44.9 kJ mol^{-1} and the rate constant is 1.54×10^{-6} mol^{-1} dm^3 s^{-1}.
Use this information to calculate the pre-exponential factor, A, for the reaction at 298 K.

A = ... mol^{-1} dm^3 s^{-1}

(2 marks)

3 This question is about reactions involving propan-1-ol.

(a) 5.00 cm^3 of 13.5 mol dm^{-3} propan-1-ol was reacted with 5.00 cm^3 of 17.4 mol dm^{-3} ethanoic acid.
This produced the ester propyl ethanoate and water, as shown by the equation below.

$$C_3H_7OH_{(l)} + CH_3COOH_{(l)} \rightleftharpoons CH_3COOC_3H_{7(l)} + H_2O_{(l)}$$

(i) Write the expression for K_c for this reaction.

....

(1 mark)

Once the reaction mixture had reached equilibrium, it was made up to a volume of 250 cm^3 by adding deionised water.

25.0 cm^3 samples of this solution were then titrated against 0.200 mol dm^{-3} sodium hydroxide solution to determine the number of moles of ethanoic acid present. The equation for this titration reaction is:

$$CH_3COOH + NaOH \rightarrow CH_3COONa + H_2O$$

The average titre of sodium hydroxide needed was 42.6 cm^3.

(ii) Use the information given to determine the number of moles of ethanoic acid present in the equilibrium mixture and hence calculate the equilibrium concentration of propyl ethanoate.

You may assume that the number of moles of each of the organic species present following dilution of the reaction mixture was the same as the number of moles present at equilibrium.

equilibrium concentration of propyl ethanoate = ... mol dm^{-3}
(6 marks)

(b) Propan-1-ol can be produced from 1-bromopropane through a nucleophilic substitution reaction. There are two possible mechanisms for this reaction.

Mechanism A	Step 1: $C_3H_7Br \rightarrow C_3H_7^+ + :Br^-$	Slow
	Step 2: $C_3H_7^+ + :OH^- \rightarrow C_3H_7OH$	Fast
Mechanism B	$C_3H_7Br + :OH^- \rightarrow C_3H_7OH + :Br^-$	

(i) State what is meant by the term rate-determining step.

....

....
(1 mark)

The rate equation for the nucleophilic substitution of 1-bromopropane is:

$$\text{rate} = k[C_3H_7Br][:OH^-]$$

(ii) Use the information provided to deduce whether mechanism A or mechanism B is the correct mechanism for this reaction. Give your reasoning.

....

....
(1 mark)

EXAM TIP

The various forms of the Arrhenius equation can look a bit daunting, what with all those exponentials and logs, but the good news is you'll always be given it if you need it in the exam. Make sure you get plenty of practice rearranging it beforehand though — you'll be less likely to make a mistake when it matters if you're already familiar with the different rearrangements.

Score

33

pH — 1

You'll need all your concentration to find the solutions to this section — it's not as basic as it seems...

For each of questions 1-4, give your answer by writing the correct letter in the box.

1   An acidic buffer solution can be made up of which of the following?

    A   Excess of a weak alkali and a strong acid

    B   Excess of a strong alkali and a strong acid

    C   Excess of a weak acid and a strong alkali

    D   Excess of a strong acid and a strong alkali

    Your answer ☐

    (1 mark)

2   An acid has a K_a value of 2.24×10^{-5} mol dm^{-3}. What is the pK_a value of the acid?

    A   4.65   **B**   10.7

    C   1.00   **D**   6.29

    Your answer ☐

    (1 mark)

3   Lithium hydroxide is a strong base. At 298 K the value of K_w is 1.00×10^{-14} mol^2 dm^{-6}. What is the pH of a 0.500 mol dm^{-3} solution of lithium hydroxide at this temperature?

    A   13.4   **B**   14.6

    C   14.3   **D**   13.7

    Your answer ☐

    (1 mark)

4   The acid dissociation constants, K_a, of two weak acids are shown in the table below.

Acid	Chloric(I) acid	Ethanoic acid
K_a	3.7×10^{-8}	1.7×10^{-5}

    Which of the following statements are true?

    1. The weakest acid in the table has the lowest pK_a.
    2. The pK_a of ethanoic acid is 4.8 (2 s.f.)
    3. Ethanoic acid is the stronger of the two acids.

    A   1, 2 and 3   **B**   Only 1 and 2

    C   Only 2 and 3   **D**   Only 1

    Your answer ☐

    (1 mark)

Module 5 : Physical Chemistry and Transition Elements

5   The Brønsted-Lowry theory can be used to explain the reactions of acids and bases.

Sodium hydroxide is an example of a Brønsted-Lowry base.

(a)   State the meaning of the term Brønsted-Lowry base.

....
(1 mark)

Hydrochloric acid and sulfuric acid are examples of strong Brønsted-Lowry acids.

(b)   State and explain the relative difference in the K_a value of a strong acid compared with that of a weak acid.

....

....

....
(3 marks)

(c)   (i)   Write an equation to show how hydrochloric acid acts as a strong acid when added to water.

....
(1 mark)

     (ii)   Calculate the pH of a 0.0500 mol dm^{-3} solution of hydrochloric acid.

pH = ...
(1 mark)

(d)   A student is using a pH meter to measure the pH of a solution of 1.0×10^{-3} mol dm^{-3} sulfuric acid.

     (i)   Describe how the student could calibrate the pH meter before use.

....

....

....

....
(4 marks)

     (ii)   The student found the solution to have a pH of 2.7. The uncertainty in this reading is ±0.05. Calculate the percentage uncertainty in the student's measurement of the pH of the solution. Give your answer to 1 significant figure.

Percentage uncertainty = ... %
(1 mark)

     (iii)   Write an equation to show the first ionisation of sulfuric acid in water.

....
(1 mark)

     (iv)   Identify a conjugate acid-base pair in your answer to part **(iii)**.

Conjugate acid: ....

Conjugate base: ....
(1 mark)

6 Carboxylic acids, such as propanoic acid, are weak acids.

(a) Write an equation to show how propanoic acid (CH_3CH_2COOH) acts as a weak acid when added to water.

....

(1 mark)

The pH of a weak acid can be calculated using the acid dissociation constant, K_a.

(b) Write the K_a expression for propanoic acid.

....

(1 mark)

A student prepared a solution of propanoic acid with a volume of 150 cm^3.
The solution contained 12.0 g of propanoic acid. The K_a value for propanoic acid is 1.34×10^{-5} mol dm^{-3}.

(c) Calculate the pH of the solution of propanoic acid.

pH = ...

(5 marks)

(d) Hydrofluoric acid (HF) is a weak acid with a K_a value of 5.6×10^{-4} mol dm^{-3}.
Explain why using K_a to calculate the pH of a solution of hydrofluoric acid would give a less accurate result than the same calculation for propanoic acid.

....

....

....

(3 marks)

EXAM TIP

Even if you're confident you know what you're doing, it's always a good idea to write out your working in full. That way if you do slip up and end up with the wrong numbers, the examiner will still be able to understand what you're trying to do and give you some marks for it. If you're worried any stage of your working is unclear, you can just add in a brief note to explain it.

Score

27

pH — 2

1 The ionic product of water can be used to calculate the pH of solutions of strong bases.

(a) Give the expression for the ionic product of water.

....
(1 mark)

The dissociation of water is an equilibrium process. The value of K_w varies with temperature.

(b) As temperature increases, the position of equilibrium shifts to the right.
Explain the effect of increasing temperature on the value of K_w.

....

....
(2 marks)

At a temperature of 298 K the value of K_w is 1.00×10^{-14} mol^2 dm^{-6}.

(c) Calculate the pH of a 0.800 mol dm^{-3} solution of the strong base potassium hydroxide at 298 K.

pH = ...
(3 marks)

When the temperature was increased to 373 K, the same solution
of potassium hydroxide was found to have a pH of 12.19.

(d) Calculate the value of K_w for the solution at this higher temperature.

K_w = ... mol^2 dm^{-3}
(2 marks)

(e) Potassium hydroxide can be used to neutralise a solution of hydrochloric acid. A suitable indicator
for this titration is resazurin (R-H). In solution, resazurin establishes the following equilibrium:

$$\text{R-H} \rightleftharpoons \text{H}^+ + \text{R}^-$$
$$\text{Orange} \qquad\qquad \text{Purple}$$

(i) State the colour that resazurin would be in a basic solution.

....
(1 mark)

(ii) Explain why the solution containing resazurin changes colour over the course of the titration.

....

....

....

....

(3 marks)

2   A student adds 25 cm^3 of 0.050 mol dm^{-3} propanoic acid solution to a beaker containing 100 cm^3 of 0.125 mol dm^{-3} sodium propanoate solution. An acidic buffer solution is produced.

(a)   Write an equation for the dissociation of sodium propanoate.

....

(1 mark)

(b)   The K_a value for propanoic acid is 1.34 × 10^{-5} mol dm^{-3}.
Calculate the pH of the acidic buffer solution produced.

pH = ...

(5 marks)

(c)   A small amount of dilute hydrochloric acid was added to the buffer solution.
State and explain the effect that this would have on the pH of the solution.

....

....

....

....

(4 marks)

(d)   Give the chemical formula of the compounds in the conjugate acid-base pair
that acts a buffer system in the human bloodstream.

Conjugate acid: ....

Conjugate base: ....

(1 mark)

3   The pH changes which occur during an acid-base titration
can be measured and used to produce a pH curve.

The graph below shows a typical pH curve for a titration involving a strong acid and a weak base.

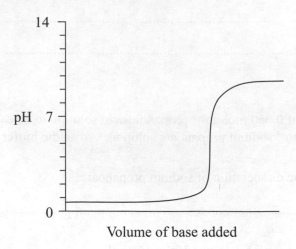

Indicators are chemicals which are used to detect the end point of an acid-base titration.
Some commonly used indicators, along with their pH ranges and
colours in acidic and basic solutions, are shown in the table below.

Indicator	Colour in acidic solution	Colour in basic solution	pH range over which the colour change occurs
Methyl orange	Red	Yellow	3.10 - 4.40
Phenolphthalein	Colourless	Pink	8.30 - 10.00
Phenol red	Yellow	Red	6.80 - 8.20

(a)   (i)   Explain how the equivalence point on a pH curve can be used to determine the most
suitable indicator to use in an acid-base titration.

....

....

....
(2 marks)

(ii)   Use the pH curve shown above and the information in the table to select the
most appropriate indicator to use in a titration of a strong acid with a weak base.
Give the colour change that would occur at the end point of the titration.

Indicator: ....

Colour change: ....
(1 mark)

(iii)   Explain why an indicator cannot be used to determine the equivalence point
in a titration between a weak acid and a weak base.

....

....
(2 marks)

The value of the acid dissociation constant, K_a, for a weak acid such as butanoic acid ($CH_3CH_2CH_2COOH$) can be determined from the pH curve produced during a reaction of the weak acid with a strong base.

(b) Write a balanced symbol equation for the neutralisation reaction that occurs when butanoic acid is titrated with sodium hydroxide, NaOH.

....

(1 mark)

(c) In a titration involving 0.0500 mol dm⁻³ butanoic acid and 0.0500 mol dm⁻³ sodium hydroxide, the equivalence point was reached after 25.0 cm³ of the sodium hydroxide had been added.

(i) At the half-neutralisation point, enough sodium hydroxide had been added to neutralise exactly half of the butanoic acid originally present. Calculate the concentrations of the acid and its salt at the half-neutralisation point. Give your answers to an appropriate number of significant figures.

Concentration of acid = ... mol dm⁻³

Concentration of salt = ... mol dm⁻³

(6 marks)

(ii) Write an expression for K_a for butanoic acid.

....

(1 mark)

(iii) The pH at the half-neutralisation point was 4.80.
Use this information and your answers to parts **(i)** and **(ii)** to calculate the value of K_a for butanoic acid.

K_a = ... mol dm⁻³

(2 marks)

For questions involving K_a it's always a good idea to start by writing out the expression for K_a for the reaction you're interested in. That way you can see what data you have, what data you need, and how you need to rearrange the expression. You won't always just be given numbers to plug in, sometimes you might need to use the reaction equation to help you with your calculation.

Score

38

Energy — 1

You can calculate how many biscuits you'll need for this section if you know your enthalpy change of revision...

For each of questions 1-4, give your answer by writing the correct letter in the box.

1   Which of the following would **not** be used in a standard hydrogen electrode?

A   A 2 mol dm^{-3} solution of HCl   **B**   A temperature of 298 K

C   A platinum electrode   **D**   Hydrogen gas at a pressure of 100 kPa

Your answer ☐

(1 mark)

2   A reaction is endothermic and is accompanied by a positive entropy change.
Which statement best describes the feasibility of the reaction?

A   It is never feasible.

B   It is feasible below a certain temperature.

C   It is always feasible.

D   It is feasible above a certain temperature.

Your answer ☐

(1 mark)

3   The table below shows some standard electrode potentials.

Electrode half-equation	$E^{⦵}$/V
$Al^{3+} + 3e^- \rightleftharpoons Al$	−1.66
$2H^+ + 2e^- \rightleftharpoons H_2$	0.00
$Fe^{3+} + e^- \rightleftharpoons Fe^{2+}$	+0.77
$Cl_2 + 2e^- \rightleftharpoons 2Cl^-$	+1.36

Which of the species shown in the table could reduce hydrogen ions?

A   Both Fe^{2+} and Cl^- **B** Al^{3+} only

C   Al only   **D**   Both Al^{3+} and Fe^{3+}

Your answer ☐

(1 mark)

4   The lattice enthalpy of barium chloride is −2056 kJ mol^{-1}, the enthalpy of solution is −36 kJ mol^{-1} and the enthalpy of hydration of a Cl^- ion is −364 kJ mol^{-1}.
What is the enthalpy of hydration of a barium ion?

A   −1364 kJ mol^{-1} **B**   + 1656 kJ mol^{-1}

C   −1728 kJ mol^{-1} **D**   + 1292 kJ mol^{-1}

Your answer ☐

(1 mark)

5 Strontium chloride and rubidium chloride are both soluble metal chlorides.

(a) (i) State the meaning of the term enthalpy change of solution.

....

....
(1 mark)

(ii) Write a symbol equation that represents the process of dissolving strontium chloride.

....
(1 mark)

(iii) Use the data in the table below to calculate the enthalpy of solution of strontium chloride.

Enthalpy change	$\Delta H^\ominus$ / kJ mol^{-1}
Enthalpy of hydration of Sr^{2+}	-1445
Enthalpy of hydration of Cl^-	-364
Lattice enthalpy of strontium chloride	-2156

Enthalpy of solution of strontium chloride = ... kJ mol^{-1}
(2 marks)

(b) (i) The enthalpy of solution of rubidium chloride is slightly endothermic at 298 K.
Suggest why rubidium chloride is reasonably soluble in water at room temperature.

....

....

....

....
(3 marks)

(ii) The enthalpy of hydration of Rb^+ is -296 kJ mol^{-1}. Explain why the enthalpy of hydration of Sr^{2+} is so much more exothermic than that of Rb^+.

....

....

....
(2 marks)

6   Nitrogen monoxide reacts with oxygen to form nitrogen dioxide.

$$2NO_{(g)} + O_{2(g)} \rightarrow 2NO_{2(g)} \qquad \Delta H^\ominus = -114.0 \text{ kJ mol}^{-1}$$

(a)   Explain whether you would expect the entropy change for this reaction to be positive or negative. Use the reaction equation to justify your answer.

....

....

....

(2 marks)

(b)   (i)   The table shows the standard entropies of the substances involved in the reaction.

Substance	NO	O_2	NO_2
$S^\ominus$ / J K^{-1} mol^{-1}	210.8	205.3	240.0

Use the data provided to determine a value for the entropy change of the reaction.

Entropy change = ... J K^{-1} mol^{-1}

(2 marks)

(ii)   Use the value you calculated in (i) and the given enthalpy change for the reaction to explain whether this reaction is feasible at all temperatures.

....

....

....

(2 marks)

(c)   At standard pressure, nitrogen dioxide condenses at 21.2 °C.
Explain the effect that condensation has on its entropy.

....

....

....

(2 marks)

You won't be able to get top marks in your exam just by calculating everything correctly (though that is important) — you need to be able to explain what's going on qualitatively too. That means understanding what all the numbers actually tell you about a system, and being able to suggest what might happen if conditions change without having to do the whole calculation again...

Score

21

Energy — 2

1   A Born-Haber cycle for calcium oxide is shown below.

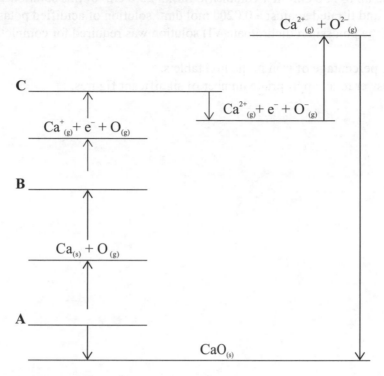

(a)   Complete the cycle by writing expressions to show the changes in the
      species involved on each of the three blank lines labelled **A**, **B** and **C**.

(3 marks)

(b)   Use the Born-Haber cycle and the data in the table below to calculate the enthalpy of atomisation of oxygen.

Enthalpy change	$\Delta H^{\ominus}$ / kJ mol^{-1}
Enthalpy of formation of calcium oxide	−635
Lattice enthalpy of calcium oxide	−3513
Enthalpy of atomisation of calcium	+193
First electron affinity of oxygen	−142
First ionisation energy of calcium	+590
Second electron affinity of oxygen	+844
Second ionisation energy of calcium	+1150

Enthalpy of atomisation of oxygen = ... kJ mol^{-1}

(2 marks)

2 Fe^{2+} ions are oxidised by Cr$_2$O$_7^{2-}$ ions according to the equation:

$$6Fe^{2+} + Cr_2O_7^{2-} + 14H^+ \rightarrow 6Fe^{3+} + 2Cr^{3+} + 7H_2O$$

A 2.00 g sample of iron tablets containing Fe^{2+} was dissolved in excess dilute sulfuric acid and the solution made up to 250 cm^3 in a volumetric flask. 25.0 cm^3 of this solution was pipetted into a conical flask and titrated against a 0.0200 mol dm^{-3} solution of acidified potassium dichromate(VI). 23.85 cm^3 of the potassium dichromate(VI) solution was required for complete oxidation.

Calculate the percentage of iron in the iron tablets.
Give your answer to an appropriate number of significant figures.

Percentage of iron = ...%

(6 marks)

3 A student is investigating reactions in electrochemical cells.
The student has access to the half-cells **A-G** shown in the table below.

Half-cell	Electrode half-equation	E° / V
A	$Zn^{2+}_{(aq)} + 2e^- \rightleftharpoons Zn_{(s)}$	-0.76
B	$Fe^{2+}_{(aq)} + 2e^- \rightleftharpoons Fe_{(s)}$	-0.44
C	$2H^+_{(aq)} + 2e^- \rightleftharpoons H_{2(g)}$	0.00
D	$Cu^{2+}_{(aq)} + 2e^- \rightleftharpoons Cu_{(s)}$	$+0.34$
E	$I_{2(aq)} + 2e^- \rightleftharpoons 2I^-_{(aq)}$	$+0.54$
F	$Fe^{3+}_{(aq)} + e^- \rightleftharpoons Fe^{2+}_{(aq)}$	$+0.77$
G	$MnO_4^-{}_{(aq)} + 8H^+_{(aq)} + 5e^- \rightleftharpoons Mn^{2+}_{(aq)} + 4H_2O_{(l)}$	$+1.51$

(a) Identify a material that the electrodes in half-cells **C**, **E**, **F** and **G** could be made from and suggest **two** reasons why this is a suitable material for these electrodes.

material: ....

reasons: ....

....

(3 marks)

(b) The student connects some of the half-cells together as shown in the table below.
Complete the table by writing the equations, including state symbols, for the overall reactions that occur.

Half-cells	Reaction equation
A and **C**	
B and **D**	
E and **F**	
B and **G**	

(4 marks)

(c) Calculate a value for the cell potential, E°_{cell}, of the cell produced when half-cells **B** and **G** are connected.

$$E^{\circ}_{cell} = \text{..} \text{ V}$$

(1 mark)

(d) (i) Draw a labelled diagram to show an experimental set-up that the student could use to measure the standard electrode potential for half-cell **E**.
State the temperature at which the student should take their measurements.

Temperature: ....

(4 marks)

(ii) A salt bridge connects the two half-cells together in an electrochemical cell. Describe the function of the salt bridge.

....

....

....

(2 marks)

4   Hydrated ethanedioic acid has the formula $C_2O_4H_2.xH_2O$, meaning that for every 1 mole of $C_2O_4H_2$ present in a sample, there are x moles of H_2O. The value of x can be determined by reacting a solution of $C_2O_4H_2.xH_2O$ with acidified potassium manganate(VII) solution. The equation for this reaction is:

$$5C_2O_4^{2-} + 2MnO_4^- + 16H^+ \rightarrow 10CO_2 + 2Mn^{2+} + 8H_2O$$

A 1.20 g sample of solid hydrated ethanedioic acid is dissolved in sulfuric acid and the solution made up to 250 cm³ with distilled water in a volumetric flask. 25.0 cm³ samples are taken from this solution and titrated against 0.0200 mol dm⁻³ $KMnO_4$ solution. An average of 19.10 cm³ of $KMnO_4$ solution is required to reach the equivalence point of the titration.

Determine the value of x in the formula $C_2O_4H_2.xH_2O$.

$x =$ ....

(6 marks)

In your exam, you could be asked how you'd set up an electrochemical cell to measure its EMF. One thing you can do to really improve the accuracy of your results is to clean the electrodes with emery paper before you pop them into the solutions, and again before taking any repeat measurements. That'll get rid of any impurities that might affect the reactions in the half-cells.

Score

31

Energy — 3

1 Carbon, in the form of graphite, reacts with oxygen to produce carbon dioxide.

$$C_{(s)} + O_{2(g)} \rightarrow CO_{2(g)}$$

The table shows some thermodynamic data relating to the reaction.

Substance	$\Delta_f H$ / kJ mol^{-1}	$S^{\ominus}$ / J K^{-1} mol^{-1}
C	0	5.7
O$_2$	0	205.3
CO$_2$	−394	214.0

(a) Explain why carbon has a much lower entropy under standard conditions than oxygen.

....

....

....

(2 marks)

(b) (i) Use the data provided to deduce the enthalpy change for the reaction.

....

(1 mark)

(ii) Use your answer to (i), and the data in the table, to determine a value for the free energy change, ΔG, of the reaction at 298 K. Give your answer to 3 significant figures.

Free energy change = ... J mol^{-1}

(4 marks)

(iii) Graphite is an allotrope of carbon. With reference to the feasibility of the reaction, suggest why the graphite in pencil lead does not spontaneously combust at room temperature.

....

....

(2 marks)

Module 5 : Physical Chemistry and Transition Elements

2   Lithium fluoride is an ionic solid with a structure similar to that of sodium chloride.
     Some thermodynamic data about lithium fluoride is given in the table.

Enthalpy change	$\Delta H^{\ominus}$ / kJ mol^{-1}
Enthalpy of formation of lithium fluoride	−612
Enthalpy of atomisation of lithium	+161
First ionisation energy of lithium	+519
Enthalpy of atomisation of fluorine	+79
Lattice enthalpy of lithium fluoride	−1022

(a) (i)   State the meaning of the term lattice enthalpy.

     ....

     ....

                                                                                                        (1 mark)

     (ii) The lattice enthalpy of sodium chloride is −787 kJ mol^{-1}.
           Explain why lithium fluoride has a more exothermic lattice enthalpy than sodium chloride.

     ....

     ....

     ....

                                                                                                        (3 marks)

(b) Use the data in the table to construct a Born-Haber cycle and
     calculate a value for the first electron affinity of fluorine.

                              First electron affinity of fluorine = ... kJ mol^{-1}

                                                                                                        (5 marks)

3 The diagram shows a rechargeable lead-acid cell being discharged to power a motor.

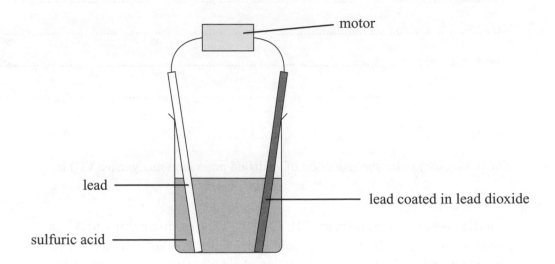

The half-equations for the reactions taking place at the electrodes as the cell discharges are:

$$PbSO_{4(s)} + 2e^- \rightleftharpoons Pb_{(s)} + SO_4^{2-}{}_{(aq)} \qquad E^\circ = -0.36$$
$$PbO_{2(s)} + SO_4^{2-}{}_{(aq)} + 4H^+{}_{(aq)} + 2e^- \rightleftharpoons PbSO_{4(s)} + 2H_2O_{(l)} \qquad E^\circ = +1.69$$

(a) (i) On the diagram, label the positive and negative electrodes during discharge.
Draw an arrow to show the direction of electron flow across the motor during discharge.

(2 marks)

(ii) Combine the half-equations given to show a full equation for the cell reaction during discharge.

....

(1 mark)

(iii) During the discharge reaction, which species acts as the
oxidising agent and which species acts as the reducing agent?

Oxidising agent: ....

Reducing agent: ....

(2 marks)

(b) (i) Calculate the cell voltage produced by the lead-acid cell as it discharges.

cell voltage = ... V

(1 mark)

(ii) Suggest why the voltage produced by the cell in everyday use may be different to that calculated in (i).

....

....

....

(2 marks)

(c) State **one** advantage and **one** disadvantage of using electrochemical cells to power vehicles, in place of conventional internal combustion engines.

Advantage:..

....

Disadvantage: ....

....

(2 marks)

4 The half-equation for the reduction of acidified potassium manganate(VII) is:
$$MnO_4^- + 8H^+ + 5e^- \rightarrow Mn^{2+} + 4H_2O$$

Acidified potassium manganate(VII), $KMnO_{4(aq)}$, can oxidise metal ions X^{2+} in aqueous solution. A 25.0 cm³ sample of a 0.160 mol dm⁻³ solution of X^{2+} was titrated against a 0.0300 mol dm⁻³ solution of acidified potassium manganate(VII). 26.7 cm³ of the potassium manganate(VII) solution was required for complete oxidation.

Determine the oxidation state of the metal **X** following the oxidation reaction.

Oxidation state = ...

(5 marks)

If you're unsure how to approach a calculation question, think about the data you've been given, and the kind of calculations you would usually use that data for. Even if you don't get to the end of the question, you might pick up some marks for making a start, or it might just become more obvious what you need to do next.

Score

33

Energy — 4

1   Many metals are extracted from their ores using carbon.

The reaction between aluminium oxide and carbon is shown in the equation below.

$$Al_2O_{3(s)} + 3C_{(s)} \rightarrow 2Al_{(s)} + 3CO_{(g)}$$

The table shows some thermodynamic data relating to the reaction.

Substance	$\Delta_f H$ / kJ mol^{-1}	$S^{\ominus}$ / J K^{-1} mol^{-1}
Al_2O_3	−1675.7	50.9
Al	0	28.3
C	0	5.7
CO	−110.5	197.6

(a) (i)   Calculate a value for the free energy change, ΔG, of the reaction at 277 °C.
         Give your answer to an appropriate number of significant figures.

Free energy change = ... J mol^{-1}

(6 marks)

(ii) Use your answer to (i) to deduce whether the reaction is feasible at 277 °C.
      Give a reason for your answer.

....

....

(1 mark)

(b) Determine a value for the minimum temperature, in K, at which the reaction is feasible.

Minimum temperature = ... K

(2 marks)

Module 5 : Physical Chemistry and Transition Elements

(c) Suggest **one** reason why reduction with carbon is not used to extract aluminium metal from its oxide.

....

(1 mark)

2 Standard electrode potentials can be used to make predictions about the feasibility of reactions and the direction in which a reaction equilibrium will shift.
Some typical electrode potential values are shown in the table below.

Half-cell equation	E° / V
$O_{2(g)} + 4H^+ + 4e^- \rightleftharpoons 2H_2O_{(l)}$	+1.23
$Ag^+_{(aq)} + e^- \rightleftharpoons Ag_{(s)}$	+0.80
$Fe^{2+}_{(aq)} + 2e^- \rightleftharpoons Fe_{(s)}$	−0.44
$Zn^{2+}_{(aq)} + 2e^- \rightleftharpoons Zn_{(s)}$	−0.76
$Mn^{2+}_{(aq)} + 2e^- \rightleftharpoons Mn_{(s)}$	−1.19

(a) Which of the species in the table is the strongest reducing agent? Give your reasoning.

....

....

(2 marks)

(b) (i) Using the electrode potential values in the table, explain why
silver metal should react with oxygen gas in acidic solution.

....

....

....

(2 marks)

(ii) Suggest a reason why this reaction is not observed under standard conditions,
and a practical way in which this limiting factor could be overcome.

....

....

....

(2 marks)

A student connected an $Fe^{2+}_{(aq)}/Fe_{(s)}$ half-cell to an $Mn^{2+}_{(aq)}/Mn_{(s)}$ half-cell and found the cell potential to be 0.75 V under standard conditions. They then increased the concentration of the Fe^{2+} solution whilst keeping the concentration of the Mn^{2+} solution the same, and measured the cell potential again.

(c) Suggest and explain how this increase in Fe^{2+} concentration will affect the electrode
potential value for the $Fe^{2+}_{(aq)}/Fe_{(s)}$ half-cell and so the overall cell potential value.

....

....

....

(2 marks)

3   Sodium thiosulfate ($Na_2S_2O_3$) is commonly used in redox titrations with iodine solutions (I_2) to deduce the concentration of oxidising agents such as chlorate ions (ClO^-) ions.

(a) (i)   State, in terms of electron movement, what is meant by the term oxidising agent.

....

(1 mark)

(ii) Deduce the oxidation state of the chlorine in the chlorate ion.

....

(1 mark)

(b) Chlorate ions oxidise iodide ions to iodine molecules in acidic solution and are themselves converted into chloride ions and water. The half-equations for these reactions are:

$$2I^-_{(aq)} \rightleftharpoons I_{2(aq)} + 2e^-$$
$$ClO^-_{(aq)} + 2H^+_{(aq)} + 2e^- \rightleftharpoons Cl^-_{(aq)} + H_2O_{(l)}$$

Write the overall equation for the reaction between iodide ions and chlorate ions in acidic solution.

....

(1 mark)

(c) The iodine solution produced can then be titrated against a standard solution of sodium thiosulfate and the results used to determine the concentration of the chlorate ions.
A suggested practical method for this iodine-sodium thiosulfate titration is outlined below:

1. Transfer the iodine solution produced into a conical flask.
2. Fill a burette with sodium thiosulfate of known concentration.
3. Place the conical flask containing the iodine solution below the burette and start to slowly add the sodium thiosulfate from the burette.
4. As the iodine solution changes to a pale yellow colour, add 2 cm³ of starch solution to the flask and continue to add the sodium thiosulfate slowly until the end-point is reached.

(i)   Suggest why the sodium thiosulfate must be added slowly.

....

....

(1 mark)

(ii) Starch reacts with iodine to form a blue-black complex. Explain why the solution changes colour from blue-black to colourless when the end-point of the titration is reached.

....

....

....

(1 mark)

(iii) During the titration, the thiosulfate ions ($S_2O_3^{2-}$) are oxidised to tetrathionate ions ($S_4O_6^{2-}$) whilst the iodine molecules are reduced to iodide ions. The overall equation for this reaction is:

$$2S_2O_3^{2-}{}_{(aq)} + I_{2(aq)} \rightarrow S_4O_6^{2-}{}_{(aq)} + 2I^-_{(aq)}$$

Write the half-equation for the oxidation of thiosulfate ions to tetrathionate ions.

....

(1 mark)

(d) Chlorate ions are the active ingredient in household bleach. A student was investigating the concentration of chlorate ions in household bleach. A 25.0 cm³ sample of household bleach was made up to 250 cm³ of solution using distilled water. Three 25.0 cm³ samples of the resulting solution were then individually mixed with excess potassium iodide and titrated against 0.250 mol dm⁻³ sodium thiosulfate solution using starch as an indicator. The results from this titration are summarised in the table below.

	Rough titration	Titration 1	Titration 2	Titration 3
Initial burette reading / cm³	0.00	0.00	0.10	0.00
Final burette reading / cm³	22.75	22.50	22.65	22.55
Total titre / cm³	22.75	22.50	22.55	22.55

(i) Use these results, along with the equations given, to calculate the concentration of chlorate ions (ClO^-) in the original 25.0 cm³ sample of bleach.
Show **all** your working.
Give your answer to an appropriate number of significant figures.

concentration of ClO^- = ... mol dm⁻³

(6 marks)

(ii) The burette the student used had an uncertainty of 0.05 cm³.
Calculate the percentage uncertainty in their value for the total titre in Titration 2.

percentage uncertainty = ...%

(2 marks)

It's easy to trip up over units when you're calculating free energy change. Unless you're told to use a particular unit, it doesn't matter whether you give your final answer in kJ mol⁻¹ or J mol⁻¹, but you'll usually be given ΔH in kJ mol⁻¹ and ΔS in J K⁻¹ mol⁻¹, so you'll need to convert one of them before you can plug them into the equation for ΔG.

Score

32

Module 5 : Physical Chemistry and Transition Elements

Transition Elements — 1

Have you heard the story of the student who stayed up all night practising inorganic chemistry? They found him wandering the streets at sunrise, blabbering about atomic radii. That's what you get for not taking periodic breaks.

For each of questions 1-4, give your answer by writing the correct letter in the box.

1   Aqueous Fe^{3+} ions are reacted with an excess of aqueous sodium hydroxide. What is the product formed?

A $[Fe(OH)_6]^{3-}$ **B** $[Fe(OH)_3(H_2O)_3]$

C $[Fe(OH)_4(H_2O)_2]^-$ **D** $[Fe(OH)_4]^{3-}$

Your answer

(1 mark)

2   The table below shows some electron configurations. Which row or rows of the table are correct?

	Species	Electron configuration
1	Cu	$1s^2\,2s^2\,2p^6\,3s^2\,3p^6\,3d^9\,4s^2$
2	Cr	$1s^2\,2s^2\,2p^6\,3s^2\,3p^6\,3d^5\,4s^1$
3	Mn^{2+}	$1s^2\,2s^2\,2p^6\,3s^2\,3p^6\,3d^5$

A   1 and 3 only   **B**   2 only

C   2 and 3 only   **D**   1, 2 and 3

Your answer

(1 mark)

3 $[Cu(H_2O)_6]^{2+}$ is a blue complex formed when copper(II) chloride dissolves in water. Addition of excess ammonia produces a deep blue coloured complex.

What is the formula of this complex?

A $[Cu(OH)_2(H_2O)_4]$ **B** $[Cu(NH_3)_6]^{2+}$

C $[Cu(NH_3)_4(H_2O)_2]^{2+}$ **D** $[Cu(NH_3)_3(OH)_3]^-$

Your answer

(1 mark)

4 $[Cr(NH_2(CH_2)_2NH_2)_3]^{3+}$ is a complex ion which forms optical isomers.

Which of the following statements is/are true?

1: $NH_2(CH_2)_2NH_2$ is a bidentate ligand.
2:   The complex has an octahedral shape.
3:   The terms cis and trans are used to describe the optical isomers.

A   1, 2 and 3   **B**   Only 1 and 2

C   Only 1 and 3   **D**   Only 1

Your answer

(1 mark)

5 Transition metals such as cobalt are capable of forming a wide range of complex ions.

(a) State the full electron configurations of cobalt and zinc.
Use the electron configurations to explain why cobalt is regarded as a transition metal but zinc is not.

....

....

....

....

....

....

(4 marks)

(b) (i) Give the name of the type of bonding responsible for the formation of transition metal complexes.

....

(1 mark)

(ii) State the meaning of the term ligand.

....

....

(1 mark)

(c) (i) Draw a diagram to show the three-dimensional shape of $[CoCl_4]^{2-}$.
Label the bond angles in your diagram.

(2 marks)

(ii) In aqueous solution, $[CoCl_4]^{2-}$ ions exist in equilibrium with $[Co(H_2O)_6]^{2+}$ ions.
Suggest an equation for the ligand substitution reaction which produces this equilibrium.

....

(1 mark)

(iii) Explain why the change in ligand leads to a change in the overall charge of the complex ion.

....

....

(1 mark)

(iv) Suggest a ligand which can substitute with the water in $[Co(H_2O)_6]^{2+}$ without causing a change in the co-ordination number or the overall charge.

....

(1 mark)

6   The flowchart below shows some reactions involving chromium.

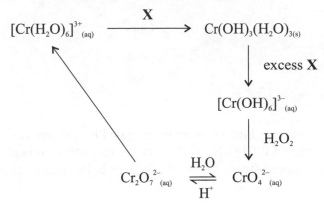

(a) (i) Reagent **X** is an ionic compound. Identify reagent **X**.

....

(1 mark)

(ii) Reagent **Y** can be used instead of reagent **X** to convert $[Cr(H_2O)_6]^{3+}$ to $Cr(OH)_3(H_2O)_3$.
Reagent **Y** is a compound that is **not** ionic. Identify reagent **Y**.

....

(1 mark)

(b) What colour is the complex $[Cr(OH)_6]^{3-}$?

....

(1 mark)

(c) Name the type of reaction which converts $[Cr(OH)_6]^{3-}$ to CrO_4^{2-}.

....

(1 mark)

(d) (i) Using oxidation numbers, explain why the reaction which
produces $[Cr(H_2O)_6]^{3+}$ from $Cr_2O_7^{2-}$ is a reduction.

....

....

(2 marks)

(ii) Identify the reagent(s) used to carry out this reduction.

....

(1 mark)

7   This question is about some applications of transition metals and their compounds.

(a) Cis-platin is a platinum complex with the formula $Pt(NH_3)_2Cl_2$ that is used as
an anti-cancer drug. Only the cis isomer will inhibit cell division.

(i) Cis-platin works by bonding to two nitrogen atoms on the DNA molecule of a cancerous cell.
Which of cis-platin's ligands are displaced to allow this to happen?

....

(1 mark)

(ii) Draw a diagram to show the trans isomer of $Pt(NH_3)_2Cl_2$.

(1 mark)

(iii) Another platinum complex which has been investigated for anti-cancer properties has the formula $PtCl_4(NH_3)_2$. This also exists as **two** isomers. Draw the three-dimensional structures of both isomers below and label each as cis or trans.

(3 marks)

(iv) The NH_3 ligands in cis-platin can be substituted for the ligand $NH_2CH_2CH_2NH_2$. Suggest an equation for this reaction.

....

(1 mark)

(b) Catalytic behaviour is a characteristic property of transition metals and their compounds.

(i) Give **two** examples of reactions in which transition metals or their compounds act as catalysts. Include the name or formula of the catalyst involved in each reaction.

1 ....

....

2 ....

....

(2 marks)

(ii) Suggest **one** advantage and **one** disadvantage of the use of transition metals and their compounds as catalysts in the chemical manufacturing industry.

Advantage: ....

Disadvantage: ....

(2 marks)

EXAM TIP

There's less new information than you might think in this section — you just need to think about stuff you already know in slightly different ways. Everything you learnt about structure and bonding back in Year 1 comes in really handy, as do electron configurations, redox reactions, isomerism... Pull all that together, and you'll be writing some really fantastic exam answers.

Score

32

Transition Elements — 2

1   Iron is a transition metal that has two stable ions, Fe^{2+} and Fe^{3+}. In aqueous solution, they become hydrated to form the complex ions $[Fe(H_2O)_6]^{2+}$ and $[Fe(H_2O)_6]^{3+}$.

(a)   Write the electron configuration, in terms of sub-shells, of an Fe^{3+} ion.

....

(1 mark)

(b) Fe^{2+} ions react with acidic hydrogen peroxide. Half-equations for the reaction are shown below.
$$H_2O_2 + 2H^+ + 2e^- \rightarrow 2H_2O$$
$$Fe^{3+} + e^- \rightarrow Fe^{2+}$$

(i)   Construct an overall equation for the reaction of Fe^{2+} with H_2O_2.

....

(1 mark)

(ii) H_2O_2 is colourless in solution. Describe the colour change
you would expect to observe over the course of this reaction.

....

(1 mark)

(iii)   Identify the reducing agent in this reaction.

....

(1 mark)

(c)   State what you would observe when ammonia is added to a solution
containing $[Fe(H_2O)_6]^{2+}$ ions and to a solution containing $[Fe(H_2O)_6]^{3+}$ ions.
Give the formula of the iron-containing species formed in each case.

$[Fe(H_2O)_6]^{2+}$: ....

....

$[Fe(H_2O)_6]^{3+}$: ....

....

(4 marks)

(d)   If a solution containing ethanedioate ions ($C_2O_4^{2-}$) is added to a solution containing
$[Fe(H_2O)_6]^{3+}$, a ligand substitution reaction occurs to form the complex ion $[Fe(C_2O_4)_3]^{3-}$.

(i)   Write an equation for this ligand substitution reaction.

....

(1 mark)

(ii)   Suggest how the ethanedioate ion acts as a bidentate ligand.

....

....

(1 mark)

(e)   Haemoglobin is a complex ion containing 6 coordinate bonds.

    (i)   Identify the central metal ion in the haemoglobin complex.

....

(1 mark)

    (ii)   Outline how haemoglobin is involved in the transport of oxygen in the body.

....

....

....

(2 marks)

---

2   Transition metals and their compounds can be identified by their distinctive colours.

(a)   State the colour of the following complex ions.

$Mn(H_2O)_6{}^{2+}$: ....

$CuCl_4{}^{2-}$: ....

(2 marks)

(b)   A double salt is a salt containing more than one cation or anion.
A double salt with the general formula $AB_2X_2.6H_2O$ is being investigated. **A** and **B** are positive ions, with **A** being a transition metal ion. **X** is a negative ion. To identify the ions, the salt was dissolved in water and an excess of sodium hydroxide was added to a sample of the solution. A green precipitate was formed. This sample was then warmed up and the vapour given off turned red litmus paper blue. Adding hydrochloric acid and barium chloride to another sample of the solution produced a white precipitate.

    (i)   Identify ions **A**, **B** and **X**. For each ion, write an ionic equation for the reaction described that allowed you to make the identification.

       A: ....

....

       B: ....

....

       X: ....

....

(6 marks)

    (ii)   Write the formula of the salt and predict the colour of its solution.

       Formula: ....

       Colour of solution: ....

(2 marks)

EXAM TIP

There's no way around it — there are a lot of facts you just need to learn to answer the questions in this section really well. Precipitate and solution colours aren't TOO bad (you can make yourself some snazzy coloured revision notes), but equations and formulae can be trickier. Try grouping equations for ions with the same charge together to make them easier to learn.

Score

23

Aromatic Compounds and Carbonyls — 1

And now we move on to a delicate and finely-spiced blend of organic compounds, with a fragrance reminiscent of tropical fruits, a greenhouse in bloom, and the last days of summer... Or rather, I hope you like drawing hexagons.

For each of questions 1-3, give your answer by writing the correct letter in the box.

1   A student has three samples of the compound shown below. They warm the first sample with Tollens' reagent, add Na_2CO_3 to the second and warm the third with acidified $K_2Cr_2O_7$.

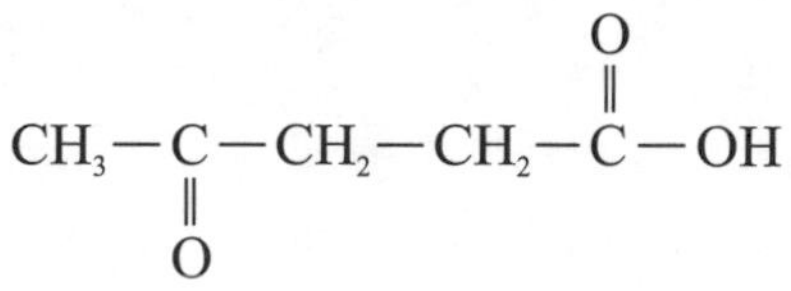

$$CH_3-\overset{\displaystyle O}{\underset{\displaystyle \parallel}{C}}-CH_2-CH_2-\overset{\displaystyle O}{\overset{\displaystyle \parallel}{C}}-OH$$

Which of the substances would this compound react with?

A   Tollens' reagent only   B   Both Tollens' reagent and Na_2CO_3

C Na_2CO_3 only   D   Both Na_2CO_3 and acidified $K_2Cr_2O_7$

Your answer ☐

(1 mark)

2   Which of the following statements about dimethylbenzene ($C_6H_4(CH_3)_2$) is **not** correct?

A   Dimethylbenzene undergoes electrophilic substitution reactions.

B   All carbon-carbon bond lengths are equal in dimethylbenzene.

C   There are four structural isomers of dimethylbenzene that contain a benzene ring.

D   It can react with an acyl chloride to produce an aromatic ketone.

Your answer ☐

(1 mark)

3   The diagram below shows the structure of a chloro-substituted phenol.

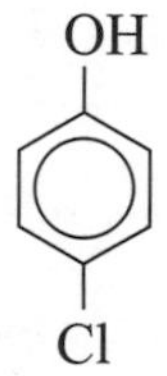

Which of the following statements about the molecule shown is/are correct?

       1: The OH group is 2,4 directing.
       2: 2-chlorophenol is a structural isomer of the molecule.
       3: The OH group is electron withdrawing.

A   1, 2 and 3   B   Only 1 and 2

C   Only 2 and 3   D   Only 1

Your answer ☐

(1 mark)

4   Ethanoic acid, CH_3COOH, is a very soluble carboxylic acid that shows the typical properties of weak acids.

(a)   Ethanoic acid is very soluble in water because it is able to form hydrogen bonds with water molecules. Draw a diagram to show **one** molecule of ethanoic acid hydrogen bonding to a water molecule, showing all partial charges.

(2 marks)

(b)   Examples of substances that react with ethanoic acid are shown in the flowchart below.

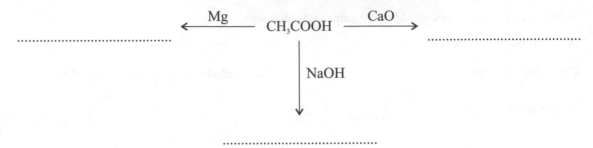

Complete the flowchart by writing the formulae of **all** the products formed in each of these reactions.

(3 marks)

(c)   Ethanoyl chloride takes part in many of the same organic reactions as ethanoic acid, but reacts much more vigorously. It can be made by reacting ethanoic acid with thionyl chloride, $SOCl_2$.

(i)   Write an equation for the reaction of ethanoic acid with thionyl chloride.

....

(1 mark)

(ii)   Suggest a compound that could be reacted with ethanoyl chloride to produce ethanoic acid.

....

(1 mark)

(iii)   The ester, amide and substituted amide below can all be produced in reactions involving acyl chlorides. Write equations to represent each of these reactions.

Ester: $C_3H_7COOC_2H_5$

....

Amide: $C_2H_5CONH_2$

....

Substituted amide: $CH_3CONHC_2H_5$

....

(3 marks)

(iv)   Name the ester $C_3H_7COOC_2H_5$.

....

(1 mark)

5 Benzene is a cyclic compound that can react with certain electrophiles.

(a) Explain why electrophiles do not undergo addition reactions with benzene under standard conditions.

....

(1 mark)

Benzene was once incorrectly thought to have the structure of the theoretical compound cyclohexa-1,3,5-triene. Both benzene and cyclohexa-1,3,5-triene have the formula C_6H_6.
The hydrogenation reactions of benzene, cyclohexa-1,3,5-triene and cyclohexene are shown below.

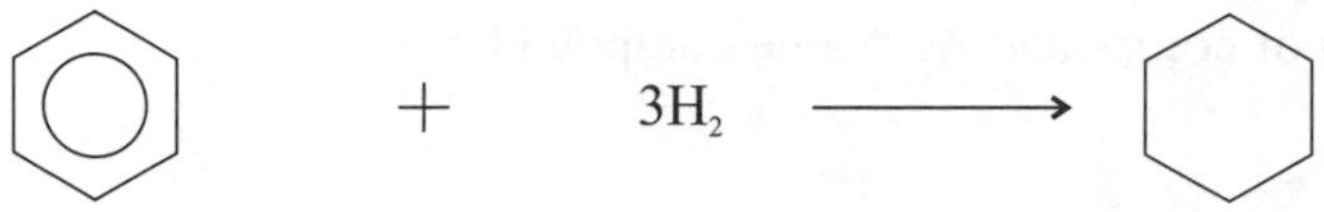

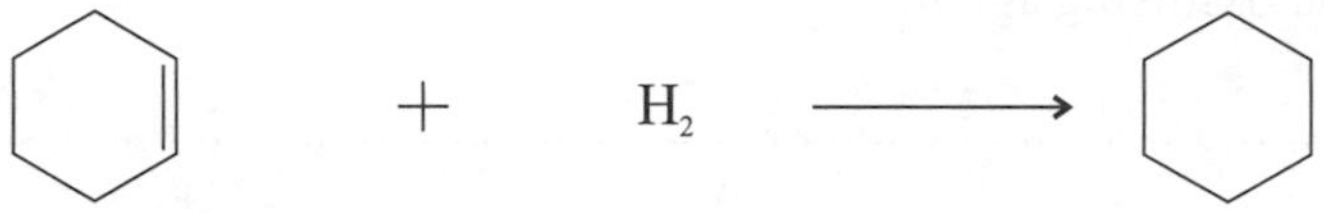

Benzene $+$ $3H_2$ ⟶ $\Delta H = -208$ kJ mol^{-1}

Cyclohexa-1,3,5-triene $+$ $3H_2$ ⟶

Cyclohexene $+$ H_2 ⟶ $\Delta H = -120$ kJ mol^{-1}

(b) Compare the structure and bonding and the reactivity of benzene to that of cyclohexa-1,3,5-triene.
In your answer you should show how the information given above provides evidence that benzene does **not** have the structure of cyclohexa-1,3,5-triene.

....

....

....

....

....

....

....

....

....

....

....

....

(6 marks)

EXAM TIP — It's almost certain that you'll encounter an extended response question at some point during your chemistry exams. These questions test your chemistry knowledge (obviously), but they also test whether you can structure your answer in a logical way — so it's worth spending a bit of time having a good think about how best to order all the stuff you want to include in your answer.

Score

21

Aromatic Compounds and Carbonyls — 2

1   Compound **A** is an organic liquid with the molecular formula C_3H_6O.

When a few drops of **A** were added to acidified sodium dichromate and warmed,
product **B** was formed and the solution turned from orange to dark green.

When **A** was reacted with 2,4-dinitrophenylhydrazine, a bright orange crystalline product, **C**, was formed.

(a)   Draw the displayed formula of compound **A**. Name compound **A**.

Displayed formula:

Name: ....
(2 marks)

(b)   (i)   Write an equation for the reaction of compound **A** with the acidified sodium dichromate.
Use [O] to represent the oxidising agent.

....
(1 mark)

(ii)   Describe a test that could be used to confirm the identity of the purified product **B**.
State what you would expect the result of the test to be.

....

....
(2 marks)

(c)   Describe a further test that could be carried out after the reaction with
2,4-dinitrophenylhydrazine to confirm the identity of compound **A**.

....

....

....
(2 marks)

(d)   Compound **D** is a structural isomer of compound **A**. It has a different functional group to **A**,
but also produces a crystalline solid when it reacts with 2,4-dinitrophenylhydrazine.

(i)   Draw the displayed formula of compound **D**. Name compound **D**.

Displayed formula:

Name: ....
(2 marks)

(ii)   Suggest what would happen if acidified sodium dichromate
were added to a test tube containing compound **D**.

....
(1 mark)

2 The flowchart below shows some reactions of benzene.

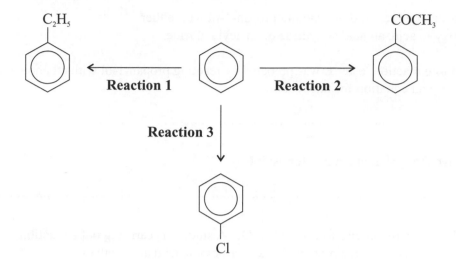

Each reaction involves one reagent and a halogen carrier.
The same halogen carrier is used in all three reactions.

(a) Identify a suitable reagent for each reaction.

Reaction 1: ....

Reaction 2: ....

Reaction 3: ....

(3 marks)

(b) (i) Suggest a suitable halogen carrier for the three reactions.

....

(1 mark)

(ii) Explain the role of the halogen carrier in these reactions.

....

....

....

(2 marks)

(c) Draw the mechanism for reaction 3, showing curly arrows and relevant dipoles.
Your answer should include all steps in the mechanism.

(4 marks)

3 This question is about esters.

(a) Ester **E** can be prepared by reacting propan-1-ol with either
a carboxylic acid, an acid anhydride or an acyl chloride.

    (i) In **one** reaction, ester **E** was prepared by reacting propan-1-ol with ethanoic anhydride, $(CH_3CO)_2O$.
Write an equation for this reaction.

....

(1 mark)

    (ii) Give the systematic name for ester **E**.

....

(1 mark)

(b) Ester **F** has the molecular formula $C_5H_{10}O_2$. A student is carrying out a reaction
to produce ester **F** from a branched chain carboxylic acid and methanol.

    (i) Using structural formulas, write an equation for this reaction.

....

(2 marks)

    (ii) Explain why it is likely that the carboxylic acid will still be present in the product mixture.

....

....

(2 marks)

(c) The hydrolysis of esters is a reversible reaction.

    (i) Write an equation for the acid-catalysed hydrolysis of the ester 1-methylpropyl ethanoate.
Use skeletal formulae to represent any organic reactants and products.

(2 marks)

    (ii) State how you could shift the equilibrium to the right to increase the yield of this reaction.

....

(1 mark)

    (iii) Lactones are cyclic esters that can be hydrolysed under acidic conditions
in a similar way to the ester in part (i). The structure of a lactone is shown below.

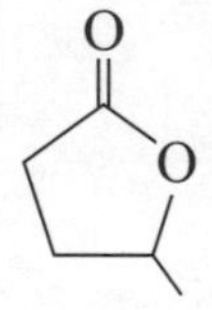

The acid hydrolysis of lactones produces only one product.
Predict the structure of the product formed by the acid hydrolysis of the lactone shown above.

(1 mark)

4   Benzaldehyde is an aromatic aldehyde with a distinctive almond smell.
Some of its reactions are shown in the flowchart below.

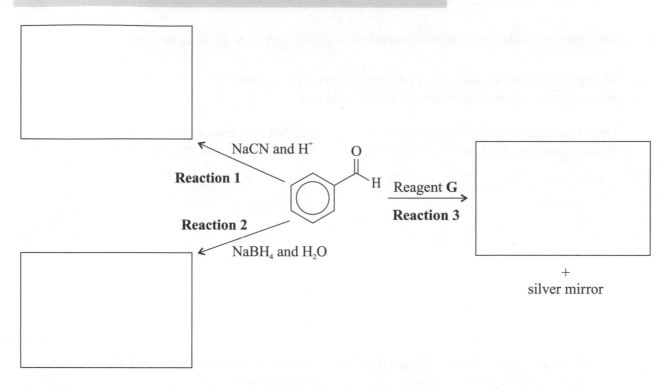

(a) (i) Fill in the boxes to show the organic products of reactions 1,2 and 3.

(3 marks)

(ii) Identify reagent **G**.

....

(1 mark)

(b) Reactions 1 and 2 have a similar mechanism.

(i) Name this type of reaction mechanism.

....

(1 mark)

(ii) Reaction 2 is a two step reaction. In the first step, the BH_4^- ion breaks up into BH_3 and an H^- ion.
In the second step, the H^- ion goes on to react with benzaldehyde.
Draw the mechanism for this second step, using curly arrows and showing relevant dipoles.

(5 marks)

If you get stuck halfway through drawing a mechanism, don't panic — you can often work out
what the next step should be by looking out for any way that a negative charge (or a lone pair,
or a δ⁻ atom) can attack a positive charge (or a δ⁺ atom). For example, if you've got a molecule
with a lone pair of electrons, it's pretty likely that it'll attack a δ+ carbon in another molecule.

Score

40

Aromatic Compounds and Carbonyls — 3

1   This question is about electrophilic substitution reactions of aromatic compounds.

(a)   Multiple substitution reactions can occur when benzene is heated
with a mixture of concentrated nitric and sulfuric acids.

Draw a mechanism to show the formation of 1,3-dinitrobenzene from nitrobenzene.
Include equations to show how the electrophile is generated at the start of the reaction.

(4 marks)

(b)   (i)   Write an equation for the formation of 2,4,6-tribromophenol from phenol and bromine,
showing the structures of any organic reactants and products.

(2 marks)

(ii)   Write an equation for the formation of 2-nitrophenol from phenol and dilute nitric acid,
showing the structures of any organic reactants and products.

(2 marks)

(iii) Explain how the reaction described in part (ii) shows that phenol
undergoes electrophilic substitution more readily than benzene.

....

....

(1 mark)

(c)   Fuming sulfuric acid is the name given to a solution of sulfur trioxide in sulfuric acid.
When fuming sulfuric acid reacts with nitrobenzene, an electrophilic substitution reaction occurs.
An $-SO_3H$ group is substituted on to the ring structure.

Draw the structure of the product of this reaction.

(1 mark)

2 Arenes **X** and **Y** are structural isomers that both contain an OH group.

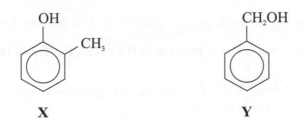

X   Y

(a) Name arene **X**.

....

(1 mark)

(b) (i) Explain why **X** undergoes electrophilic substitution more readily than **Y**.

....

....

....

(3 marks)

(ii) Suggest why **X** is weakly acidic.

....

....

....

(2 marks)

(c) Samples of arene **X** are added to each of the following reagents.
For each reagent:

- State whether a reaction occurs.
- If a reaction does occur, write the reaction equation,
  showing the structures of any organic reactants and products.
- If a reaction does not occur, explain why not.

Sodium hydroxide:

Sodium carbonate:

(3 marks)

Nitrogen Compounds, Polymers and Synthesis — 1

And here are yet more different types of compounds and reactions to get your head around, you lucky thing...

For each of questions 1-4, give your answer by writing the correct letter in the box.

1 Terylene™ can be formed from the monomers benzene-1,4-dicarboxylic acid and ethane-1,2-diol. What is the structure of the repeat unit of Terylene™?

A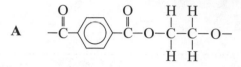

B

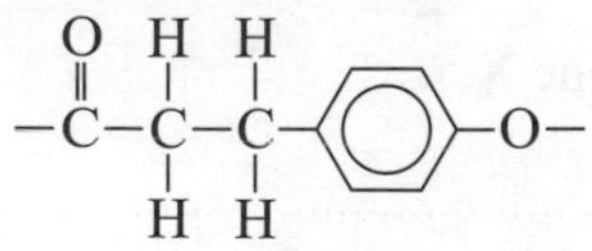

C

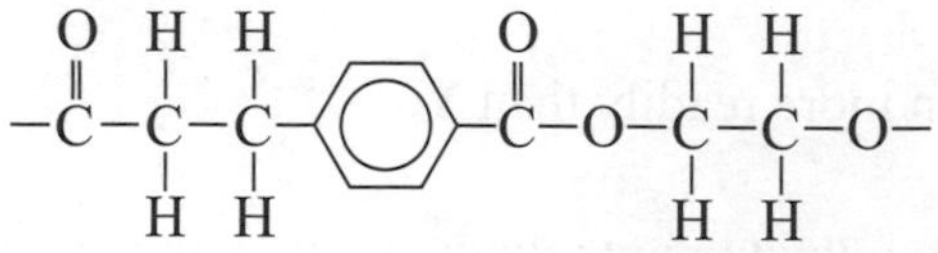

D

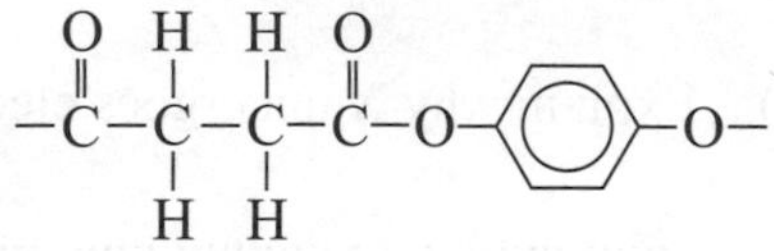

Your answer ☐

(1 mark)

2 Which process is **not** involved in the reaction sequence shown below?

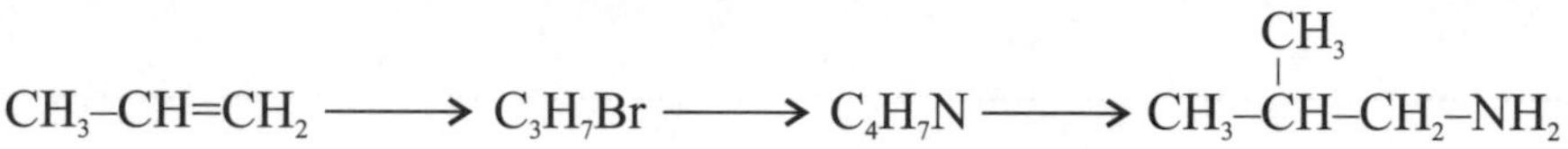

$$CH_3-CH=CH_2 \longrightarrow C_3H_7Br \longrightarrow C_4H_7N \longrightarrow CH_3-\overset{CH_3}{\underset{}{CH}}-CH_2-NH_2$$

A Substitution

B Reduction

C Addition

D Elimination

Your answer ☐

(1 mark)

3 Which amine may be formed when methylamine is heated with bromoethane?

A $H_3C-\overset{}{\underset{H}{N}}-CH_3$

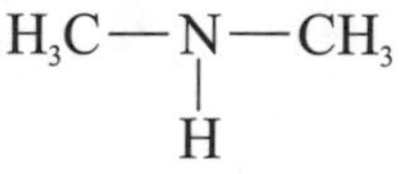

B $H_3C-\overset{}{\underset{CH_2CH_3}{N}}-CH_3$

C $H_3CH_2C-\overset{CH_2CH_3}{\underset{}{N}}-CH_3$

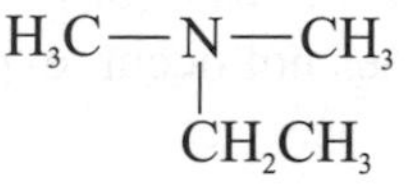

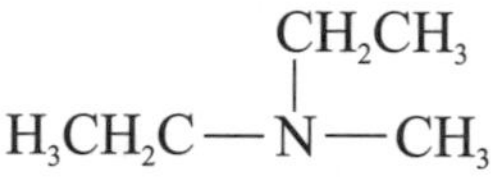

D $H_3CH_2C-\overset{CH_2CH_3}{\underset{CH_2CH_3}{\overset{+}{N}}}-CH_2CH_3$

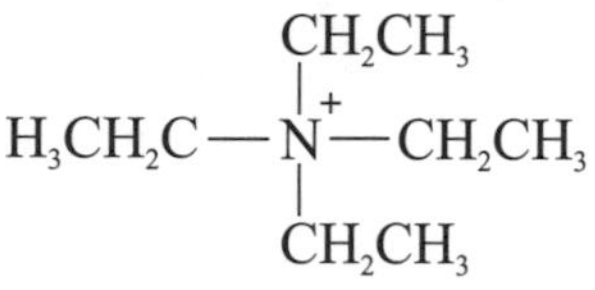

Your answer ☐

(1 mark)

4 Which statement about organic synthesis is **not** correct?

A Acyl chlorides can be converted into primary amides in one step.

B Acyl chlorides can be converted into carboxylic acids in one step.

C Haloalkanes can be converted into carboxylic acids in one step.

D Haloalkanes can be converted into alcohols in one step.

Your answer ☐

(1 mark)

5　The structure of the α-amino acid glycine is shown in the diagram below.

$$
\begin{array}{c}
H \quad\quad H \quad\quad\quad O \\
\diagdown \quad\quad | \quad\quad\quad \diagup\diagup \\
N-C-C \\
\diagup \quad\quad | \quad\quad\quad \diagdown \\
H \quad\quad H \quad\quad OH
\end{array}
$$

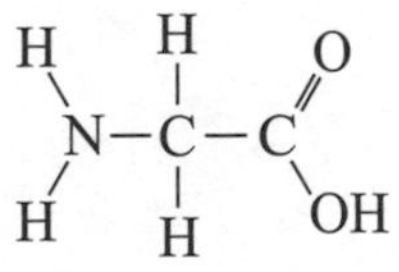

(a)　State the general formula for an α-amino acid.

....

(1 mark)

(b)　Draw the displayed formula of the organic compound formed when glycine reacts with ethanol in the presence of concentrated sulfuric acid.

(1 mark)

(c)　Explain, with reference to the behaviour of the different functional groups, how α-amino acids are able to react with both acids and alkalis.

....

....

....

(2 marks)

6　Polymers are long-chain molecules formed when large numbers of smaller molecules join together. Two common groups of polymers are polyesters and polyamides.

(a)　Polyesters are formed when dicarboxylic acids react with diols.

(i)　Name the type of polymerisation reaction that takes place.

....

(1 mark)

A section of a polyester, **C**, is shown in the diagram below.

$$
\begin{array}{c}
\quad\quad H \quad H \quad\quad\quad\quad O \quad CH_3 \; H \quad H \quad\quad O \\
\quad\quad | \quad\; | \quad\quad\quad\quad || \quad\; | \quad\quad | \quad\; | \quad\quad || \\
-O-C-C-O-C-C-C-C-C- \\
\quad\quad | \quad\; | \quad\quad\quad\quad\quad\quad | \quad\quad | \quad\; | \\
\quad\quad CH_3 \; H \quad\quad\quad\quad\quad CH_3 \; H \quad H
\end{array}
$$

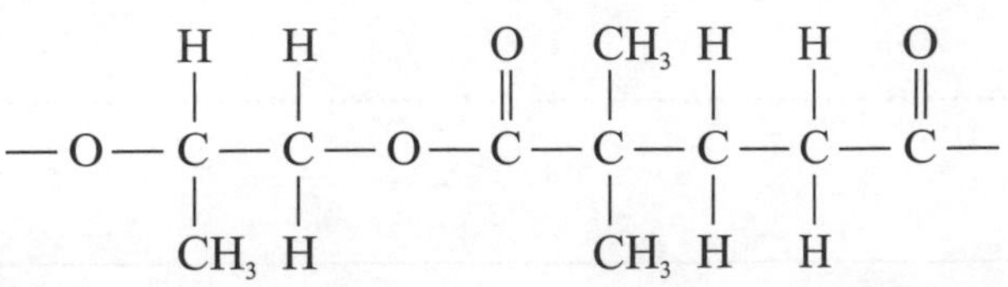

(ii) Draw the skeletal formulae of the two products that form when polyester **C**
undergoes base hydrolysis with excess sodium hydroxide.

(2 marks)

(b) Kevlar® and nylon-6,6 are examples of polyamides.

(i) Kevlar® is produced in a polymerisation reaction between
the monomers benzene-1,4-dioic acid and benzene-1,4-diamine.
Draw the repeat unit of Kevlar®.

(1 mark)

(ii) Identify the other product of this polymerisation reaction.

....

(1 mark)

(iii) A section of nylon-6,6 is shown in the diagram below.

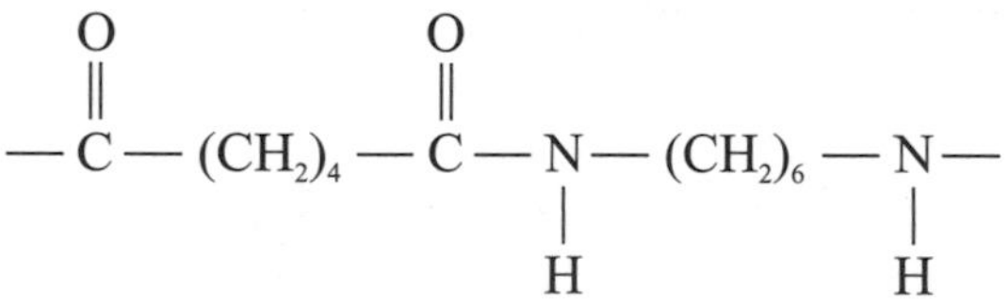

$$-\overset{\overset{\displaystyle O}{\|}}{C}-(CH_2)_4-\overset{\overset{\displaystyle O}{\|}}{C}-\underset{\underset{\displaystyle H}{|}}{N}-(CH_2)_6-\underset{\underset{\displaystyle H}{|}}{N}-$$

Draw the structures of the two products that form when nylon-6,6 undergoes
hydrolysis with dilute hydrochloric acid. Give the name of each product.

Product 1:   Product 2:

Name of product 1: ....

Name of product 2: ....

(4 marks)

Nitrogen Compounds, Polymers and Synthesis — 2

1 Compounds **A** and **B** both demonstrate optical isomerism.
The displayed formulae of compounds **A** and **B** are shown in the diagrams below.

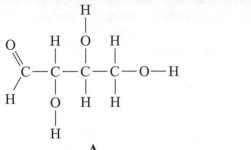

          A   **B**

(a) State what is meant by the term optical isomers.

....

....

(1 mark)

(b) (i) Identify the chiral centre(s) present in compounds **A** and **B**.
Mark each chiral centre on the diagrams above using an asterisk, *.

(2 marks)

(ii) Explain your choice of chiral centres in (b)(i).

....

....

(1 mark)

(c) Draw 3D diagrams to represent the optical isomers of compound **B**.

(1 mark)

2 The structures of two molecules that contain amine groups are shown below.

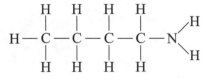

         butan-1-amine   1-aminobutan-2-one

(a) (i) Explain why amines can behave as both bases and nucleophiles.

(2 marks)

(ii) Use structural formulae to write an equation for the neutralisation reaction
that occurs when dilute hydrochloric acid is added to butan-1-amine.

....

(1 mark)

(b) A scientist is investigating the organic reactions of butan-1-amine.
She adds butan-1-amine to an excess of bromomethane and heats the reaction mixture.
A mixture of products is formed. One of the products is a secondary amine.

(i) Draw the displayed formula of this secondary amine.

(1 mark)

(ii) Suggest why a mixture of products is formed by the reaction.

....

....

(1 mark)

(c) The scientist reacts 1-aminobutan-2-one with ethanoyl chloride.
Draw the displayed formula of the organic product formed in this reaction.

(1 mark)

3   Organic compounds that contain a $-C\equiv N$ functional group are known as nitriles.
Nitriles are produced in several different reactions.

(a) The reaction between pentan-2-one and hydrogen cyanide produces a compound containing a $-C\equiv N$ group.
Outline the mechanism for this reaction.
In your answer, include the name of the mechanism, curly arrows and relevant dipoles.

Name of mechanism: ....

Mechanism:

(5 marks)

(b) Nitriles can also be produced from haloalkanes.

   (i) State the reagents needed to produce a nitrile from a haloalkane.

   ....
   (1 mark)

   (ii) Draw the mechanism for the reaction of 1-bromobutane that produces a nitrile.
   Clearly show all the products of the reaction, and include curly arrows and relevant dipoles.

   (3 marks)

(c) Nitriles can be reduced to primary amines.

   (i) Suggest a suitable reducing agent for this process.
   Include any other necessary reagents or conditions in your answer.

   ....

   ....
   (2 marks)

   (ii) Write an equation to represent the reduction reaction that occurs when ethanenitrile
   is reduced to ethylamine. Use [H] to represent the reducing agent.

   ....
   (1 mark)

(d) A scientist heats 2-hydroxypentanenitrile under reflux with dilute hydrochloric acid.
The reaction forms an organic product, **D**, and one inorganic product.

   (i) Draw and name organic product **D**.

   Name: ....
   (2 marks)

   (ii) Name the inorganic product formed.

   ....
   (1 mark)

Nitrogen Compounds, Polymers and Synthesis — 3

1 The flowchart below shows some reactions of an aromatic compound, **E**.

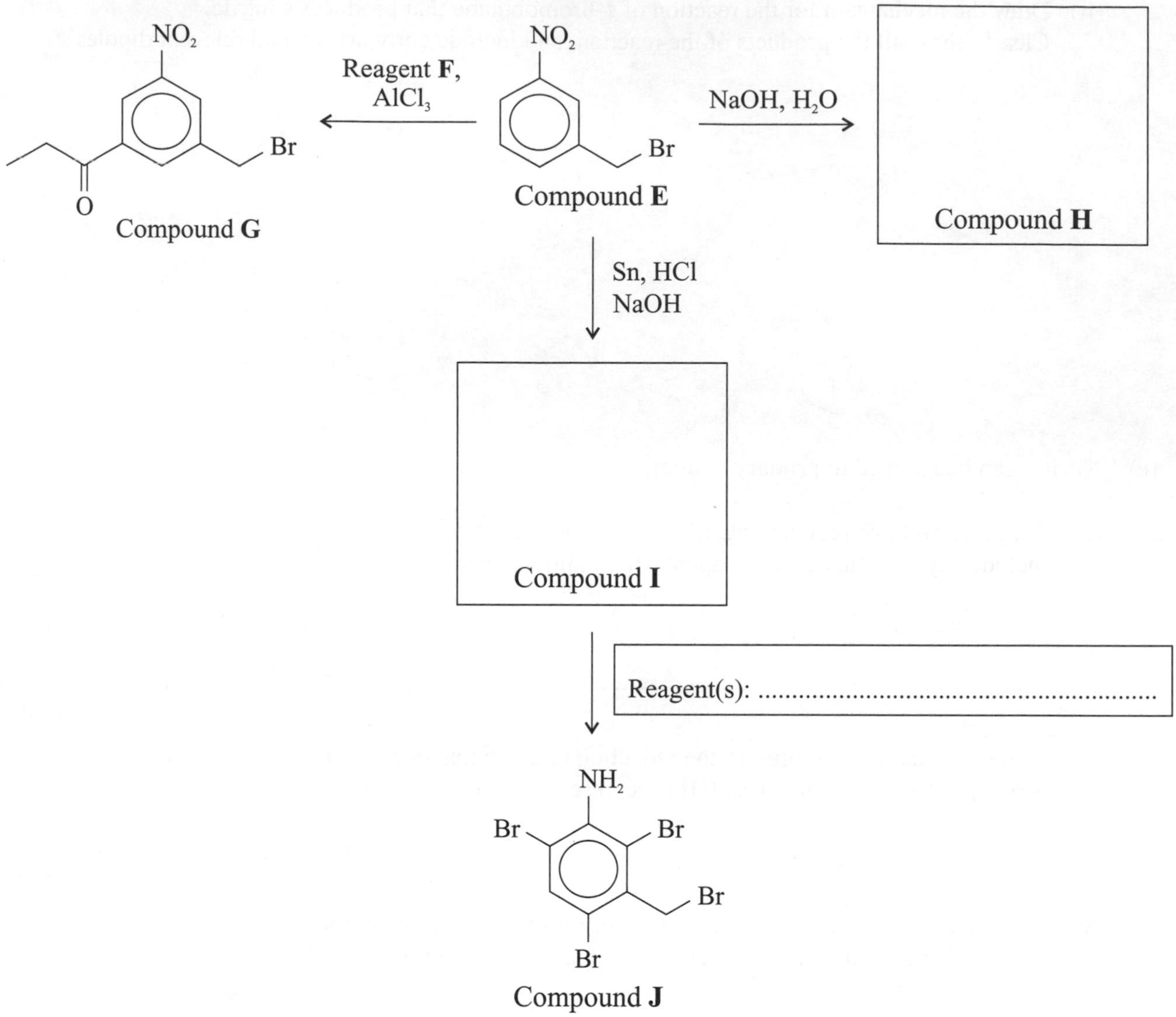

(a) Complete the flowchart above. Show the structures of compounds **H** and **I** and suggest the formula(e) of the reagent(s) that could be used to convert compound **I** to compound **J**.

(3 marks)

(b) Compound **E** reacts with reagent **F** in the presence of $AlCl_3$ to produce compound **G**.

(i) State the name given to this type of reaction.

....

(1 mark)

(ii) Give the displayed formula and systematic name of reagent **F**.

Name: ....

(2 marks)

(c) The bromomethyl group of compound **E** is weakly electron-donating.
Using this information and your knowledge of the directing effects of other aromatic
substituents, state and explain how the yield of compound **J** would change if the
order of the steps in its synthesis from compound **E** was reversed.

....

....

....

....

(2 marks)

2   Aspirin can be prepared in an esterification reaction between 2-hydroxybenzoic acid
and ethanoic anhydride. The reaction is carried out in the presence of an acid catalyst.
The aspirin produced precipitates out of the reaction mixture as the mixture cools.

(a)* Describe how the techniques of reflux and vacuum filtration can be used to produce aspirin from
2-hydroxybenzoic acid and ethanoic anhydride. Suggest why these techniques are suitable for this process.
In your answer you should include details of all equipment and conditions required.
You may use labelled diagrams in your answer.

....

....

....

....

....

....

....

....

....

....

....

....

(6 marks)

Module 6 : Organic Chemistry and Analysis

(b) The solid aspirin crystals obtained from the refluxed reaction mixture may be impure. Impurities can be removed by the process of recrystallisation. A possible method for recrystallisation is outlined below.

    1.   The crystals are dissolved in the minimum possible amount of hot solvent.
    2.   The saturated solution is left to cool slowly, allowing crystals of aspirin to form.
    3.   The crystals are removed by filtration under reduced pressure and washed with ice-cold solvent.
    4.   The crystals are dried.

(i) Why should the **minimum** possible amount of solvent be used in step 1?

....

....

(1 mark)

(ii) Explain why the choice of solvent in step 1 is important.

....

....

....

(2 marks)

(iii) Explain why the crystals are washed with **ice-cold solvent** in step 3.

....

....

....

(2 marks)

(c) The melting point of the aspirin produced can be used to assess the purity of the sample.
Describe **one** way in which experimental melting point data could indicate that the sample is impure.

....

....

(1 mark)

---

3 Scientists use their understanding of the reactions of different functional groups to devise efficient synthetic routes.

(a) The skeletal formula of an organic compound, **K**, is shown below.

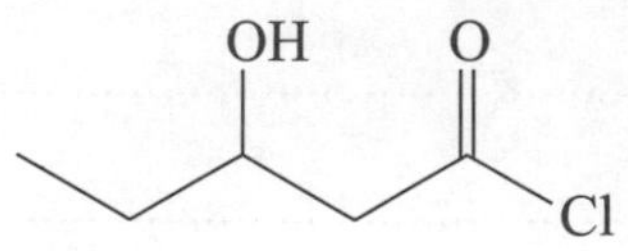

K

(i) Name the functional groups present in compound **K**.
You do not need to include the alkane functional group in your answer.

....

(2 marks)

(ii) Draw the displayed formula of the organic product formed when compound **K** reacts with ethanol.

(1 mark)

(b) Ethene can be converted into a primary amine using a three stage synthetic route as shown in the flowchart below.

$$\text{Ethene} \xrightarrow{\text{Stage 1}} \text{Ethane} \xrightarrow[\text{UV}]{\text{Cl}_2} \textbf{L} \xrightarrow{\text{Stage 3}} \text{Primary amine}$$

(i) State the type of reactions occurring in stages 1 and 2.

Stage 1: ....

Stage 2: ....

(2 marks)

(ii) Compound **L** contains one chlorine atom. Give the systematic name of compound **L**.

....

(1 mark)

(iii) For stage 3 of the synthetic route

- state the type of reaction occurring,
- give the reagents and conditions required,
- name the primary amine formed.

Type of reaction: ....

Reagents and conditions: ....

Name of primary amine: ....

(4 marks)

(iv) The synthetic route shown is not the shortest route from the starting material to the product. Suggest how the number of stages could be reduced, including any reagents required.

....

....

....

(2 marks)

Score

32

Analysis — 1

You can't always be sure a reaction's produced the product you're after, so analysis techniques are super-important.

For each of questions 1-3, give your answer by writing the correct letter in the box.

1 Which structure has the fewest peaks in its ^{13}C NMR spectrum?

A

CH_2CH_3
CH_3

B

CH_2CH_3
CH_2CH_3

C

CH_3
CH_3

D

CH_3
CH_2CH_3

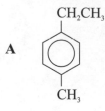

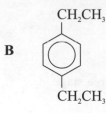

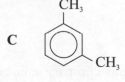

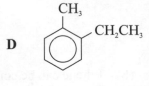

Your answer ☐

(1 mark)

2 The diagram below shows the structure of an organic molecule.

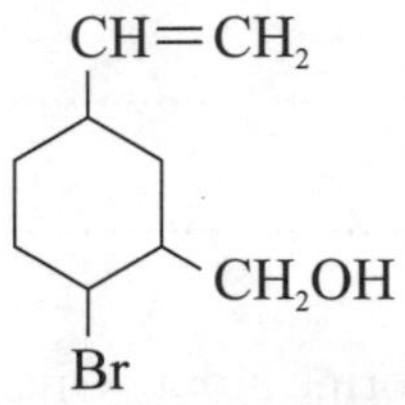

$CH=CH_2$
CH_2OH
Br

Which of these reagents would give a positive result in a test to identify a functional group in the molecule?

1: Tollens' reagent
2: aqueous silver nitrate in ethanol
3: acidified sodium dichromate solution

A 1, 2 and 3

B Only 1 and 2

C Only 2 and 3

D Only 3

Your answer ☐

(1 mark)

3 The diagram below shows the structure of Z-2-buten-2-ol.

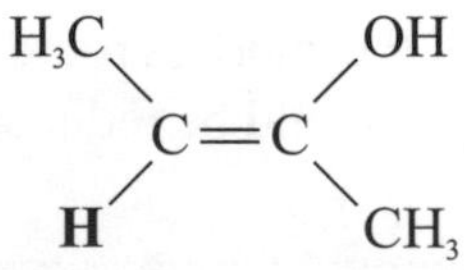

H_3C
OH
C=C
H
CH_3

A high resolution proton NMR spectrum of Z-2-buten-2-ol is run in $CDCl_3$.
Which statement correctly describes a feature of this spectrum?

A The spectrum has three signals with relative peak areas in the ratio 3:1:1.

B The **H** signal is a quartet.

C The OH signal is a doublet.

D One of the CH_3 signals is a triplet.

Your answer ☐

(1 mark)

4 **X** and **Y** are two mixtures of amino acids. A scientist used thin layer chromatography (TLC) to separate and identify the amino acids present in each mixture.

The scientist's chromatogram is shown below.
The table gives the R_f values of some amino acids for the solvent used.

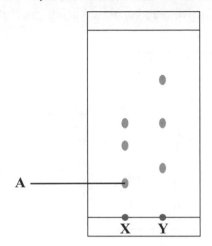

Amino acid	R_f value
Glycine	0.26
Alanine	0.38
Tyrosine	0.50
Leucine	0.73

(a) Which of the amino acids shown in the table adsorbs most strongly to the solid coating on the TLC plate?

....
(1 mark)

(b) (i) State the formula used to calculate an R_f value.

....
(1 mark)

(ii) Use the chromatogram to calculate the R_f value of the amino acid labelled **A**.

R_f value = ...
(1 mark)

(c) (i) Use the chromatogram and the information in the table to suggest the identity of the amino acid that is present in both mixtures. Give your reasoning, including any relevant calculations.

....

....
(2 marks)

(ii) Explain how the scientist could use another TLC experiment to confirm the identity of this amino acid.

....

....

....
(2 marks)

You'll need to know the reagents, method and expected results for ALL the tests for organic functional groups you've encountered during the course. Remembering specific quantities and concentrations isn't important, but you will need to make sure you describe the results correctly. Don't go saying a solution is "clear" when you mean "colourless", for example.

Score

10

Analysis — 2

1   A company was investigating the possibility of using an equimolar mixture of
octan-1-ol and hexan-1-ol in a perfume. It was necessary to test the mixture for impurities.
A solution of the mixture was made with a suitable solvent and analysed using gas chromatography.

The chromatogram produced is shown below. An impurity appears to be present in the sample.

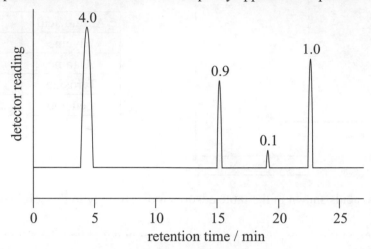

The table below shows the boiling points and retention times of a range of suspected impurities.
Information about octan-1-ol and hexan-1-ol is also included. The retention times were obtained using
the same conditions that were used to produce the chromatogram shown above.

Compound	Boiling point / °C	Retention time / min
Octane	126	9.7
Hexanal	130	10.8
Hexan-1-ol	157	15.2
Butanoic acid	164	16.5
Phenol	182	19.1
Octan-1-ol	195	22.6

(a) Relative peak integration values are given above each peak in the chromatogram.
What information about the substances present in the sample do these values provide?

....

(1 mark)

(b) (i)   State what is meant by the term retention time.

....

....

(1 mark)

(ii) Suggest why 50 °C would not be a suitable operating temperature
for the gas chromatograph in this experiment.

....

....

(2 marks)

(iii) Suggest which component of the sample produced the large peak at approximately 4 minutes.

....

(1 mark)

(c) (i) Use the data provided to suggest the identity and the source of the impurity.
Explain each of your suggestions.

Identity of impurity: ....

....

Source of impurity: ....

....

(2 marks)

(ii) Suggest how the identity of the impurity could be confirmed using gas chromatography.

....

....

(2 marks)

(iii) The company wishes to know the concentration of the impurity.
Outline a method involving gas chromatography that could be used to determine this concentration.

....

....

....

....

....

....

(5 marks)

2   Two esters, **A** and **B**, both have the molecular formula $C_4H_8O_2$.
Both esters have a proton NMR spectrum with three peaks and a carbon-13 NMR spectrum with four peaks.

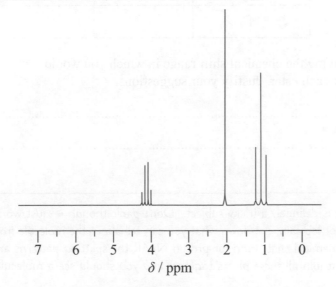

Ester **A**   Ester **B**

(a)   The proton NMR spectra for **one** of these esters is shown below.

(i)* Explain the splitting patterns observed and the positions of the peaks in the spectrum on the previous page. Identify which of the esters, **A** or **B**, produced this spectrum and explain your reasoning.

....

....

....

....

....

....

....

....

....

....

....

(6 marks)

(ii) A third ester with molecular formula $C_4H_8O_2$ also has three peaks in its proton NMR spectrum. Draw the displayed formula of this isomer.

(1 mark)

(b) The table below shows data from the carbon-13 NMR spectra for esters **A** and **B**.

Peak number	δ / ppm	
	A	**B**
1	15	10
2	23	28
3	60	52
4		

Complete the table by giving the chemical shift range in which you would expect to find peak 4 for each ester. Justify your suggestions.

....

....

(2 marks)

Analysis — 3

1 Compound **C** is an aliphatic compound found in coffee.
It contains only carbon, hydrogen and oxygen atoms.

(a) The infrared spectrum for compound **C** contains peaks at 3400 cm^{-1} and 1700 cm^{-1}.
Identify the functional groups that could have caused each of these peaks.

....

....

(2 marks)

(b) (i) When Tollens' reagent is added to a sample of compound **C**, no change is observed.
State what this shows about the functional groups present in compound **C**.

....

(1 mark)

(ii) Outline **two** more chemical tests that could be used to further investigate the presence
of the functional groups you identified in **(a)**.

....

....

....

(2 marks)

(c) The mass spectrum of compound **C** is shown below.

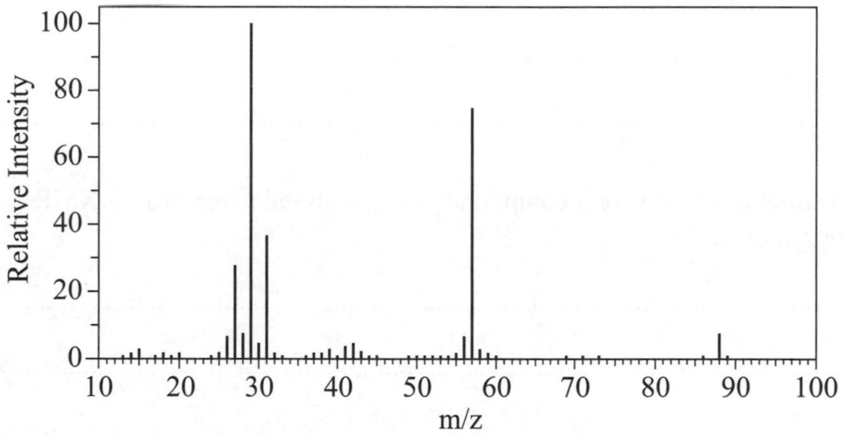

(i) Compound **C** has the following percentage composition by mass:
C: 55%; H: 9%; O: 36%
Determine the empirical formula of compound **C**.

empirical formula = ...

(2 marks)

(ii) Deduce the molecular formula of compound **C**.

molecular formula = ...

(1 mark)

(iii) Suggest the formula of the fragment ion responsible for each of the following peaks in the mass spectrum:

m/z = 29: ....

m/z = 31: ....

m/z = 57: ....

(3 marks)

(d) Deduce the displayed formula of compound **C**. Name compound **C**.

Displayed formula:

Name: ....

(2 marks)

2 Proton and carbon-13 NMR spectroscopy are techniques frequently used by organic chemists to determine the structures of molecules they have synthesised.

(a) (i) Tetramethylsilane (TMS) is used as a standard substance in both proton and carbon-13 NMR. The chemical formula of TMS is $Si(CH_3)_4$. Draw the displayed formula of TMS. Suggest why the structure of TMS makes it suitable for use as a standard substance in proton NMR.

....

....

(3 marks)

(ii) Suggest a suitable solvent for a compound being analysed using proton NMR. Justify your choice.

....

....

(2 marks)

Compound **D** is an organic compound with the molecular formula $C_4H_6O_4$. The carbon-13 and proton NMR spectra of compound **D** are shown below.

Carbon-13 NMR spectrum:

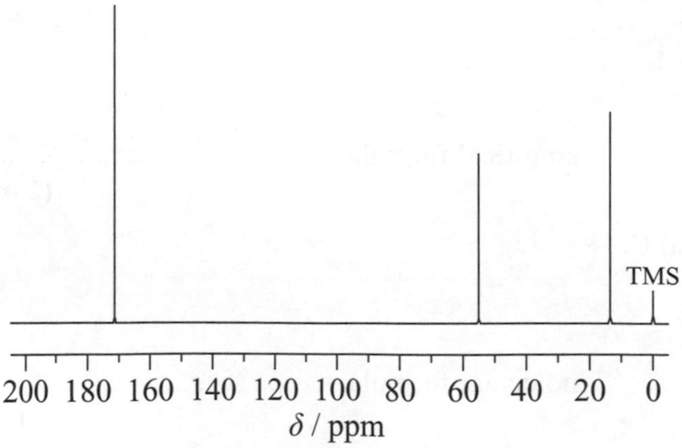

Proton NMR spectrum:

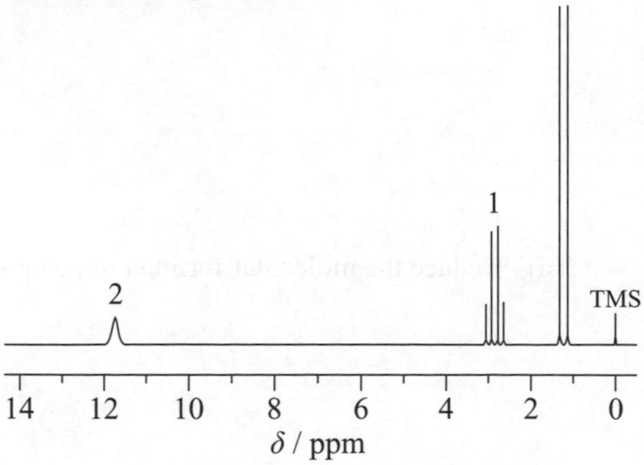

(b)* Use all of the information given to deduce the structure of compound **D**.
Give your reasoning.

....

....

....

....

....

....

....

....

....

(6 marks)

(c) The structure of another organic compound, **E**, is shown below.

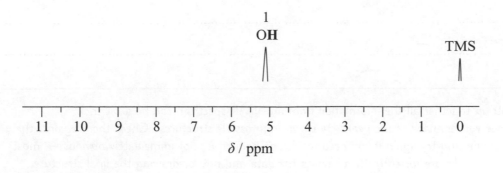

(i) Using the structure shown above, complete the high resolution proton NMR spectrum for compound **E**. Include predicted relative peak areas. The peak for the –OH hydrogen is already shown.

(5 marks)

(ii) Describe and explain a method that could be used to confirm that the signal at 5.1 ppm was produced by the –OH hydrogen atom.

....

....

(2 marks)

3 Compound **F** is a carbonyl compound with the molecular formula $C_7H_{14}O$.
It cannot be oxidised under normal laboratory conditions.

Data from the proton NMR spectrum of compound **F** is shown in the table below.

δ / ppm	2.4	1.1	0.9
Relative area	2	3	9
Splitting pattern	Quartet	Triplet	Singlet

Deduce the displayed formula of compound **F**.
Use all the information provided and explain your reasoning fully.

....

....

....

....

....

....

....

....

....

....

....

....

(8 marks)

EXAM TIP

Putting together all the information from an NMR spectrum can be a bit tricky. Once you've analysed the peaks start drawing possible structures. Check them against the spectrum and try again if you need to. Don't panic if it's not immediately obvious — most of the marks are for correctly analysing the data and not for drawing the final structure.

Score

39

Mixed Questions — 1

I hope you had a large helping of your wholegrain, wheat-based, high-fibre breakfast cereal this morning, because this section will test you on material from the whole of the course. It's time to bring it all together.

For each of questions 1-4, give your answer by writing the correct letter in the box.

1 Which statement about chemical reactions is correct?

A Magnesium reacts more vigorously than barium with water.

B Adding a catalyst means that, on average, the reactant molecules have more kinetic energy.

C Reactant molecules move slower at higher temperatures.

D Increasing the temperature shifts the Boltzmann distribution curve to the right.

Your answer ☐

(1 mark)

2 What is the chemical equation for the 2nd ionisation energy of sulfur?

A $S_{(g)} \rightarrow S^{2+}_{(g)} + 2e^-$ **B** $S^+_{(g)} \rightarrow S^{2+}_{(g)} + e^-$

C $S^{2+}_{(g)} + e^- \rightarrow S^+_{(g)}$ **D** $S^{2+}_{(g)} \rightarrow S^{3+}_{(g)} + e^-$

Your answer ☐

(1 mark)

3 What is the oxidation number of hydrogen in MgH_2?

A +2   **B** +1

C −1   **D** −2

Your answer ☐

(1 mark)

4 Which compound could be produced if 2-bromopentan-3-ol was heated with aqueous NaOH?

A 2,3-dibromopentane

B 2-bromopentane-2,3-diol

C pentane-2,3-diol

D 2-bromopentan-3-one

Your answer ☐

(1 mark)

5 A student is investigating the rate of the reaction between calcium and water.

She uses the following method:

1. Add 150 cm³ of water to a conical flask.
2. Add 142 mg of calcium to the conical flask and connect a 100 cm³ gas syringe.
3. Use a stopwatch to record the time taken for 80 cm³ of gas to be produced.

The reaction is carried out at a pressure of 100 kPa and a temperature of 298 K.

(a) The reaction of calcium with water is an example of a redox reaction.
Write a half-equation for the oxidation process occurring during the reaction.

....
(1 mark)

(b) Give the oxidation number of hydrogen in a molecule of water.

....
(1 mark)

(c) Use the ideal gas equation to calculate the maximum mass of calcium that the student could use without exceeding the capacity of the gas syringe.
Give your answer to an appropriate number of significant figures.

mass = ... mg
(5 marks)

(d) Suggest why the amount of gas collected during the experiment may be less than the amount of gas produced during the reaction.

....

....
(1 mark)

(e) The student repeats the experiment twice more, but uses strontium and barium instead of calcium.
Predict which metal produced 80 cm³ of gas in the shortest time. Justify your answer.

....

....
(2 marks)

6 The industrial production of aluminium chloride ($M_r = 133.5$) involves heating aluminium metal with chlorine at a temperature of 750 °C.

The equation for the reaction is:

$$2Al + 3Cl_2 \rightarrow 2AlCl_3$$

(a) Write the electron configuration, in terms of sub-shells, of an aluminium atom.

....
(1 mark)

(b) Give the oxidation number of aluminium and chlorine in aluminium chloride.

Aluminium oxidation number: .... Chlorine oxidation number: ....

(1 mark)

(c) The melting points of aluminium and chlorine are 660 °C and −102 °C respectively.
Explain the difference in the melting points of these two substances in terms of their structure and bonding.

....

....

....

....

(4 marks)

(d) In a reaction, 2.00 kg of aluminium is heated with excess chlorine. 7.14 kg of aluminium chloride is formed.
Calculate the percentage yield of this reaction.
Give your answer to an appropriate number of significant figures.

percentage yield = ... %

(3 marks)

Above a certain temperature, gaseous aluminium chloride forms an equilibrium mixture of $AlCl_3$ and Al_2Cl_6:

$$2AlCl_3 \rightleftharpoons Al_2Cl_6$$

(e) Write an expression for the equilibrium constant, K_c, for this reaction.

....

(1 mark)

(f) Al_2Cl_6 contains two Cl-Al dative covalent bonds, with each Al atom bonded to 4 Cl atoms.
There are no lone pairs around the Al atoms.

(i) Predict the bond angle around each Al atom in Al_2Cl_6.

....

(1 mark)

(ii) Deduce the shape of a molecule of Al_2Cl_6.
Hence draw a 3D diagram showing the bonding and shape of an Al_2Cl_6 molecule.

(2 marks)

EXAM TIP

Being presented with an unfamiliar compound in the exam can be a bit daunting, but don't be alarmed. Try and work out whether it shares any similarities with a compound that you've studied before — you can use this as a guide to predict the properties of the new compound.

Score

27

Mixed Questions — 2

1 Hex-1-ene and 3-methylpent-2-ene are structural isomers that belong to the homologous series of alkenes.

(a) (i) Write the structural formula of 3-methylpent-2-ene.

....

(1 mark)

(ii) 3-methylpent-2-ene exists as a pair of stereoisomers.
Draw the structure of the E isomer of 3-methylpent-2-ene.

(1 mark)

During combustion, hydrocarbons such as hex-1-ene and 3-methylpent-2-ene are oxidised to produce carbon dioxide and water.

(b) (i)* Describe and explain how the shapes and polarities of carbon dioxide and water molecules determine their physical states at room temperature (25 °C).

....

....

....

....

....

....

....

....

....

....

....

....

(6 marks)

(ii) Write a balanced symbol equation for the complete combustion of hex-1-ene.

....

(1 mark)

(iii) The enthalpies of combustion of hex-1-ene, carbon and hydrogen are shown in the table below.

Compound	$\Delta_c H$ / kJ mol^{-1}
$H_2C=CH(CH_2)_3CH_{3(l)}$	−4003.4
$C_{(s)}$	−393.5
$H_{2(g)}$	−285.8

Use the data in the table to calculate the enthalpy of formation of hex-1-ene.
The equation for the reaction is: $6C_{(s)} + 6H_{2(g)} \rightarrow H_2C=CH(CH_2)_3CH_{3(l)}$

enthalpy of formation = ...kJ mol^{-1}

(3 marks)

(c) Hex-1-ene reacts readily by electrophilic addition.

(i) Draw a mechanism for the addition reaction of hex-1-ene with hydrogen iodide, HI, to form 2-iodohexane.

(4 marks)

(ii) Hexan-2-ol can be produced by the steam hydration of hex-1-ene.
State a suitable catalyst for this reaction.

....

(1 mark)

(iii) Explain why hexan-2-ol is less volatile than hex-1-ene.

....

....

....

(2 marks)

Mixed Questions

2 The diagram shows the structure of the alkene chloroethene.

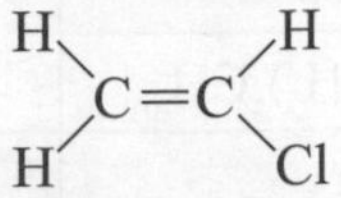

$$\underset{H}{\overset{H}{\diagdown}}C=C\underset{Cl}{\overset{H}{\diagup}}$$

(a) (i) Predict the shape and bond angle around each carbon atom in chloroethene.

Shape:...

Bond angle: ....

(2 marks)

(ii) Explain why chloroethene does **not** exhibit E/Z isomerism.

....

(1 mark)

(b) Describe **one** feature of the double bond in chloroethene that leads to the compound's high reactivity.

....

....

(1 mark)

(c) Chloroethene can undergo an addition polymerisation reaction to form poly(chloroethene) (PVC).

(i) Draw the displayed formula of a section of PVC three repeat units long.

(1 mark)

(ii) One method of disposing of polymers involves burning them to produce energy. Describe **one** problem with disposing of PVC in this way.

....

....

(1 mark)

(d) Chloroethene can also undergo a polymerisation reaction involving chlorine free radicals. The initiation step in this reaction is:

$$Cl_2 \xrightarrow{\text{UV}} 2Cl\cdot$$

The first reaction in the propagation step forms a radical by opening up the C=C double bond. The second results in the formation of a trichlorobutyl radical.

(i) Write equations to represent the first two reactions in the propagation step.

It's fine if you only use molecular formulas here.

....

....

(2 marks)

(ii) Suggest how the amount of chlorine added to the mixture affects the length of the polymer chains in the final product.

....

....

(2 marks)

3 A scientist has a sample of a compound, **X** ($M_r = 88.0$).
The displayed formula of compound **X** is shown below.

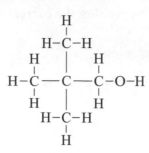

(a) Name compound **X**.

....

(1 mark)

The scientist uses mass spectrometry to analyse a sample of compound **X**.

(b) Explain how the presence of ^{13}C in the sample affects the mass spectrum.

....

....

(1 mark)

(c) The ionisation of molecules during mass spectrometry can cause some of the bonds
within a molecule to break. This produces additional ions which are also detected
by the mass spectrometer. These ions are known as fragment ions.

    (i) A peak with m/z = 57 is present in the mass spectrum of compound **X**.
       Suggest the displayed formula of the fragment ion that was responsible for this peak.

(1 mark)

    (ii) Suggest why the ion you drew in (c)(i) is particularly stable.

....

....

....

(2 marks)

Score

34

Mixed Questions — 3

For each of questions 1-4, give your answer by writing the correct letter in the box.

1 Which of the following is a valid rate equation?

A Rate = $k[NO]_2[O_2]$

B Rate = $k[NO]^2[O_2]$

C Rate = $k[NO]^2[O]_2$

D Rate = $k[2NO_2][O]$

Your answer [ ]

(1 mark)

2 Which reagents could **not** be used to prepare $CH_3CH_2CH_2COOH$?

A $CH_3CH_2CH_2COCl + H_2O$

B $CH_3CH_2CH_2COH + K_2Cr_2O_7 + H_2SO_4$

C $CH_3CH_2CH_2C{\equiv}N$ + dilute HCl

D $CH_3CH_2CH_2CH_2Br + KOH + H_2O$

Your answer [ ]

(1 mark)

3 Phosphoric acid (H_3PO_4) is a tribasic acid. What mass of calcium hydroxide is required to neutralise 30 cm³ of a solution of 1.2 mol dm⁻³ H_3PO_4?

A 2.7 g

B 2.5 g

C 4.0 g

D 1.8 g

Your answer [ ]

(1 mark)

4 The skeletal formulas of three organic compounds are shown below.

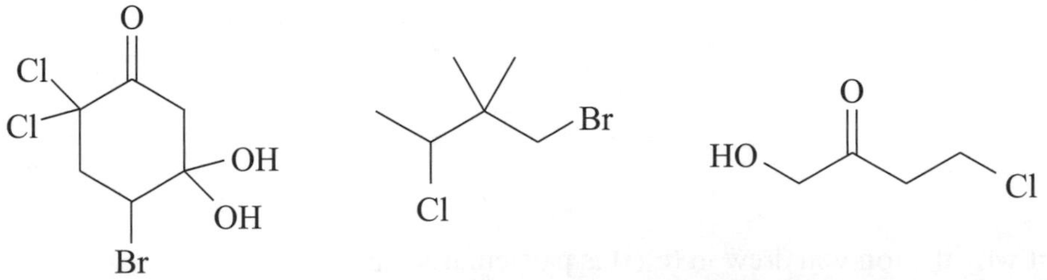

Which of the following is the **minimum** amount of information required to fully distinguish the compounds?

A The number of peaks in the carbon-13 and proton NMR spectra.

B The number of peaks in the carbon-13 NMR spectrum only.

C The number of peaks in the proton NMR spectrum only.

D The IR spectrum in the range 1630-1820 cm⁻¹ and the number of peaks in the carbon-13 and proton NMR spectra.

Your answer [ ]

(1 mark)

5 Ethylbenzene can be produced by the Friedel-Crafts alkylation of benzene, in which benzene reacts with chloroethane in the presence of an aluminium chloride catalyst. The diagram below shows the structure of ethylbenzene.

(a) In the first stage of the reaction, the chloroethane reacts with the aluminium chloride to produce an electrophile.

(i) State what is meant by the term electrophile.

....

(1 mark)

(ii) Write an equation for the reaction that produces the electrophile.
Use structural formulae for any organic reactants and products.

....

(1 mark)

(iii) Suggest a mechanism for the Friedel-Crafts alkylation reaction that produces ethylbenzene. In your answer you should include curly arrows and relevant charges, and show how the aluminium chloride catalyst is reformed during the reaction. Use skeletal formulae to show the organic reactants and products.

(4 marks)

(b) In industry, most ethylbenzene is converted to styrene in the gas-phase equilibrium reaction shown below.

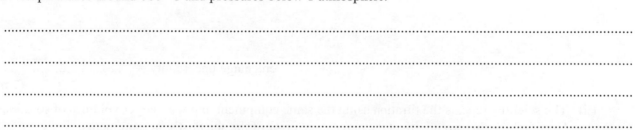

$\Delta_r H = +124.9 \text{ kJ mol}^{-1}$

Suggest and explain why the highest yields for this reaction are obtained at temperatures around 600 °C and pressures below 1 atmosphere.

....

....

....

....

(2 marks)

EXAM TIP

When you're drawing diagrams in the exam, make sure you make them as large and clear as possible. That way you'll have plenty of space for labelling partial charges and the like, and there shouldn't be any confusion as to where exactly any arrows are pointing. So it should be super-easy for the examiner to see everything you're trying to show and give you those marks.

Score

12

Mixed Questions — 4

1   A scientist carried out a redox titration using acidified manganate(VII) ions
to determine the concentration of 150 cm^3 of a solution of chloride ions.

Some information about the processes occurring during the redox reaction is shown in the table below.

Half-equation	E° / V
$Cl_{2(aq)} + 2e^- \rightleftharpoons 2Cl^-_{(aq)}$	+1.36
$MnO_{4\ (aq)}^- + 8H^+_{(aq)} + 5e^- \rightleftharpoons Mn^{2+}_{(aq)} + 4H_2O_{(l)}$	+1.51

(a)   Use the information in the table above to construct a balanced ionic equation for the redox reaction.

....

(1 mark)

(b)   Calculate the E° value for the redox reaction.

E° = ... V

(1 mark)

(c)   35.0 cm^3 of the chloride solution was titrated against a 0.230 mol dm^{-3} solution of acidified MnO_4^- ions.
18.7 cm^3 of the MnO_4^- solution was required for complete oxidation of the chloride ions.
Calculate the number of chloride ions in the scientist's 150 cm^3 solution.

number of ions = ...

(4 marks)

(d)   The scientist plans to reduce the percentage error of the measurements taken during the titration.
(i)   The burette the scientist used had an uncertainty of 0.05 cm^3.
Calculate the percentage uncertainty in their measurement of the volume of MnO_4^- solution added.

Percentage uncertainty = ... %

(2 marks)

(ii)   The scientist repeats the titration using the same equipment, but with larger volumes of solutions.
Explain how this would affect the percentage error of the scientist's measurements.

....

....

....

(2 marks)

2 Urease is a protein found in soils that catalyses the hydrolysis of urea into carbon dioxide and ammonia. The reaction scheme for this process is shown below.

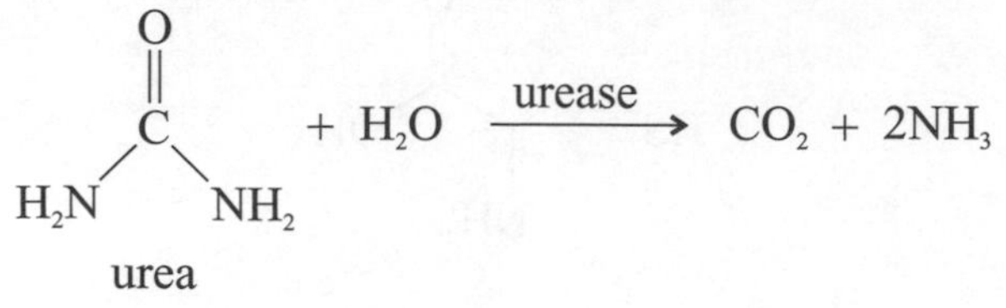

$$\text{urea} + H_2O \xrightarrow{\text{urease}} CO_2 + 2NH_3$$

(a) (i) Suggest why soils that contain high concentrations of urease may have a relatively high pH.

....

....

(2 marks)

(ii) In the absence of urease, the hydrolysis of urea at 298 K has a rate constant of 1.46×10^{-7} s^{-1}. The pre-exponential factor for the reaction is 7.098×10^3 s^{-1}. Use the Arrhenius equation to calculate the activation energy of the hydrolysis of urea, in kJ mol^{-1}, at 298 K.

activation energy = ... kJ mol^{-1}

(2 marks)

(b) Urease inhibitors prevent urease from catalysing the hydrolysis of urea. The structure of the urease inhibitor phenyl phosphorodiamidate (PPDA) is shown below.

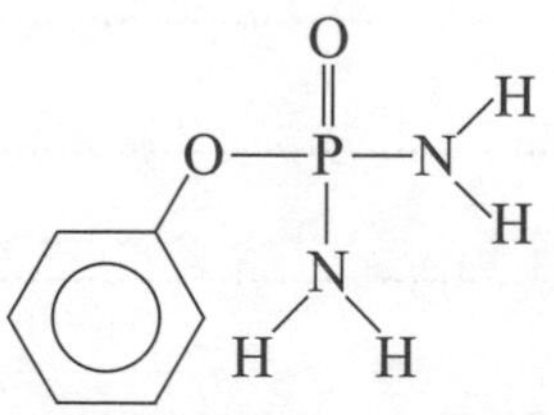

(i) How many signals would appear in the proton NMR spectrum of PPDA?

....

(1 mark)

(ii) Deduce how many atoms in the structure of PPDA can form a hydrogen bond.

....

(1 mark)

(iii) Under the basic conditions found in some soils, PPDA can be hydrolysed in a similar way to an ester. Suggest which bond in PPDA is broken by this hydrolysis.

....

(1 mark)

(c) Urease typically contains the amino acid cysteine.
The structure of cysteine is shown below.

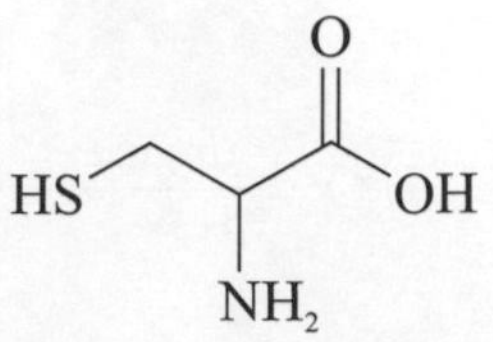

(i) Cysteine contains a chiral centre. On the diagram above,
label the chiral centre in cysteine using an asterisk (*).

(1 mark)

(ii) The amino acids in urease are joined together in long chains by amide links.
Draw the skeletal formula of the compound that forms
when two cysteine molecules are joined by an amide link.

(1 mark)

(d) The structure of two more amino acids, lysine and leucine, are shown below.

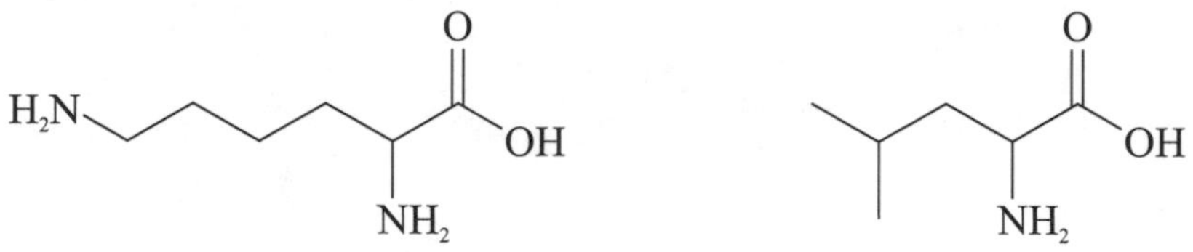

Lysine   Leucine

(i) Suggest and explain which of the amino acids shown is more soluble in water.

....

....

....

(2 marks)

(ii) Two students analysed a sample of lysine using thin-layer chromatography.
The amino acid was found to have a different R_f value on each of the two students' chromatograms.
Suggest **two** possible reasons for this difference.

....

....

....

(2 marks)

Score

It's really important that you pay close attention to units when you're doing calculation
questions in the exam. For example, if you've got a concentration in g dm⁻³ and a volume in
cm³, you'll need to do a bit of maths to get them to be in the same units (e.g. g dm⁻³ and dm³).

EXAM TIP

23

Mixed Questions — 5

1 Tris(ethane-1,2-diamine)cobalt(III) is a complex ion that exists as a pair of optical isomers.
The complex ion has the formula $[Co(en)_3]^{3+}$ (where en = ethane-1,2-diamine, $NH_2CH_2CH_2NH_2$).
One of the optical isomers of $[Co(en)_3]^{3+}$ is shown below.

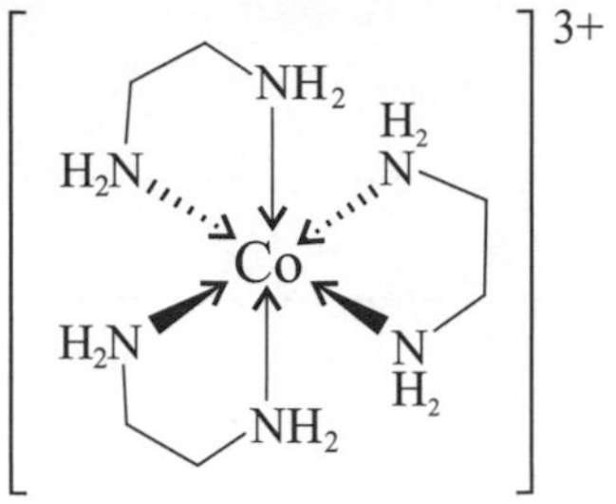

(a) (i)   Draw the other optical isomer of $[Co(en)_3]^{3+}$.

(1 mark)

(ii) Deduce the oxidation number of Co in $[Co(en)_3]^{3+}$.

....
(1 mark)

(iii) State the coordination number of Co in $[Co(en)_3]^{3+}$.

....
(1 mark)

(iv) Suggest why the entropy change for the ligand substitution reaction of $[Co(en)_3]^{3+}$
with H_2O does not lead to a favourable change in the free energy.

....

....

....
(2 marks)

(b) Ethane-1,2-diamine can be used as a starting point for the synthesis of the multidentate ligand EDTA.
The skeletal formula of EDTA is shown below.

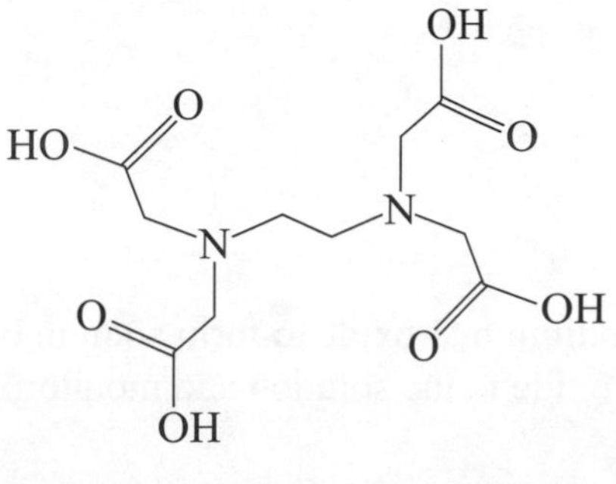

(i)   Use the skeletal formula shown above to deduce the molecular formula of EDTA.

....
(1 mark)

(ii) Suggest the name of a compound that could be reacted with ethane-1,2-diamine to produce EDTA.

....

(1 mark)

A scientist has a solution with a pH of 7. She attempts to dissolve a sample of EDTA in the solution, but finds that most of the EDTA does not dissolve.

(iii) Suggest a reagent that could be used to increase the solubility of the EDTA sample. Explain your answer.

....

....

....

....

....

(3 marks)

2 The structures of three aromatic compounds are shown below.

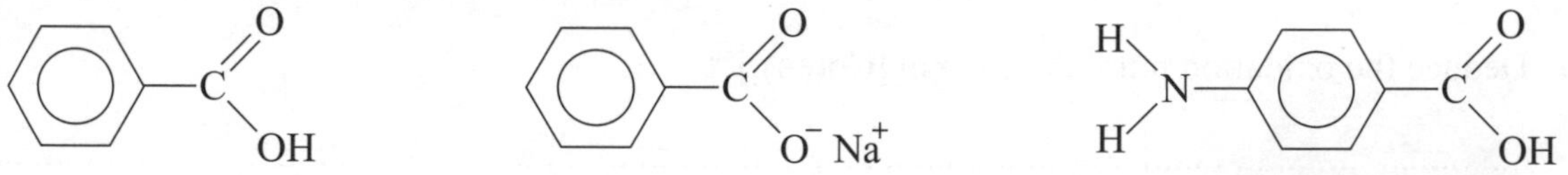

Benzoic acid   Sodium benzoate   4-aminobenzoic acid

Benzoic acid is a weak acid.
A scientist makes up 750 cm³ of a solution of benzoic acid (C_6H_5COOH) with a concentration of 0.025 mol dm⁻³. The acid dissociation constant, K_a, for benzoic acid is 6.3×10^{-5} mol dm⁻³.

(a) (i) Calculate the pH of the solution of benzoic acid.

pH = ...

(3 marks)

Benzoic acid can react with sodium hydroxide to form sodium benzoate. The scientist slowly adds small amounts of solid sodium hydroxide to the solution and monitors the pH change during the reaction.

(ii) Write an ionic equation for the reaction that occurs between benzoic acid and sodium hydroxide.

....

(1 mark)

(iii) The scientist keeps adding more sodium hydroxide until it is in excess.
He finds that the pH of the resulting solution is 12.2. The experiment was carried out at 298 K.
Use this information to calculate the mass of sodium hydroxide that was added to the benzoic acid solution over the course of the experiment.
You may assume that adding the sodium hydroxide did not change the volume of the solution.
Give your answer to an appropriate number of significant figures.

mass = ... g

(7 marks)

(b) (i) 4-aminobenzoic acid can be synthesised from benzoic acid in a two-step process.
Suggest reagents and conditions for each step in the synthesis.

Step 1: ....

....

Step 2: ....

....

(5 marks)

(ii) State the number of peaks that you would expect to be produced in the proton and carbon-13 NMR spectra of 4-aminobenzoic acid.

Number of peaks in proton spectrum: ....

Number of peaks in carbon-13 spectrum: ....

(2 marks)

(iii) Under certain conditions, 4-aminobenzoic acid undergoes a polymerisation reaction to form a polyamide. Draw the repeating unit of the polyamide formed from 4-aminobenzoic acid.

(1 mark)

EXAM TIP

Some of the trickier questions in the exam may require you to bring together knowledge from different areas of chemistry, so take your time to read each question part carefully so you understand what it's asking. You don't want to go into autopilot and start writing about acids and bases, when the question is actually testing you on your knowledge of redox titrations, for example.

Score

29

Answers

Module 2 — Foundations in Chemistry

Pages 3-6: Atoms, Compounds and Equations

1   C *[1 mark]*
All copper atoms have 29 protons in their nuclei, so copper-64 must have 64 − 29 = 35 neutrons.

2   A *[1 mark]*
Caesium is in Group 1 of the Periodic Table, so it forms 1+ ions. Selenium is in Group 6 of the Periodic Table, so it forms 2− ions. Two caesium ions are needed to balance out the charge on one selenide ion.

3   B *[1 mark]*
To have a charge of +1, the Ag ion must have 1 fewer electrons than protons.

4   B *[1 mark]*
m is the mass of the missing isotope.
$$\frac{(21 \times 0.3) + (20 \times 90.5) + (m \times 9.2)}{100} = 20.187$$
1816.3 + 9.2m = 2018.7
9.2m = 202.4
* m = 22*

5 a) i)   Isotopes are atoms of the same element with different numbers of neutrons *[1 mark]*.
    ii) mass number: 17
         atomic number: 8 *[1 mark for both correct]*
   b)   10 *[1 mark]*
   c)   E.g. the model is easy to draw and understand *[1 mark]* and fits well with most observations of e.g. bonding or ionisation energy trends *[1 mark]*.

6 a) i) Na_2SO_4 *[1 mark]*
    ii) $Cu^{2+}_{(aq)} + 2OH^-_{(aq)} \rightarrow Cu(OH)_{2(s)}$ *[1 mark]*
  b) i) $2NaOH + H_2SO_4 \rightarrow Na_2SO_4 + 2H_2O$ *[1 mark]*
    ii) $2Na^+ + 2OH^- + 2H^+ + SO_4^{2-} \rightarrow 2Na^+ + SO_4^{2-} + 2H_2O$
         [1 mark]. $2Na^+$ and SO_4^{2-} are on both sides of the equation so cancel out, giving $2H^+ + 2OH^- \rightarrow 2H_2O$ which can be divided by 2 to give the required equation *[1 mark]*.

If you've shown this visually by crossing through the species which appear on both sides of the equation, rather than explaining in words, you still get the mark.

7 a) $A_r = \dfrac{(84 \times 0.56) + (86 \times 9.86) + (87 \times 7.02) + (88 \times 82.56)}{100}$
         = 87.7102
         = 87.7 (1 d.p.)
         [2 marks for correct answer given to 1 d.p. or 1 mark for correct method for calculating A_r.]
  b)   Strontium *[1 mark]*

8 a) $2CO + 2NO \rightarrow N_2 + 2CO_2$ *[2 marks — 1 mark for correctly identifying carbon dioxide and 1 mark for a correctly balanced symbol equation]*
  b) $M_r = (3 \times 12.0) + (6 \times 1.0) + (2 \times 16.0)$
         = 74.0 *[1 mark]*
  c) i) $4NH_3 + 5O_2 \rightarrow 4NO + 6H_2O$ *[1 mark]*
         $3Cu + 8HNO_3 \rightarrow 3Cu(NO_3)_2 + 2NO + 4H_2O$ *[1 mark]*
    ii) copper(II) nitrate *[1 mark]*
    iii) Cu^{2+} and NO_3^- *[1 mark for both correct]*
Multiples of any of the balanced equations in question 8 are also correct answers.

9 a)   The weighted mean mass of an atom of an element *[1 mark]* compared to 1/12th of the mass of an atom of carbon-12 *[1 mark]*.
  b)   Isotopic mass is the exact mass of an atom of a particular isotope, and not a mean value like relative atomic mass *[1 mark]*.
  c) $M_r = 63.5 + 4(14.0 + (3 \times 1.0)) + 2((2 \times 1.0) + 16.0))$
         = 167.5 *[1 mark]*
  d) Cl_2 ($M_r = 71.0$) *[1 mark]* and $MnCl_2$ ($M_r = 125.9$) *[1 mark]*

Pages 7-9: Amount of Substance, Acids and Redox — 1

1   B *[1 mark]*
For every mole of PCl_5 molecules, there are 5 moles of Cl atoms. So the number of chlorine atoms is $5 \times 6.02 \times 10^{23} = 3.01 \times 10^{24}$.

2   C *[1 mark]*
The sum of the oxidation numbers in $VOSO_4$ is zero. The sulfate ion has an oxidation number of −2 and the oxygen has an oxidation number of −2, so the oxidation number of vanadium is 0 − (−2) − (−2) = +4

3   C *[1 mark]*
Mass of oxygen in oxide = 4.26 − 1.86 = 2.40 g.
Moles of P in oxide = 1.86 ÷ 31.0 = 0.06 moles
Moles of O in oxide = 2.40 ÷ 16.0 = 0.15 moles.
Now find the simplest whole number ratio of moles:
0.06 ÷ 0.06 = 1 and 0.15 ÷ 0.06 = 2.5.
Ratio of P to O atoms = 1:2.5 = 2:5. So the empirical formula is P_2O_5.

4   C *[1 mark]*
The number of moles of $BaSO_4$ is 3.16 ÷ 233.4 = 0.0135 moles. The balanced equation shows that one mole of $CuSO_4$ reacts to form one mole of $BaSO_4$. So you need 0.0135 ÷ 0.650 = 0.0208 dm^3 = 20.8 cm^3 of $CuSO_4$ solution to form 3.16 g of $BaSO_4$.

5 a)   Divide by the A_r of each element:
         C: 40.9 ÷ 12.0 = 3.4083...
         H: 4.5 ÷ 1.0 = 4.5
         O: 54.6 ÷ 16.0 = 3.4125
         Divide through by the smallest number:
         C: 3.4083... ÷ 3.4083... = 1.00
         H: 4.5 ÷ 3.4083... = 1.32...
         O: 3.4125 ÷ 3.4083... = 1.00...
         Simplest whole-number ratio of C:H:O = 3:4:3
         Empirical formula = $\mathbf{C_3H_4O_3}$
         [2 marks for correct answer, otherwise 1 mark for dividing by the A_r of each element.]
  b)   Empirical mass = $(3 \times 12.0) + (4 \times 1.0) + (3 \times 16.0) = 88.0$
         Number of empirical units = 176.0 ÷ 88.0 = 2
         Molecular formula = $2 \times (C_3H_4O_3) = \mathbf{C_6H_8O_6}$ *[1 mark]*
  c)   Mass of ascorbic acid in grams = 300 ÷ 1000 = 0.300 g
         Moles of ascorbic acid = 0.300 ÷ 176.0 = 0.0017045...
         = 0.00170 (3 s.f.) *[1 mark]*
You could also give your answer in standard form i.e. 1.70×10^{-3} moles.

6 a)   volume of acid *[1 mark]*
  b) i)

		Titre		
	Rough	1	2	3
Initial reading / cm^3	11.10	28.50	11.25	27.60
Final reading / cm^3	28.50	45.15	27.60	44.30
Volume of HCl added / cm^3	17.40	16.65	16.35	16.70

         [2 marks for all four answers correct to 4 significant figures, otherwise 1 mark for three answers correct to 4 significant figures.]
    ii) mean titre = (16.65 + 16.70) ÷ 2 = 16.675
         = 16.68 cm^3 (4 s.f.)
         [2 marks for correct answer, otherwise 1 mark for including only concordant results in the calculation.]
Concordant results are ones that are very similar to each other (usually within 0.10 cm^3). The result for titre 2 is not concordant with titres 1 and 3, so it shouldn't be included when calculating the mean titre.

iii) Moles of HCl = 0.100 × 0.016675 = 1.6675 × 10^{-3} mol
The equation shows that there are 2 moles of HCl
for each mole of Ca(OH)$_2$.
Moles of Ca(OH)$_2$ in 25 cm^3 of diluted solution
= 1.6675 × 10^{-3} ÷ 2 = 8.3375 × 10^{-4} mol
Moles of Ca(OH)$_2$ in original sample
= (8.3375 × 10^{-4} ÷ 25.0) × 250 = 8.3375 × 10^{-3} mol
Concentration of Ca(OH)$_2$ = 8.3375 × 10^{-3} ÷ 0.0250
= 0.3335
= **0.334 mol dm^{-3} (3 s.f.)**
*[4 marks for correct answer, otherwise 1 mark for correct
number of moles of HCl, 1 mark for correct number of
moles of Ca(OH)$_2$ in 25 cm^3 of diluted solution, 1 mark for
correct number of moles of Ca(OH)$_2$ in original sample.
Allow error in mean titre value carried forward from
question 6 b)ii) throughout.]*

*Be careful with units in calculations like this. The volumes you're given are
in cm^3, but the concentrations are in mol dm^{-3}. So you need to convert the
volume of the Ca(OH)$_2$ solution to dm^3 before calculating its concentration.
(That's why you divide by 0.250 in the last step rather than by 250.)*

7 a) $p = (nRT) ÷ V$
= ((2.50 ÷ 58.0) × 8.314 × (10.0 + 273)) ÷ (750 × 10^{-6})
= 135221.954 Pa = 135.22... kPa = **135 kPa (3 s.f.)**
*[4 marks for correct answer, otherwise 1 mark for
correctly working out moles of C$_4$H$_{10}$, 1 mark for correctly
rearranging the ideal gas equation, 1 mark for substituting
correct values into the equation.]*

*Again, be careful with units here. For the ideal gas equation, volume must
be in m^3, so in the first step you need to divide by 750 × 10^{-6} m^3 rather
than 750 cm^3. Temperature must be in K, so you need to add 273 on to
the given value of 10 °C. And your answer for pressure will be in Pa, so
you'll need to divide it by 1000 to convert it to kPa.*

b) Moles of O$_2$ = 3.84 ÷ (2 × 16.0) = 0.120
Moles of C$_4$H$_{10}$ = 0.120 ÷ 6.5 = 0.0184...
Mass of C$_4$H$_{10}$ = 0.0184... × 58.0 = 1.070... = **1.07 g (3 s.f.)**
*[3 marks for correct answer, otherwise 1 mark for correct
number of moles of O$_2$, 1 mark for correct number of moles
of C$_4$H$_{10}$.]*

Pages 10-13: Amount of Substance, Acids and Redox — 2

1 a) Any two from: e.g. rinse the weighing boat into the flask
after transferring the solid/re-weigh the weighing boat after
transferring the solid to determine the precise mass of solid
added to the flask. / Dissolve the solid in a beaker of water
before transferring to the volumetric flask. / Use a funnel to
add the solid/solution to the volumetric flask. / Use a pipette
to add the last few drops of distilled water to the volumetric
flask.
[2 marks — 1 mark for each correct answer.]

b) i) E.g. moles of NaHCO$_3$ = 0.30 × (250 ÷ 1000) = 0.075
M_r(NaHCO$_3$) = 23.0 + 1.0 + 12.0 + (3 × 16.0) = 84.0
Mass of NaHCO$_3$ = 0.075 × 84.0 = **6.3 g**
*[2 marks for correct answer, otherwise 1 mark for
correct working.]*

*You could also have worked this out by finding the mass of NaHCO$_3$
required to make 1 dm^3 of 0.30 mol dm^{-3} solution, and dividing it by 4
to find the mass needed to make 250 cm^3 of the solution.*

ii) E.g. moles of NaHCO$_3$ in 100 cm^3 = 0.075 × (100 ÷ 250)
= 0.030
Concentration of NaHCO$_3$ = 0.030 ÷ (250 ÷ 1000)
= **0.12 mol dm^{-3}**
*[2 marks for correct answer, otherwise 1 mark for correct
number of moles of NaHCO$_3$.]*

*Another way of finding the number of moles of NaHCO$_3$ in 100 cm^3
would be by multiplying the concentration of the standard solution by the
volume of the portion removed (100 cm^3 ÷ 1000 = 0.1 dm^3).*

c) Error 1 would decrease the mean titre volume, as the
concentration of the standard solution would be higher
than intended, meaning less would be needed to neutralise
the hydrochloric acid. *[1 mark]*. Error 2 would increase
the mean titre volume, as the concentration of the standard
solution would be lower than intended, meaning more would
be needed to neutralise the hydrochloric acid *[1 mark]*.

2 a) i) Moles of PbS = (4.50 × 10^6) ÷ 239.3 = 18804.84... mol
Moles of O$_2$ = 18804.84... × (3 ÷ 2) = 28207.27... mol
Mass of O$_2$ = 28207.27... × (2 × 16.0) = 902632.67... g
= 902.632... kg = **903 kg (3 s.f.)**
*[3 marks for correct answer, otherwise 1 mark for correct
number of moles of PbS and 1 mark for correct number of
moles of O$_2$.]*

ii) E.g. 2 moles of PbS react to give 2 moles of PbO in step 1.
2 moles of PbO reacts to give 2 moles of Pb in step 2.
So 2 moles of PbS reacts to give 2 moles of Pb.
Moles of Pb = 18804.84... mol
Mass of Pb = 207.2 × 18804.84... = 3896364.39... g
= 3896.364... kg = **3900 kg (3 s.f.)**
*[2 marks for correct answer, otherwise 1 mark for
correct working.]*

*You could also have worked this out by finding the mass of lead in
4.5 tonnes of PbS: (4.50 × 10^6) × (207.2 ÷ 239.3) = 3896364.39... g.*

b) Atom economy of reaction A = (A_r(Ti) ÷ M_r(reactants)) × 100
= 47.9 ÷ ((47.9 + (4 × 35.5)) + (2 × 24.3)) × 100
= **20.1% (3 s.f.)**
Atom economy of reaction B = (A_r(Ti) ÷ M_r(reactants)) × 100
= 47.9 ÷ ((47.9 + (4 × 35.5)) + (4 × 23.0)) × 100
= **17.0% (3 s.f.)**
[2 marks — 1 mark for each correct atom economy.]

*When you're calculating atom economy, you can divide the molecular mass
of the desired product by the total molecular mass of all the reactants or all
the products — they'll both be the same.*

c) i) MnO$_2$ *[1 mark]*
ii) iron(III) oxide *[1 mark]*

3 a) i) The copper has been oxidised *[1 mark]*. Its oxidation
number has increased from 0 to +2 *[1 mark]*. At the same
time, the nitrogen has been reduced *[1 mark]*. Its oxidation
number has decreased from +5 to +2 *[1 mark]*.

ii) When a species is reduced, it gains electrons (from another
species) *[1 mark]*.

b) i) E.g. moles of Cu = 3.60 ÷ 63.5 = 0.0566... mol
2 moles of Cu are produced from 1 mole of Cu_2S,
so moles of Cu_2S that reacted = 0.0566... ÷ 2 = 0.0283... mol.
The percentage yield of the reaction was 92.4%, so:
Total moles of Cu_2S in sample = 0.0283... × (100 ÷ 92.4)
= 0.0306...

Mass of Cu_2S sample = 0.0306... × ((2 × 63.5) + 32.1)
= 4.8808... = **4.88 g**

[4 marks for correct answer, otherwise 1 mark for correct number of moles of Cu, 1 mark for correct number of moles of Cu_2S that reacted, 1 mark for correct total number of moles of Cu_2S in the sample.]

You could also work this out by finding the theoretical mass of Cu that would have formed had all of the Cu_2S reacted, converting the mass to moles, and then using that figure to find the moles and mass of Cu_2S in the sample.

ii) Atom economy = $(M_r(2Cu) ÷ M_r(\text{reactants})) × 100$
= [(2 × 63.5) ÷ (((2 × 63.5) + 32.1) + (2 × 16.0))] × 100
= **66.5% (3 s.f.)** *[1 mark]*

Again, it's fine if you divided by the total molecular mass of the products rather than the reactants to reach your answer here.

iii) E.g. reactions with high atom economies produce less waste so are less polluting *[1 mark]*. Reactions with high atom economies make more efficient use of raw materials so are more sustainable *[1 mark]*.

You could also have written your answer in terms of why reactions with low atom economies are less sustainable.

4 a) i) $V = (nRT) ÷ p$
= (0.0820 × 8.314 × 298) ÷ (101 × 10³)
= 2.011... × 10⁻³ m³
= 2.01... dm³ = **2.01 dm³ (3 s.f.)**

[3 marks for correct answer, otherwise 1 mark for correctly rearranging the ideal gas equation, 1 mark for substituting correct values into the equation.]

ii) 0.0820 × 6.02 × 10²³ = 4.9364 × 10²²
= **4.94 × 10²² (3 s.f.)** *[1 mark]*

b) Percentage of oxygen = 100 − (40.0 + 14.3) = 45.7%
In 100 g of the compound, there would be:
40.0 ÷ 14.0 = 2.85... moles of N
14.3 ÷ 1.0 = 14.3 moles of H
45.7 ÷ 16.0 = 2.85... moles of O
Divide through by the smallest number:
N: 2.85... ÷ 2.85... = 1.00
H: 14.3 ÷ 2.85... = 5.00 (3 s.f.)
O: 2.85... ÷ 2.85... = 1.00 (3 s.f.)
Empirical formula = NH_5O

[3 marks — 1 mark for correct percentage of oxygen, 1 mark for dividing by the A_r of each element, 1 mark for dividing through by the smallest number of moles.]

c) i) $NH_3 + H_2O → NH_4^+ + OH^-$ *[1 mark]*
ii) NH_4NO_3 *[1 mark]*

Pages 14-16: Amount of Substance, Acids and Redox — 3

1 a) $HClO \rightleftharpoons H^+ + ClO^-$ *[1 mark]*

Since this question specifically asks for 'the dissociation reaction', you still get a mark if you used an ordinary arrow instead of the reversible reaction sign.

b) +1 *[1 mark]*

c) i) Alkalis are bases that are soluble in water *[1 mark]* and release OH^- ions in aqueous solution *[1 mark]*.

ii) sodium chlorate(I) *[1 mark]*

*The ClO^- ion contains oxygen, so it must be a chlor**ate**. You get the (I) from the oxidation state of the chlorine: the overall oxidation state of ClO^- is −1, and the oxygen has an oxidation state of −2, so the chlorine must have an oxidation state of +1.*

iii) $H^+_{(aq)} + OH^-_{(aq)} → H_2O_{(l)}$ *[1 mark]*

2 a) Containing water of crystallisation within the crystal structure *[1 mark]*.

b) Result: mass of crucible/32.2 g *[1 mark]*
Explanation: this result has not been recorded to 2 decimal places *[1 mark]*.

c) i) mass of water = 34.64 − 34.28 = **0.36 g** *[1 mark]*

ii) E.g. the student could have heated the crucible until its mass remained constant *[1 mark]*.

d) Mass of $BaCl_2$ = 34.28 − 32.2 = 2.08 g
Molar mass of $BaCl_2$ = 137.3 + (2 × 35.5) = 208.3 g mol⁻¹
Moles of $BaCl_2$ = 2.08 ÷ 208.3 = 0.00999... ≈ 0.01
Molar mass of H_2O = (2 × 1.0) + 16.0 = 18.0 g mol⁻¹
Moles of H_2O = 0.36 ÷ 18.0 = 0.02
Ratio of $BaCl_2$ to H_2O = 0.01 : 0.02 = 1 : 2, therefore **n = 2**

[3 marks for correct answer, otherwise 1 mark for calculating moles of $BaCl_2$ and 1 mark for calculating moles of H_2O.]

e) *n* would be too high, as the calculated mass of water would include the mass of the lost crystals/there would be too few moles of $BaCl_2$ in the sample after heating *[1 mark]*.

3 a) Moles of H_2 = 138 ÷ 24 000 = 0.00575
From the reaction equation the ratio of metal X to H_2 is 1:1, therefore moles of metal X = 0.00575
Molar mass of metal X = 0.14 g ÷ 0.00575 mol
= 24.3 g mol⁻¹ (3 s.f.)
metal X = magnesium/Mg

[3 marks — 1 mark for calculating moles of H_2, 1 mark for calculating molar mass of metal X, 1 mark for identifying metal X as magnesium.]

b) $n = (pV) ÷ (RT)$
= ((101 × 10³) × (28.9 × 10⁻⁶)) ÷ (8.314 × 293)
= 1.19... × 10⁻³ moles of H_2 produced
1 mole of H_2 is produced from 1 mole of Y,
so moles of Y = 1.19... × 10⁻³ mol.
Molar mass of metal Y = mass ÷ moles
= 0.0784 ÷ (1.19... × 10⁻³) = 65.4 g mol⁻¹ (3 s.f.)
metal Y = zinc/Zn

[4 marks — 1 mark for correctly rearranging the ideal gas equation, 1 mark for correct number of moles of H_2, 1 mark for calculating molar mass of metal Y, 1 mark for identifying metal Y as zinc.]

c) Source of error: gas escaping once the metal has been added before the bung is replaced *[1 mark]*.
Improvement: e.g. put the metal in a vial in the acid, replace the bung and tip the flask to mix the acid and the metal.
[1 mark for any sensible suggestion.]

d) Moles of Li = 0.0245 ÷ 6.9 = 3.550... × 10⁻³
From the reaction equation the ratio of Li to H_2 is 2:1,
Therefore moles of H_2 = (3.550... × 10⁻³) ÷ 2
= 1.775... × 10⁻³
Volume of H_2 = (1.775... × 10⁻³) × 24 000 = 42.608...
= **42.6 cm³ (3 s.f.)**

[3 marks for correct answer, otherwise 1 mark for calculating moles of Li, 1 mark for deducing moles of H_2.]

You could also have calculated the volume of H_2 in dm³ first and then converted to cm³.

Pages 17-19: Amount of Substance, Acids and Redox — 4

1 a) How to grade your answer:

Level 0: There is no relevant information. *[No marks]*

Level 1: One section is covered well OR two sections are covered but they are incomplete and not always accurate. The answer is not in a logical order. *[1 to 2 marks]*

Level 2: Two sections are covered well OR all 3 sections are covered but they are incomplete and not always accurate. The answer is mostly in a logical order. *[3 to 4 marks]*

Level 3: All 3 sections are covered and are complete and accurate. The answer is coherent and is in a logical order. *[5 to 6 marks]*

Indicative scientific content may include:

Carrying out a titration

Use a pipette to add a set volume of one of the acids to a conical flask.

Add a few drops of an appropriate indicator to the flask.

Fill a burette with the standard solution of sodium hydroxide.

Do a rough titration to get an idea where the end point is.

Add the alkali to the acid using a burette, giving the flask a regular swirl.

Then do an accurate titration. Run the alkali in to within 2 cm^3 of the end point. When you get to this stage, add it dropwise.

Repeat the titration several times.

Repeat these steps for the other acid.

Collecting and processing results

Work out the amount of alkali used to neutralise the acid in each accurate titration by subtracting the initial burette reading from the final reading.

Use the results from each repeat to calculate the mean volume of alkali required to neutralise each acid.

Leave out any anomalous results when calculating the mean.

Identifying the acids

The equations for the two reactions are:

$H_2SO_4 + 2NaOH \rightarrow Na_2SO_4 + 2H_2O$

$HCl + NaOH \rightarrow NaCl + H_2O$

H_2SO_4 reacts with NaOH in a 1:2 molar ratio and HCl reacts with NaOH in a 1:1 molar ratio.

So, the acid that required twice as much NaOH to neutralise it is H_2SO_4.

b) i) Oxidation is the loss of electrons *[1 mark]*.

ii) Magnesium has been oxidised, as its oxidation number has increased from 0 to +2 *[1 mark]*.

iii) Effervescence/bubbles of gas *[1 mark]* and the magnesium metal decreasing in size/disappearing *[1 mark]*.

2 a) $n = (pV) \div (RT)$

$= ((101 \times 10^3) \times (280 \times 10^{-6})) \div (8.314 \times (22 + 273))$

$= 0.0115...$ mol of CO_2 produced

1 mole of CO_2 is produced from 1 mole of $CaCO_3$,

so moles of $CaCO_3 = 0.0115...$ mol

Mass of $CaCO_3 = 0.0115... \times (40.1 + 12 + (3 \times 16.0))$

$= 1.15...$ g

Percentage of $CaCO_3$ in sample $= (1.15... \div 1.75) \times 100$

$= 65.954...$

$= \mathbf{66.0\% \text{ (3 s.f.)}}$

[5 marks for correct answer, otherwise 1 mark for correctly rearranging the ideal gas equation, 1 mark for correct number of moles of CO_2, 1 mark for correct number of moles of $CaCO_3$, 1 mark for correct mass of $CaCO_3$.]

b) i) An acid which only partially dissociates in solution *[1 mark]*.

ii) $2CH_3COOH + CaCO_3 \rightarrow Ca(CH_3COO)_2 + CO_2 + H_2O$ *[1 mark]*

iii) HCl is a strong acid *[1 mark]*, so releases more H^+ ions per mole in solution/has a higher concentration of H^+ ions in the same volume of acid *[1 mark]*.

c) i) $2HCl + CaO \rightarrow CaCl_2 + H_2O$ *[1 mark]*

ii) acid-base/neutralisation *[1 mark]*

iii) This reaction is not a redox reaction, as no element undergoes a change in oxidation number *[1 mark]*.

3 a) Water of crystallisation is the water incorporated into the lattice of a hydrated salt crystal *[1 mark]*.

b) Divide by the A_r of each element:

Mn: $0.668 \div 54.9 = 0.01216...$

Cl: $0.861 \div 35.5 = 0.02425...$

H: $0.097 \div 1.0 = 0.097$

O: $0.776 \div 16.0 = 0.0485$

Divide through by the smallest number:

Mn: $0.01216... \div 0.01216... = 1$

Cl: $0.02425... \div 0.01216... = 1.993...$

H: $0.097 \div 0.01216... = 7.972...$

O: $0.0485 \div 0.01216... = 3.986...$

Simplest whole-number ratio of Mn:Cl:H:O = 1:2:8:4

An 8:4 ratio of H to O indicates that there are 4 molecules of water in the formula.

Formula of compound C = $MnCl_2.4H_2O$

[3 marks for correct answer, otherwise 1 mark for dividing through by the A_r of each element, 1 mark for finding the whole number ratio.]

Pages 20-23: Electrons, Bonding and Structure — 1

1   C *[1 mark]*

Remember, the 4s orbital fills before the 3d orbital to produce the lowest energy arrangement of electrons.

2   D *[1 mark]*

F_2 doesn't contain any polar bonds, but CBr_4, CO_2 and PF_3 all do. In CBr_4 and CO_2, the polar bonds are arranged symmetrically:

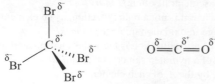

So neither CBr_4 nor CO_2 has an overall dipole.

But in PF_3 (which is trigonal pyramidal), thanks to the polar bonds, the bottom of the molecule is slightly negative and the top is slightly positive:

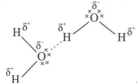   *So PF_3 does have an overall dipole.*

3   C *[1 mark]*

NCl_3 has 3 bonding electron pairs around the central nitrogen atom, and one lone pair — so it must be pyramidal.

4   C *[1 mark]*

5   B *[1 mark]*

Remember, for negative ions you need to add electrons to the atomic electron configuration, and for positive ions you need to take them away.

6 a)   (giant) ionic (lattice) *[1 mark]*

The key idea here is that it's ionic — if you said that, you get the mark.

   b)   It takes a lot of energy to overcome the strong electrostatic attractions between the positive and negative ions *[1 mark]*.

   c)   Melting or dissolving the substance allows the ions to move and carry a charge *[1 mark]*.

7 a)   E.g.

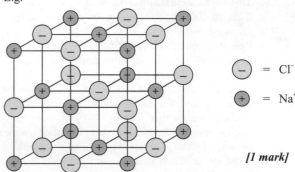

[1 mark]

Oxygen is very electronegative, and so the O–H bonds in water molecules are highly polarised *[1 mark]*, with the O atom having a partial negative charge and the H atoms having partial positive charges *[1 mark]*. Attraction between an H atom from one molecule and a lone pair of electrons on the O atom of another molecule produces a hydrogen bond *[1 mark]*.

You still get the mark for partial charges if you've just labelled them on your diagram and not mentioned them in your explanation.

   b)   E.g. the molecules gain enough energy to overcome some of the hydrogen bonds holding them in place in the ice crystal *[1 mark]*.

   c)   When liquid water freezes into ice, the number of hydrogen bonds between the molecules increases, producing a regular lattice structure *[1 mark]*. This regular structure holds the molecules further apart on average than the molecules in water/creates empty spaces between the molecules, making ice less dense than water *[1 mark]*.

8 a)   An ionic bond is an electrostatic attraction between a positive ion and a negative ion/two oppositely charged ions *[1 mark]*.

   b)   E.g.

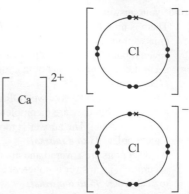

[3 marks — 1 mark for showing Ca^{2+} ion correctly with no (or eight) electrons, 1 mark for showing Cl^- ion correctly with eight electrons, one of which is represented by a different symbol, 1 mark for indicating that there are 2 Cl^- ions]

You could just draw one Cl^- ion with a 2 in front of it for the mark, but it's best to draw both Cl^- ions out in full if you've got time.

   c) $1s^2\ 2s^2\ 2p^6$ *[1 mark]*

   d)   E.g.

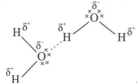

= Cl^-

= Na^+

[1 mark]

In an ionic compound like NaCl, the ions are packed together in a regular structure called a (giant ionic) lattice *[1 mark]*. The oppositely charged ions *[1 mark]* are strongly attracted to one another in all directions *[1 mark]*.

If you described the alternating arrangement of Na^+ and Cl^- ions instead of showing it on the diagram, you'd still get the mark.

   e)   There is a large difference in the electronegativities of Na and Cl, meaning bonds between Na and Cl are strongly polarised and so ionic *[1 mark]*. The difference in the electronegativities of H and Cl is much smaller, and so bonds between them are not strongly polarised and are covalent *[1 mark]*.

9   How to grade your answer:

Level 0:   There is no relevant information. *[No marks]*

Level 1:   There is a good explanation of why one of the molecules given has the observed polarity, or an incomplete explanation of why two of the molecules given have the observed polarities. *[1 to 2 marks]*

Level 2:   There is a good explanation of why two of the molecules given have the observed polarity, or an incomplete explanation of why all three of the molecules given have the observed polarities. *[3 to 4 marks]*

Level 3   There is a complete and accurate explanation of why all three of the molecules given have the observed polarities. The answer is coherent. *[5 to 6 marks]*

Indicative scientific content may include:

Br_2

The Br–Br bond in Br_2 is non-polar, as both atoms have the same electronegativity.

So the molecule has no overall dipole.

Diagram to show molecule: Br——Br

CCl₄

All of the C–Cl bonds in CCl₄ are polar, because chlorine is more electronegative than carbon.
But the polar bonds in CCl₄ are arranged symmetrically. This means that the charges cancel out, so the molecule has no permanent dipole and is non-polar.
Diagram to show symmetry:

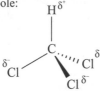

CHCl₃

All of the C–Cl bonds in CHCl₃ are polar.
Hydrogen is less electronegative than chlorine.
The negative charge is pulled towards the chlorine atoms, making them slightly negative.
So the carbon and hydrogen atoms become slightly positive, creating a permanent dipole.
Diagram to show dipole:

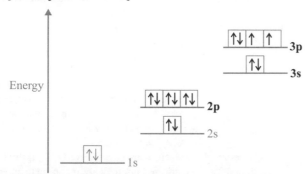

Pages 24-27: Electrons, Bonding and Structure — 2

1 a) i) An atomic orbital is a region around the nucleus that can hold up to two electrons *[1 mark]* with opposite spins *[1 mark]*.
   ii) A: p-orbital
       B: s-orbital
       [1 mark for both correct]

   b)

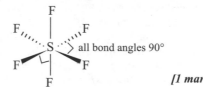

   [3 marks — 1 mark for correct 2p, 3s and 3p labels, 1 mark for showing the correct number of electrons in each orbital, 1 mark for showing opposite spins]

   c) i) 1s² 2s² 2p⁶ 3s² 3p⁶ *[1 mark]*
      ii) argon *[1 mark]*

2 a) There is a trend of increasing boiling point from H₂S to H₂Te. This is because the induced dipole-dipole interactions/London forces/Van der Waals forces increase as the number of electrons in/size of the Group 6 atoms increases *[1 mark]*.

   b) Oxygen is very electronegative, making O–H bonds highly polarised *[1 mark]*, so hydrogen bonds can form between H₂O molecules *[1 mark]*. Hydrogen bonds are stronger than induced dipole-dipole interactions/London forces/Van der Waals forces, so more energy is needed to break them *[1 mark]*.

3 a) i) A dative covalent bond is a covalent bond in which both electrons come from the same atom *[1 mark]*.
   ii)

H
↑
|
H — N⁺
| ''''H
H
 \
  H

   [2 marks — 1 mark for tetrahedral shape represented in 3-D, 1 mark for dative covalent bond shown by arrow]

b) i) The ability of an atom to attract the bonding electrons in a covalent bond *[1 mark]*.
   ii) δ⁺ indicates that the atom has a partial positive charge and δ⁻ indicates that the atom has a partial negative charge *[1 mark]*. So N is more electronegative than H *[1 mark]*.

c) E.g.

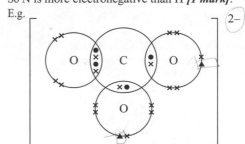

   [2 marks — 1 mark for showing bonds correctly, 1 mark for showing other electrons correctly]

   You don't need to include the brackets or the charge for the marks here, but it's a good idea to get into the habit of drawing them anyway.

d) E.g. the bonding centres around atoms 2 and 3 all repel each other equally, so are arranged in a tetrahedral shape at an angle of 109.5° to one another *[1 mark]*. This means the central carbon chain is not straight as shown *[1 mark]*, and the bonds in the molecule do not all lie in the same plane *[1 mark]*. The bond angles around carbons 1 and 4 are also shown incorrectly. There are 3 bonding centres and so the bonds are actually at 120° to one another, giving a trigonal planar shape *[1 mark]*.

4 a) i) SF₂:

S (with two lone pairs)
F   97 - 107°   F

   Diagram with bond angle between 97° and 107° *[1 mark]*.

   SF₆:

F
|
F,,,,, S ,,,,,F   all bond angles 90°
F | F
        F

   [1 mark]

   Shape of SF₂: non-linear *[1 mark]*
   Shape of SF₆: octahedral *[1 mark]*

   ii) There are two bonding pairs and two lone pairs around the sulfur atom *[1 mark]*. The electron pairs all repel one another *[1 mark]*, but the lone pairs repel more than the bonding pairs *[1 mark]*, giving SF₂ a non-linear shape.

b) Sulfur is less electronegative than fluorine, so the S–F bond is polar *[1 mark]*. In SF₆, the polar bonds are arranged symmetrically/the charge is evenly distributed across the molecule, so the molecule is non-polar *[1 mark]*. In SF₂, the fluorine atoms pull the shared electrons/negative charge in the same direction *[1 mark]*, creating an uneven distribution of charge across the molecule *[1 mark]*.

c) E.g. SF₂ is a smaller molecule than SF₆, so it will have weaker induced dipole-dipole interactions/London forces *[1 mark]*. But SF₂ also has a permanent dipole (while SF₆ is non-polar), so it will have permanent dipole-dipole interactions *[1 mark]*. Which fluoride has the higher melting point will depend on whether the strength of the SF₂ dipole is greater than the strength of the induced dipole-dipole interactions/London forces in SF₆ *[1 mark]*.

Module 3 — Periodic Table and Energy

Pages 28-30: The Periodic Table — 1

1   B *[1 mark]*
2   D *[1 mark]*
3   B *[1 mark]*
4   C *[1 mark]*

The first ionisation energies of the elements increase as you move down a group in the periodic table. In general (with a couple of exceptions) they also increase as you move across a period. The successive ionisation energies of an element also increase.

5 a) i) E.g.

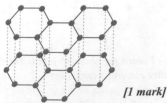

                           [1 mark]

        The carbon atoms are arranged in sheets of hexagons, with each carbon atom covalently bonded to three other carbon atoms *[1 mark]*. The fourth outer electron of each carbon atom is delocalised *[1 mark]*. The sheets of carbon atoms are held together by induced dipole-dipole/London forces *[1 mark]*.

    ii) E.g. the structure of graphene is the same as that of one of the sheets of carbon atoms in graphite *[1 mark]*.

  b) i) To melt graphite you have to break the strong covalent bonds holding the carbon atoms together *[1 mark]*, which needs a lot of energy *[1 mark]*.

    ii) Electrical conductivity: graphite conducts electricity because it contains delocalised/free electrons *[1 mark]*.
        Solubility: graphite is insoluble in any solvent because the covalent bonds between carbon atoms are too strong to be broken by the solvent *[1 mark]*.

  c) Graphene is strong because it consists of a single sheet *[1 mark]* of hexagons, where every carbon atom is joined to three other carbon atoms by strong covalent bonds *[1 mark]*.

6 a) i) $1s^2\,2s^2\,2p^6\,3s^2\,3p^5$ *[1 mark]*

    ii) $1s^2\,2s^2\,2p^6$ *[1 mark]*

  b) i) $Mg + 2HCl \rightarrow MgCl_2 + H_2$ *[1 mark]*

    ii) Magnesium has been oxidised, with its oxidation number increasing from 0 to +2 *[1 mark]*, and hydrogen has been reduced, with its oxidation number decreasing from +1 to 0 *[1 mark]*.

    iii) Strontium has a larger atomic radius *[1 mark]* and more inner shell electrons shielding the outer shell electrons from the nucleus *[1 mark]*. Overall this means the attraction between the nucleus and outer electrons is weaker *[1 mark]*, so it loses electrons more easily *[1 mark]*.

  c) i) E.g. magnesium hydroxide is used as an antacid in some indigestion tablets *[1 mark]*

    ii) The reaction between magnesium and water is very slow. *[1 mark]*

Pages 31-33: The Periodic Table — 2

1 a) The energy needed to remove 1 electron from each atom in 1 mole of gaseous atoms *[1 mark]*.

  b) The overall shape of the graph would be similar *[1 mark]* because of similar sub-shell structure across the periods *[1 mark]*. But the line for Period 2 would be higher *[1 mark]*, because the outer electrons are closer to the nucleus and also less shielded from it, and so take more energy to remove *[1 mark]*.

  c) i) $X^+_{(g)} \rightarrow X^{2+}_{(g)} + e^-$ *[1 mark]*

    ii) The 6th electron is taken from an inner shell/a shell closer to the nucleus *[1 mark]*. It also experiences less shielding by other electrons *[1 mark]*, and so the pull of the nucleus is greater/more energy is required to remove the electron *[1 mark]*.

    iii) nitrogen *[1 mark]*

There is a large difference between the fifth and sixth ionisation energies of element X, which indicates that it has 5 electrons in its outermost shell, and so must be in Group 5 of the Periodic Table. The question tells you it's in Period 2, and so element X can only be nitrogen.

2 a) The strength of the induced dipole-dipole/London forces between molecules of chlorine is weaker than between molecules of iodine *[1 mark]*. This is because the size/mass of the chlorine molecules is less than iodine molecules/chlorine molecules contain fewer electrons than iodine molecules *[1 mark]*.

Chlorine molecules are smaller than iodine molecules because they contain fewer electrons, so have fewer occupied shells and take up less space.

  (b) The reactivity of the halides decreases down the group *[1 mark]*, as the attraction between the nucleus and the outer electrons decreases *[1 mark]*. This is because the halide ions get larger/the electrons are further from the nucleus *[1 mark]*, and because the effect of shielding by the inner electrons increases down the group *[1 mark]*.

  c) i) $Cl_2 + 2Br^- \rightarrow 2Cl^- + Br_2$ *[1 mark]*

    ii) bromide ions/Br^- *[1 mark]*

    iii) white *[1 mark]*

3   How to grade your answer:

    Level 0:   There is no relevant information. *[No marks]*

    Level 1:   One stage is covered well OR two stages are covered but they are incomplete and not always accurate. The answer is not in a logical order. *[1 to 2 marks]*

    Level 2:   Two stages are covered well OR all three stages are covered but they are incomplete and not always accurate. The answer is mostly in a logical order. *[3 to 4 marks]*

    Level 3:   All three stages are covered and are complete and accurate. The answer is coherent and is in a logical order. *[5 to 6 marks]*

  Indicative scientific content may include:

  <u>Stage 1: Metallic substances</u>
  Sodium, magnesium and aluminium are metals.
  Their melting points increase across the period because the metal-metal bonds get stronger.
  The bonds get stronger because the metal ions have an increasing positive charge, an increasing number of delocalised electrons and a decreasing radius.

  <u>Stage 2: Silicon</u>
  Silicon is giant covalent.
  It has a structure made of strong covalent bonds that link all its atoms together.
  A lot of energy is needed to break these bonds, so silicon has a high melting point.

Stage 3: Molecular and monoatomic substances

Phosphorus (P_4), sulfur (S_8) and chlorine (Cl_2) are all molecular substances.

Their melting points depend upon the strength of the induced dipole-dipole/London forces between the molecules.

Induced dipole-dipole/London forces are weak and easily overcome so these elements have low melting points.

More atoms in a molecule mean stronger induced dipole-dipole/London forces.

Sulfur forms the biggest molecules, so it's got a higher melting point than phosphorus or chlorine .

Phosphorus is the next biggest, so it has a higher melting point than chlorine.

Argon has a very low melting point because it exists as individual atoms (it's monatomic). This results in very weak induced dipole-dipole/London forces.

Pages 34-37: The Periodic Table — 3

1 a) $1s^2\ 2s^2\ 2p^6\ 3s^2\ 3p^6\ 4s^2$ *[1 mark]*

   b)   The second electron is harder to remove because it is being removed from a positive ion/there are now a greater number of protons than electrons so each outer shell electron receives a greater positive pull from the nucleus *[1 mark]*. There is less repulsion from other electrons so it is held more strongly by the nucleus *[1 mark]*.

   c)   Jumps between the 2nd and 3rd and the 10th and 11th ionisation energies indicate the presence of discrete shells/energy levels *[1 mark]*, as it takes significantly more energy to remove electrons held in shells/energy levels closer to the nucleus *[1 mark]*. The jump after the 2nd electron is removed indicates two electrons in the outermost shell/energy level *[1 mark]*. The jump after the 10th electron is removed indicates 8 electrons in the next shell/energy level *[1 mark]*.

2 a)   E.g. the outermost electron of a Group 2 atom is in an s sub-shell *[1 mark]*.

   b) i)   Group 2 metals become more reactive as you descend the group, because the ionisation energy decreases/the outer electrons are more easily lost as you descend the group *[1 mark]*.

      ii) Similarity: e.g. fizzing/bubbles of gas given off *[1 mark]*. Difference: e.g. the reaction of barium would be more vigorous/bubbles of gas would be given off faster *[1 mark]*.

   c) i) $CaO_{(s)} + H_2O_{(l)} \rightarrow Ca^{2+}_{(aq)} + 2OH^-_{(aq)}$
            [2 marks — 1 mark for correct equation, 1 mark for correct state symbols]

If you've written $Ca(OH)_{2(aq)}$ on the right hand side of the equation that's also correct.

      ii) Group 2 metal oxides react with water to produce metal hydroxides *[1 mark]*. Barium hydroxide is more soluble than calcium hydroxide *[1 mark]*, so it will produce more hydroxide ions in solution and have a higher pH than the calcium hydroxide solution *[1 mark]*.

3 a) i)   Reaction 2: $Cl_2 + 2NaOH \rightarrow NaClO + NaCl + H_2O$ *[1 mark]*
            Reaction 3: $NaClO + H_2O \rightleftharpoons HClO + NaOH$ *[1 mark]*

      ii) $Cl_2 + H_2O \rightleftharpoons 2H^+ + Cl^- + ClO^-$ *[1 mark]*

      iii) Reactions 1 and 2 *[1 mark]*

   b)   Any two from: e.g. chlorine gas is very harmful if breathed in. / Liquid chlorine causes severe chemical burns. / Chlorine reacts with organic compounds in water to form chlorinated hydrocarbons. / Chlorine can react to form carcinogenic (cancer-causing) compounds. *[2 marks — 1 mark for each correct answer]*

4 a)

	Experiment 1 $Cl_{2(aq)}$	Experiment 2 $Br_{2(aq)}$	Experiment 3 $I_{2(aq)}$
$KCl_{(aq)}$		No visible change	No visible change
$KBr_{(aq)}$	Yellow solution forms		No visible change
$KI_{(aq)}$	Orange-brown solution forms	Orange-brown solution forms	

   [2 marks — 1 mark for each column correct]

   b)   Bromine solution/$Br_{2\ (aq)}$ *[1 mark]*

   c)   The halogen will dissolve in the cyclohexane *[1 mark]* to form a separate layer above the aqueous solution *[1 mark]*. The yellow aqueous solution will be orange in organic solution *[1 mark]*. The orange-brown solution will be purple in organic solution *[1 mark]*.

   d)   equation: $Cl_2 + 2I^- \rightarrow I_2 + 2Cl^-$ *[1 mark]*
        oxidising agent: chlorine/Cl_2 *[1 mark]*

   e)   No colour change would be seen *[1 mark]*. Bromine is less reactive than fluorine, and so it cannot displace the fluoride ions from solution *[1 mark]*.

There wouldn't be a colour change from a displacement reaction if you mixed bromine solution and sodium fluoride solution — although in reality you might see the colour of the bromine solution lightening, as you're mixing a coloured solution with a colourless one.

5 a) i)   The student should have added dilute acid to the test solution before adding the barium chloride solution *[1 mark]*. The acid removes any carbonate or sulfite ions, which would also give a white precipitate with barium chloride *[1 mark]*.

Remember, you can't use sulfuric acid here, because that would add sulfate ions to the solution. So you get the marks if you said acid, or a named acid like hydrochloric or nitric acid, but not if you said sulfuric acid.

      ii) Add dilute acid *[1 mark]*. The sodium carbonate solution will effervesce/fizz as carbon dioxide gas is formed *[1 mark]*. The gas collected will turn limewater cloudy *[1 mark]*.

   b)   Add dilute nitric acid to a sample of the solution *[1 mark]* followed by a few drops of silver nitrate solution *[1 mark]*. A precipitate will form, which will be cream if the solution contains sodium bromide, or yellow if it contains sodium iodide *[1 mark]*. Add concentrated ammonia to the solution *[1 mark]*. A precipitate of silver bromide will dissolve, but a precipitate of silver iodide will not *[1 mark]*.

Pages 38-41: Physical Chemistry — 1

1 A *[1 mark]*

The reaction is exothermic, so decreasing the temperature will favour the forward reaction, and there are more moles of gas on the reactant side than the product side, so increasing the pressure will also favour the forward reaction, leading to an increase in product yield.

2 D *[1 mark]*

Bonds broken: 1 C=C bond, 1 H−Cl bond

Bonds made: 1 C−C bond, 1 C−H bond, 1 C−Cl bond

ΔH = bonds broken − bonds made

= (612 + 432) − (347 + 413 + 346) = −62 kJ mol⁻¹

3 B *[1 mark]*

500 cm³ of solution has a mass of 500 g, so m = 500 g.

ΔT = 3.5 °C = 3.5 K.

$q = mc\Delta T$ = 500 g × 4.18 JK⁻¹g⁻¹ × 3.5 K = 7315 J = 7.315 kJ

Moles of NaOH = 0.5 × 0.25 = 0.125 mol

The reaction was exothermic, because the temperature rose. So:

Molar enthalpy change of reaction = $\dfrac{q}{n}$ = $\dfrac{-7.315}{0.125}$ = −59 kJ mol⁻¹ (2 s.f.)

4 C *[1 mark]*

5 a) E.g. An exothermic reaction gives out energy *[1 mark]* and so has negative enthalpy change/negative DH *[1 mark]*.

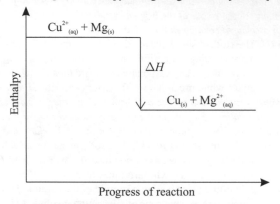

[2 marks — 1 mark for showing reactants with higher enthalpy than products, 1 mark for arrow pointing downwards labelled DH]

If you've just written 'reactants' on your higher energy line and 'products' on your lower energy line you still get the mark.

b) i) percentage uncertainty = $\dfrac{\text{uncertainty}}{\text{quantity measured}} \times 100\%$

$= \dfrac{0.1}{20} \times 100\%$ = **0.5%** *[1 mark]*

ii) E.g. the student should make sure that the copper(II) sulfate solution is disposed of correctly/not poured down the drain. / The student should wear gloves to protect their hands *[1 mark for any sensible suggestion]*.

c) 20 cm³ of solution has a mass of 20 g, so m = 20 g

ΔT = 55 °C = 55 K

$q = mc\Delta T$ = 20 × 4.18 × 55 = 4598 J = 4.598 kJ

Moles of CuSO₄ = 0.50 × (20 ÷ 1000) = 0.010 mol

$\Delta_r H$ = $\dfrac{-4.598}{0.010}$ = −459.8 = **−460 kJ mol⁻¹ (2 s.f.)**

[4 marks for correct answer given to 2 s.f. or 3 marks for correct answer not given to 2 s.f., otherwise 1 mark for correctly substituting the values into $q = mc\Delta T$ and 1 mark for correct units.]

You still get full marks if you gave a correct answer in J mol⁻¹.

d) i) E.g. heat was lost from the system to the surroundings *[1 mark]*.

ii) E.g. insulate the system more/use a polystyrene beaker/put a lid on the beaker *[1 mark]*.

6 a) A reaction where all of the reactants and products are in the same physical state/phase *[1 mark]*.

b) $K_c = \dfrac{[CH_3OH]}{[CO][H_2]^2}$ *[1 mark]*

c) There are 3 moles of gas on the reactant side and only 1 mole of gas on the product side *[1 mark]*. Increasing the pressure will shift the equilibrium to the right/towards the products (to lower the pressure again) *[1 mark]*, which will increase the yield of methanol *[1 mark]*.

d) i) At a higher temperature the molecules have more energy, so more molecules will have enough energy to react/energy above the activation energy *[1 mark]*. At a higher temperature, the molecules move more quickly, so collisions will be more frequent *[1 mark]*.

ii) The reaction is exothermic, so increasing the temperature would shift the equilibrium to the left/in the endothermic direction (to try to decrease the temperature) *[1 mark]*. This would decrease the yield of methanol *[1 mark]*. Using a catalyst is a better option because it increases the rate of reaction without affecting the position of equilibrium/yield of methanol *[1 mark]*.

e) $\Delta_r H^\ominus = \Sigma \Delta_f H^\ominus$ products − $\Sigma \Delta_f H^\ominus$ reactants

$\Delta_r H^\ominus = ((2 \times -108.7) + (2 \times -285.8)) - ((2 \times -239.1) + 0)$

$= -310.8$ **kJ mol⁻¹**

[2 marks for correct answer, otherwise 1 mark for stating the formula for $\Delta_r H^\ominus$]

It's fine if you drew a Hess's law diagram to work out what calculation you needed to do here, instead of just stating the formula.

Pages 42-44: Physical Chemistry — 2

1 a) i) A homogeneous catalyst is a catalyst which is in the same physical state/phase as the reactants *[1 mark]*.

ii) The use of catalysts means that lower temperatures and pressures can be used *[1 mark]*. Less energy is needed to create these temperatures and pressures, and so less polluting gases such as CO_2 are produced *[1 mark]*. Catalysts sometimes also allow alternative reactions with fewer steps and better atom economy to be used, creating less waste and preserving resources *[1 mark]*.

b) i) An increase in the concentration of chloride ions would make the solution bluer in colour *[1 mark]*. This colour change would occur because the position of equilibrium would shift to the right to oppose the change and decrease the concentration of chloride ions *[1 mark]*.

ii) E.g. decrease the temperature of the equilibrium mixture and examine the colour of the mixture to determine whether the reaction had moved in the forwards or backwards direction *[1 mark]*.

iii) If the forwards reaction is endothermic, decreasing the temperature will cause the solution to appear pinker in colour *[1 mark]*, as the equilibrium shifts in the exothermic direction to oppose the change *[1 mark]*.

2 a) i) E.g.

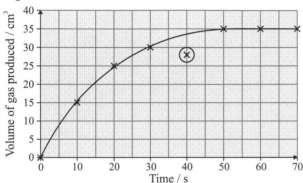

[3 marks for correctly plotted graph with appropriate trend line, otherwise 1 mark for correctly labelled axes and 1 mark for correctly plotted data points.]

ii) Point circled as on graph above *[1 mark]*.
E.g. the students might have measured or recorded the volume incorrectly *[1 mark]*.

iii) E.g.

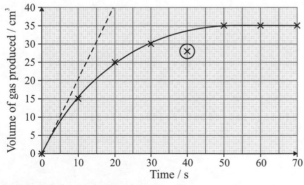

gradient = change in y ÷ change in x

= (40 − 0) ÷ (19.5 − 0)

= 2.0512... cm^3 s^{-1}

Rate = 2.1 cm^3 s^{-1} (2 s.f.)
[1 mark for tangent drawn at t = 0 s, 1 mark for calculating rate from gradient of tangent drawn]

iv) The rate of reaction depends on the frequency of successful collisions between H^+ ions and the surface of the magnesium *[1 mark]*. As the reaction proceeds, the H^+ ions are used up, so successful collisions become less frequent and the rate decreases *[1 mark]*.

b) i) At an increased temperature, a greater proportion of the particles would have at least the activation energy for the reaction and be able to react *[1 mark]*, and so the rate of reaction would increase *[1 mark]*.

ii) Increasing the concentration of HCl to 2 mol dm^{-3} would increase the number of ions in solution, meaning that collisions between the hydrogen ions and the magnesium became more frequent *[1 mark]*. More collisions in total means more successful collisions, and so the initial rate of reaction would be higher *[1 mark]*.

c) i) E.g. use a gas syringe/collect the gas over water in an upturned measuring cylinder *[1 mark]*.

ii) Any two from: e.g. the apparatus must not let any gas escape. / The apparatus must be large enough to collect all the gas produced. / The apparatus needs to have the right level of sensitivity. *[2 marks — 1 mark for each sensible factor.]*

Pages 45-47: Physical Chemistry — 3

1 a) i) Bonds broken: 2 C–C bonds, 8 C–H bonds, 5 O=O bonds
Energy absorbed = $(2 \times 347) + (8 \times 413) + (5 \times 498)$
$= 6488$ kJ mol^{-1}
Bonds made: 6 C=O bonds, 8 O–H bonds
Energy released = $(6 \times 805) + (8 \times 464)$
$= 8542$ kJ mol^{-1}
Enthalpy of reaction = energy absorbed – energy released
$= 6488 - 8542 = $**–2054 kJ mol^{-1}**
[3 marks for correct answer, otherwise 1 mark for calculating enthalpy of bonds broken and 1 mark for calculating enthalpy of bonds made.]

ii) $\Delta_c H = \Sigma \Delta_f H$ products $- \Sigma \Delta_f H$ reactants
$= ((3 \times -393.5) + (4 \times -241.8)) - (-104.5)$
$= -2147.7 + 104.5 = $**–2043.2 kJ mol^{-1}**
[3 marks for correct answer, otherwise 1 mark for stating the formula and 1 mark for correctly substituting the enthalpies of formation into the formula.]

Again, you still get the mark if you drew a Hess's law diagram here, instead of just stating the formula.

iii) Mean bond enthalpies are average values over a range of compounds *[1 mark]*. The enthalpies of formation given are for the exact compounds in this reaction *[1 mark]*.

b) 50.0 cm^3 of water has a mass of 50.0 g, so $m = 50.0$ g
$\Delta T = 74.0\ °C - 21.5\ °C = 52.5\ °C = 52.5$ K
$q = mc\Delta T = 50.0 \times 4.18 \times 52.5 = 10972.5$ J $= 10.9725$ kJ
Mass of propan-2-ol burned $= 75.2 - 74.8 = 0.4$ g
M_r of propan-2-ol $= (12.0 \times 3) + (16.0 \times 1) + (1.0 \times 8)$
$= 60.0$ g mol^{-1}
moles of propan-2-ol burnt $= \dfrac{0.4}{60.0} = 0.00666...$ mol
$\Delta_c H = \dfrac{-10.9725}{0.00666...} = -1645.875 = $**–1650 kJ mol^{-1}** (3 s.f.)
[5 marks for correct answer, otherwise 1 mark for finding the temperature change, 1 mark for calculating q using $q = mc\Delta T$, 1 mark for finding the mass of propan-2-ol burned and 1 mark for finding the number of moles of propan-2-ol burned.]

2 a) Increasing the pressure will increase the rate of reaction *[1 mark]*. At higher pressure, there will be more oxygen molecules in a given volume/the molecules will be pushed closer together *[1 mark]*, so collisions between the oxygen molecules and the potassium metal are more likely *[1 mark]*. More collisions means more successful collisions and a higher rate of reaction *[1 mark]*.

b) i)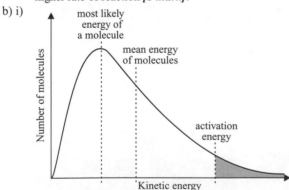
[1 mark for shading correct area.]

ii) Adding a catalyst provides a different reaction route with lower activation energy *[1 mark]*, meaning that a greater number of molecules will have sufficient energy to react *[1 mark]*.

iii)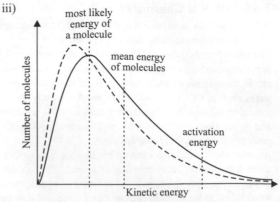
[2 marks — 1 mark for peak to left of existing peak, 1 mark for peak higher than existing peak.]

c) Measure the change in mass over time *[1 mark]*.
Measure the volume of gas given off over time *[1 mark]*.

Pages 48-49: Physical Chemistry — 4

1 a) Any two from: e.g. the forward and reverse reactions must be proceeding at the same rate. / The concentrations of the reactants and products must remain constant / The reaction must take place in a closed system. *[2 marks — 1 mark for each correct condition.]*

b) i) In this reaction, two moles of reactant give four moles of product/there are more moles of products than of reactants *[1 mark]*. Increasing the pressure would shift the equilibrium in favour of the reactants, reducing the yield of acetylene *[1 mark]*.

ii) How to grade your answer:

Level 0: There is no relevant information. *[No marks]*

Level 1: One factor from rate, yield and cost is covered well OR two factors are covered but they are covered incompletely and not always accurately. The answer is not in a logical order. *[1 to 2 marks]*

Level 2: Two factors from rate, yield and cost are covered well OR all three factors are covered but they are covered incompletely and not always accurately. The answer is mostly in a logical order. *[3 to 4 marks]*

Level 3: All three factors are covered completely and accurately. The answer is coherent and is in a logical order. *[5 to 6 marks]*

Indicative content:

Rate of reaction

Using a high temperature will increase the rate of reaction. This is because the particles have more kinetic energy on average, so they will collide more frequently and more of the collisions will be successful.

A higher rate of reaction means that the product (acetylene) can be produced more quickly.

Yield (equilibrium position)

The forward reaction is endothermic.

Using a high temperature will shift the equilibrium in favour of the product.

This will increase the yield of acetylene.

Cost

A high temperature is beneficial in terms of yield and rate of reaction.

However, high temperatures require a lot of energy to produce and maintain. This can be expensive.

High temperatures may also require specialised equipment.

Therefore a compromise temperature must be chosen that is as high as possible (to give a good rate and yield) without costing too much to produce and maintain.

c) i) $K_c = \dfrac{[H_2]^3[C_2H_2]}{[CH_4]^2}$ *[1 mark]*

ii) From the equation, 1 mole of acetylene is produced from 2 moles of methane, so 0.372 moles of acetylene must be produced from $2 \times 0.372 = 0.744$ moles of methane. Therefore there must be $1.00 - 0.744 = 0.256$ moles of methane left at equilibrium

3 moles of hydrogen are produced for every 1 mole of acetylene so $0.372 \times 3 = 1.116$ moles of hydrogen were present at equilibrium.

Equilibrium concentrations:

$[C_2H_2] = \dfrac{0.372}{3.00} = 0.124$ mol dm^{-3}

$[H_2] = \dfrac{1.116}{3.00} = 0.372$ mol dm^{-3}

$[CH_4] = \dfrac{0.256}{3.00} = 0.0853...$ mol dm^{-3}

$K_c = \dfrac{0.372^3 \times 0.124}{(0.0853...)^2} = 0.8766...$

$K_c = 0.877$ mol^2 dm^{-6} (3 s.f.)

[7 marks for correct answer given to 3 s.f. or 6 marks for correct answer not given to 3 s.f., otherwise 1 mark for number of moles of methane at equilibrium correct, 1 mark for number of moles of hydrogen at equilibrium correct, 1 mark for each equilibrium concentration correct.]

iii) K_c has increased and so the position of equilibrium must have moved towards the products/to the right *[1 mark]*. This means the yield of acetylene will increase *[1 mark]*.

Module 4 — Core Organic Chemistry

Pages 50-53: Basic Concepts and Hydrocarbons — 1

1   C *[1 mark]*

The general formula of the alkanes is C_nH_{2n+2}. So an alkane with 16 H atoms will have 7 C atoms, because $(7 \times 2) + 2 = 16$.

2   A *[1 mark]*

To figure this out, you need to use the Cahn-Ingold-Prelog priority rules. Alkene N has two F atoms attached to the first double bond carbon, so it doesn't have stereoisomers. Of the other three, alkene M is the only one that has the two higher priority groups on the same side of the double bond.

3   B *[1 mark]*

To show stereoisomerism, both of an alkene's double bond carbons must have two different groups attached to them. In 2-methylbut-2-ene, the first double bond carbon has two CH_3 groups attached to it.

4   B *[1 mark]*

The H^+ and Br^- from HBr are added to the carbons either side of where the double bond is in the original molecule.

5 a)   A/B *[1 mark]*

   b)

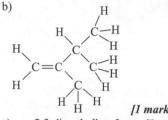

[1 mark]

   c)   2,3-dimethylbut-2-ene *[1 mark]*

   d)   E.g.

[1 mark]

Any molecule with the formula C_6H_{12} that isn't an alkene is fine here.

6 a)   E.g. saturated organic compounds contain only single bonds between carbon atoms/contain no double or triple bonds between carbon atoms *[1 mark]*.

   b)   Any two from: e.g. compounds in a homologous series have similar chemical properties. / Compounds in a homologous series have the same general formula. / Compounds in a homologous series have the same functional group. / Each successive member in a homologous series differs by a CH_2 group. *[2 marks — 1 mark for each correct answer.]*

   c) CH_3COOH *[1 mark]*

   d)   3,4-dimethylpentanoic acid *[1 mark]*

7 a) i)   22 *[1 mark]*

Don't forget to include all the C–H bonds, even though they're not shown in the skeletal formula, and the σ-bond in the double bond.

    ii) C_8H_{14} *[1 mark]*

    iii)   A and B are aliphatic compounds that have their carbon atoms arranged in a non-aromatic ring structure *[1 mark]*.

   b)   E.g.

[1 mark for a displayed formula of an aliphatic, branched-chain alkane with 8 carbon atoms.]

   c) i)   E.g. $CH_2C(CH_3)CH_2CH_2CH_3$

[1 mark for a structural formula of an alkene with the molecular formula C_6H_{12} and two identical groups bonded to the same C atom in the double bond.]

    ii)   Any two from: e.g.

[2 marks — 1 mark for each correct answer.]

    iii) $C_6H_{12} + 9O_2 \rightarrow 6CO_2 + 6H_2O$ *[1 mark]*

   d) i) $C_nH_{2n+1}Cl$ *[1 mark]*

    ii)   C and D *[1 mark]*

Both C and D have 5 carbon atoms, whereas E has 4 and F has 6.

    iii)   3-chloropentane *[1 mark]*

Pages 54-57 : Basic Concepts and Hydrocarbons — 2

1 a)

[1 mark]

For this one, it doesn't matter if you drew out all the bonds in the $-CH_2CH_3$ group (or if you showed it as C_2H_5). You could also have drawn a skeletal formula.

   b)   Both of the double-bond carbons have two different atoms or groups attached to them *[1 mark]* and there is restricted rotation around the double bond *[1 mark]*.

   c)   Any one from: e.g.

1,3-dichlorobut-1-ene:

1,4-dichlorobut-1-ene:

1,3-dichlorobut-2-ene:

2,3-dichlorobut-2-ene:

1,4-dichlorobut-2-ene:

[2 marks — 1 mark for a correct structure, 1 mark for a name that matches the structure drawn.]

There are a few more possible answers for this question — you get the marks if you correctly drew and named any isomer of $C_4H_6Cl_2$ that has a double bond with different groups attached to both double-bond carbons.

   d)   E.g. 1,1-dichlorobut-1-ene / 2,3-dichlorobut-1-ene / 3,3-dichlorobut-1-ene/ 3,4-dichlorobut-1-ene / 4,4-dichlorobut-1-ene *[1 mark]*.

You'd get a mark here for naming any alkene isomer of $C_4H_6Cl_2$ that has identical atoms or groups attached to either of the double-bond carbons.

2 a)

[1 mark]

but-2-ene *[1 mark]*

You'd get the mark for the diagram here if you just wrote 'CH_3' instead of drawing out the two methyl groups in full, or if you drew a skeletal formula.

b) i)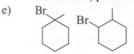

[2 marks — 1 mark for each correct structure.]

ii) A compound that contains a benzene ring *[1 mark]*.

3 a) i) Type of bond: Pi/π-bond *[1 mark]*
Explanation: This arises by sideways overlap of adjacent p-orbitals above and below the molecular axis/bonding carbon atoms *[1 mark]*.

ii) Bond angle: 120° *[1 mark]*
Explanation: There are three covalent bonds around the carbon atom which all repel evenly *[1 mark]*.

b) Of the groups attached to the left hand carbon of the C=C, CH₃ takes priority over H, since C has a higher atomic number than H *[1 mark]*. Both groups attached to the right hand carbon of the C=C contain C atoms, so it is necessary to look further down the chain *[1 mark]*. The methyl/bottom carbon is only attached to H atoms, but the ethyl/top carbon is attached to another C atom, so the ethyl/top carbon takes priority *[1 mark]*. The highest priority groups are on the same side of the double bond, so the isomer is Z *[1 mark]*. The systematic name is therefore Z-3-methylpent-2-ene *[1 mark]*.

c) i) In alkene A, each of the carbon atoms in the double bond has a methyl/CH₃ group attached to it *[1 mark]*.

ii) E.g.

[1 mark]

There are a few other possible answers for this question. Remember, an alkene will only show cis/trans isomerism if each carbon atom in the double bond is attached to two different groups, and the carbon atoms have at least one attached group in common. As long as you've drawn the structure of an alkene with the molecular formula C_6H_{12} that doesn't fit these criteria, you get the mark.

d) i)

[1 mark]

ii) The pi/π-bond in alkene A has a lower bond enthalpy than the sigma/σ-bonds in the alkane/product. / The electron density of the double bond attracts electrophiles. *[1 mark]*

e)

+ H₂O

⟶

[1 mark]

Reactions conditions: steam and an acid catalyst *[1 mark]*

4 a) The solution would be decolourised/turn from orange to colourless *[1 mark]*.

b) The double bond is a region of high electron density *[1 mark]*.

c)

[1 mark for curly arrow from C=C to bromine atom, 1 mark for curly arrow from Br–Br bond to other bromine atom.]

d) Carbocation B is more likely to be formed, as it is a tertiary carbocation, so it is more stable than A (a secondary carbocation) *[1 mark]*.

e)

[2 marks — 1 mark for each correct structure]

Pages 58-60 : Basic Concepts and Hydrocarbons — 3

1 a) i) Bond angle: 109.5° *[1 mark]*
Shape: tetrahedral *[1 mark]*

ii)

[1 mark]

b) How to grade your answer:
Level 0: There is no relevant information. *[No marks]*
Level 1: The answer covers one factor affecting the boiling points of hydrocarbons and an attempt to place the compounds in order is made. The answer has no clear structure. The information given is basic and lacking in detail. It may not all be relevant or correct. *[1 to 2 marks]*
Level 2: The answer covers both factors affecting the boiling points of hydrocarbons and the compounds are placed in the correct order. The answer has some structure. Most of the information given is relevant and there is some detail involved. *[3 to 4 marks]*
Level 3: The answers covers both factors affecting boiling points of hydrocarbons in detail and the compounds are placed in the correct order, including full reasoning. The answer has a clear and logical structure. The information given is relevant and detailed. *[5 to 6 marks]*

Indicative scientific content may include:
How chain length affects the boiling points of hydrocarbons
Hydrocarbons have covalent bonds between the atoms and induced dipole-dipole interactions/London forces between the molecules.
A larger/longer molecule has a greater number of electrons to interact.
A larger/longer molecule has stronger induced dipole-dipole interactions/London forces.
A larger/longer molecule has a greater surface area of contact.
The more induced dipole-dipole interactions/London forces, the greater the energy required to overcome them and the higher the boiling point.
How branching affects the boiling points of hydrocarbons
Branched-chain hydrocarbons cannot pack together as closely as straight-chain hydrocarbons.
They have a smaller surface area of contact.
So there are fewer induced dipole-dipole interactions/London forces between molecules.
Less energy is required to overcome fewer induced dipole-dipole interactions/London forces, and so the boiling point is lower.
Compounds A-C in order of boiling point
Compound C has the highest boiling point, as it has the longest carbon chain/is the largest molecule, and is not branched.
Compounds A and B contain the same number of carbon atoms, but compound A has a straight chain and compound B has a branched chain, therefore compound A has a higher boiling point than compound B.

c) Compound D is more reactive than compound B. The C–Cl bond has lower enthalpy than the C–H bond, therefore less energy is required to break it *[1 mark]*. There is a larger difference in electronegativity between C and Cl than between C and H, so the C–Cl bond is more polar than the C–H bond *[1 mark]*. This makes the C–Cl bond more open to (nucleophilic) attack *[1 mark]*.

d) i) When bonds break by homolytic fission, each bonded atom receives one electron from the bonded pair *[1 mark]*. Whereas when bonds break by heterolytic fission, one of the bonded atoms receives both electrons from the bonded pair *[1 mark]*.

ii) $C(CH_3)_3^+$ and Cl^- *[1 mark]*

2 a) i) Initiation: $Cl_2 \xrightarrow{UV} 2Cl\bullet$
Propagation step 1: $Cl\bullet + CH_3CH_3 \rightarrow \bullet CH_2CH_3 + HCl$
Propagation step 2: $\bullet CH_2CH_3 + Cl_2 \rightarrow CH_3CH_2Cl + Cl\bullet$
Propagation step 3: $Cl\bullet + CH_3CH_2Cl \rightarrow \bullet CH_2CH_2Cl + HCl$
Termination: $\bullet CH_2CH_2Cl + Cl\bullet \rightarrow CH_2ClCH_2Cl$
[5 marks — 1 mark for each correct step]

Remember, the total number of radicals doesn't change during a propagation reaction, so if a radical is involved in the reaction, another radical must be formed.

ii) E.g. the radicals involved in this reaction mechanism can join together in many different ways/be involved in many different termination reactions to produce a range of products (such as C_4H_{10} or C_4H_9Cl) *[1 mark]*. Some of the ethane molecules will only be substituted once by chlorine, whereas others may be substituted 3 or more times *[1 mark]*.

b) i) Any two from: e.g. combustion produces heat energy that can be used to generate electricity. / Combustion reduces the amount of waste sent to landfill. / Smaller areas of land are required for incinerators than for landfill sites. *[2 marks — 1 mark for each correct benefit]*

ii) E.g. the demand for new raw materials to produce polymers and other products is reduced. / Finite resources are conserved by processing waste in this way. / Fewer toxic by-products are produced. *[1 mark]*

c) i) E.g. biodegradable plastics can be made from renewable materials such as starch *[1 mark]*, reducing dependency on finite resources such as crude oil *[1 mark]*. Biodegradable plastics decompose quickly in the natural environment *[1 mark]*, which reduces the amount of persistent plastic waste *[1 mark]*.

ii) Biodegradable polymers need light and water in order that microorganisms can digest them *[1 mark]*, and photodegradable polymers only break down in the presence of sunlight *[1 mark]*.

Pages 61-64: Alcohols, Haloalkanes and Analysis — 1

1 B *[1 mark]*
The strength of the carbon–halogen bond determines the reactivity of a haloalkane. The bond strength decreases as you go down Group 7 — so the C–I bond breaks most easily, and 1-iodobutane will react faster than 1-chlorobutane or 1-bromobutane.

2 C *[1 mark]*
$NH_2CH_2CH_2NH_2$, $CH_3CH_2CH_2OH$ *and* CH_3COOH *all show up as having an* M_r *of 60 in a mass spectrometer, whereas* CH_3COCH_3 *has an* M_r *of 58.*

3 A *[1 mark]*
A is a primary alcohol, so you can oxidise it to an aldehyde. But you can't eliminate an H_2O *molecule, because the carbon atom next to the one with the -OH group can't donate an* H^+.

4 B *[1 mark]*
$C=O$ *bonds cause peaks in the range 1630-1820 cm^{-1}, and O–H bonds in carboxylic acid groups cause broad peaks in the range 2500-3300 cm^{-1}.*

5 a) E.g. potassium dichromate(VI) / $K_2Cr_2O_7$ *[1 mark]*
b) The method shown is distillation *[1 mark]*. The aldehyde has a lower boiling point than the alcohol, so it boils off from the reaction mixture first and can be collected as soon as it is formed *[1 mark]*.
c) A: a water bath is used to heat the alcohol instead of a naked flame as alcohols are flammable/to heat the reaction mixture more evenly/gently *[1 mark]*.
B: anti-bumping granules are used to give a smooth and even boil / prevent the formation of large bubbles *[1 mark]*.
C: an ice bath is used so that the (volatile) aldehyde does not evaporate *[1 mark]*.
d) Use reflux apparatus/vertical condenser *[1 mark]*. The vaporised substances cool and condense and return back to the reaction mixture *[1 mark]*. This ensures that the alcohol is fully oxidised to a carboxylic acid *[1 mark]*.
e) $CH_3CH_2OH + 2[O] \rightarrow CH_3COOH + H_2O$ *[1 mark]*

6 a) i)

$$
\begin{array}{c}
H \\
| \\
H-C-H \\
\quad H \quad | \quad H \quad H \\
| \quad | \quad | \quad | \\
H-C-C-C-C-H \\
| \quad | \quad | \quad | \\
H \quad O \quad H \quad H \\
| \\
H
\end{array}
$$
[1 mark]

Class of alcohol: tertiary *[1 mark]*

ii)

$$
\begin{array}{c}
H \\
| \\
H-C-H \\
\quad H \quad | \quad H \quad H \quad H \\
| \quad | \quad | \quad | \quad | \\
H-C-C-C-C-C-H \\
| \quad | \quad | \quad | \quad | \\
H \quad H \quad O \quad H \quad H \\
| \\
H
\end{array}
$$
[1 mark]

Class of alcohol: secondary *[1 mark]*

b) $C_5H_{11}OH + 7\frac{1}{2}O_2 \rightarrow 5CO_2 + 6H_2O$ *[1 mark]*

c) i) Ethanol has hydrogen bonding between the molecules *[1 mark]*. Ethane molecules have only induced dipole-dipole interactions/London forces/van der Waals forces between the molecules *[1 mark]*. Induced dipole-dipole interactions/London forces/van der Waals forces are weaker than hydrogen bonds, so they take less energy to overcome than hydrogen bonds and therefore ethane has a lower boiling point than ethanol *[1 mark]*.

ii) As the chain length increases, the alcohol becomes less soluble, because in longer chains the polar OH group makes up less of the chain's length, so the molecule is less effective overall at forming the hydrogen bonds needed to dissolve in water *[1 mark]*.

d)

H–C–H (structure)

H H H H
| | | |
H–C–C–C–C–H
| | | |
H H Cl H

[1 mark]

2-chloro-3-methylbutane *[1 mark]*

7 a) A nucleophile is an electron pair donor *[1 mark]*.

b) i) The OH⁻/hydroxide ion *[1 mark]*

ii)

H H   H H
| | | |
H–C–C^δ+ ⌒ I^δ–   ⟶   H–C–C—OH + :I⁻
| | | |
H H ⟍ :ŌH   H H

[3 marks — 1 mark for the curly arrow from the lone pair or negative charge on the OH⁻ ion to the δ+ C atom, 1 mark for the correct δ+ and δ– symbols and correct curly arrow on the C–I bond, 1 mark for showing both products correctly.]

iii) There are no polar bonds in ethane to attract the nucleophile/ OH⁻ *[1 mark]*.

c) hexane-2,3-diol *[1 mark]*

Pages 65-67: Alcohols, Haloalkanes and Analysis — 2

1 a) alkene and alcohol *[1 mark]*

b) i) Compound B will undergo an electrophilic addition reaction due to the presence of the C=C bond *[1 mark]*. The bromine water will be decolourised *[1 mark]*.

ii) An oxidation reaction takes place, because compound B contains a primary alcohol group / the alcohol will be oxidised to a carboxylic acid *[1 mark]*. The acidified potassium dichromate(VI) changes colour from orange to green *[1 mark]*.

c) i) Type of reaction: Elimination *[1 mark]*
Reagents and conditions: Concentrated sulfuric/phosphoric acid catalyst, heat *[1 mark]*

ii) Type of reaction: Addition *[1 mark]*
Reagents and conditions: H_2/hydrogen gas *[1 mark]*, nickel catalyst and temperature of 150 °C *[1 mark]*

2 a) E.g. Greenhouse gases contain bonds which absorb and re-emit infrared radiation *[1 mark]*. The peaks shown on the infrared spectrum of a molecule represent the frequencies at which its bonds absorb IR radiation *[1 mark]*. The IR spectra of water, carbon dioxide and methane will contain peaks caused by the O-H, C=O and C-H bonds which allow them to act as greenhouse gases *[1 mark]*.

b) E.g. the alcohol group contains an O-H bond, but this bond will also be present in the water vapour in the driver's breath *[1 mark]*.

c) Compound I is butanal *[1 mark]*. There is a peak at around 1750 cm⁻¹ for the C=O bond, which is only present in butanal *[1 mark]*. There is no peak at 3200-3600 cm⁻¹/1000-1300 cm⁻¹, which would be expected for the O-H/C-O peak if compound I were butanol *[1 mark]*. There is no peak at 1620-1680 cm⁻¹, which would be expected for the C=C bond if compound I were but-2-ene *[1 mark]*.

3 a) Water is a weak nucleophile *[1 mark]*.

b) Going down the group from C-F to C-I, the bond enthalpy decreases so the rate of hydrolysis will increase *[1 mark]*. The lower the bond enthalpy, the weaker the bond and the less time it takes to hydrolyse (break) the bond *[1 mark]*.

c) How to grade your answer:

Level 0: There is no relevant information. *[No marks]*

Level 1: A simple description of the method is given, which may include some errors or omissions. *[1 to 2 marks]*

Level 2: Attempts a description of the method including equations and details of how to ensure a fair test, but explanations may be incomplete. *[3 to 4 marks]*

Level 3: Gives a comprehensive description of a method that allows the trend in rate to be identified, including full, balanced equations and complete details of how to ensure a fair test. *[5 to 6 marks]*

Indicative chemistry content may include:

Carrying out the test

Fill three test tubes with ethanol.
Into the first test tube add a small amount of 1-chlorobutane.
Add a small amount of 1-bromobutane into the second tube and a small amount of 1-iodobutane into the third tube.
Heat the three tubes up in a water bath for several minutes.
Add a small amount of silver nitrate solution to each test tube. Start the stop watch immediately.
Record and compare the times taken for the three precipitates to form.
The quicker the precipitate is formed, the higher the rate of hydrolysis.

Ensuring a fair test

The same volume of ethanol should be used in each test tube.
The same number of moles of each haloalkane should be added to ensure the three haloalkanes are present in the same concentrations.
The three haloalkanes used all have the same carbon skeleton (butane) to avoid any differences in reactivity arising from halogens being bonded to different lengths of carbon chain.
The three haloalkanes used all have their halogen atoms attached at the '1' position in the carbon chain to avoid any differences in reactivity arising from halogens being bonded at different points on the carbon chain.
All three test tubes are heated in the same water bath at the same time to ensure they are all at the same temperature.
The silver nitrate should be added to all three test tubes at the same time to ensure the three reactions start at the same time.

General equations

The haloalkanes react with the water from the silver nitrate solution to form butanol, releasing a halide ion:
$CH_3CH_2CH_2CH_2X + H_2O \rightarrow CH_3CH_2CH_2CH_2OH + H^+ + X^-$
The halide ions react with silver ions to form a silver halide precipitate:
$Ag^+ + X^- \rightarrow AgX$

170

Pages 68-70: Alcohols, Haloalkanes and Analysis — 3

1 a) E.g. sulfuric acid / phosphoric acid *[1 mark]*

b) Water soluble impurities can be removed using a separating funnel *[1 mark]*. Transfer the reaction mixture to the separating funnel, add water, then seal and shake the funnel and allow the mixture to settle *[1 mark]*. The reaction mixture will separate into two layers. The 1-brombutane layer is denser and will form the lower layer *[1 mark]*. The lower layer can be run off by opening the tap at the bottom of the funnel *[1 mark]*.

c) E.g. (anhydrous) magnesium sulfate / (anhydrous) calcium chloride *[1 mark]*
The drying agent can be removed by filtration of the mixture *[1 mark]*.

d) Liquid impurities can be removed by redistillation *[1 mark]*. Heat the mixture in a round-bottomed flask connected to a Liebig condenser *[1 mark]*. A thermometer in the neck of the flask is used to monitor the temperature of the vapour *[1 mark]*. Any liquid impurities remaining will have a different boiling point to 1-bromobutane *[1 mark]*. When the boiling point of 1-bromobutane is reached, place a flask below the condenser to collect the product *[1 mark]*. When the temperature changes, a different liquid will be collected so this should be collected in a different flask *[1 mark]*.

e) Any two from: e.g. the reaction is incomplete / by-products may be produced / reagents used may be impure / some product is lost during purification / some product is lost during distillation / some of the 1-bromobutane was hydrolysed to butan-1-ol.
[2 marks — 1 mark for each valid reason.]

2 a) The M+1 peak is present due to the presence of the carbon-13 / ^{13}C isotope in the sample *[1 mark]*.

b) The m/z value of the molecular ion peak is equal to the molecular mass. / The molecular mass of compound X is 72 g mol^{-1}. *[1 mark]*

c) Ratio of C : H : O = $\frac{66.7}{12.0}$: $\frac{11.1}{1.0}$: $\frac{22.2}{16.0}$

= 5.558... : 11.1 : 1.3875

= $\frac{5.558...}{1.3875}$: $\frac{11.1}{1.3875}$: $\frac{1.3875}{1.3875}$

= 4.00... : 8 : 1

So the empirical formula of X is C_4H_8O.
[2 marks for correct empirical formula of X, otherwise 1 mark for dividing percentages of C, H and O by their relative atomic masses.]

d) How to grade your answer:
Level 0: There is no relevant information. *[No marks]*
Level 1: Interprets one or two sources of information correctly, but explanation may contain errors or omissions. *[1 to 2 marks]*
Level 2: Uses two or three of the sources of information to draw some correct conclusions about compound X but is unable to positively identify butan-2-one.
OR
Identifies compound X as butan-2-one but only partially justifies this conclusion. *[3 to 4 marks]*
Level 3: Uses relevant information from both spectra, the empirical formula and the result of the reflux experiment to deduce and fully justify that compound X is butan-2-one.
[5 to 6 marks]

Indicative chemistry content may include:
Finding the molecular formula:
The empirical formula of compound X is C_4H_8O.
The M_r of this empirical formula is
$4 \times 12.0 + 8 \times 1.0 + 16 = 72.0$.
This is equal to the molecular mass of the compound, as shown on the mass spectrum, so C_4H_8O is the molecular formula.

Identifying possible functional groups and structures:
The infrared spectrum has a sharp peak at a wavenumber of just over 1700 cm^{-1}, which suggests compound X contains a C=O/carbonyl group.
There is also a peak close to wavenumber 3000 cm^{-1}, which corresponds to the C-H groups in alkyl groups, alkenes and arenes.
There is no strong peak in the wavenumber range 3200-3600, which suggests X is not an alcohol.
There is no strong peak in the wavenumber range 1620-1680, which suggests X is not an alkene.
Compound X must therefore be one of butan-2-one ($CH_3CH_2COCH_3$), butanal ($CH_3CH_2CH_2CHO$) or 2-methypropanal ($CH_3CH(CH_3)CHO$).
This is supported by the fragmentation pattern of the mass spectrum, however the fragmentation pattern does not provide enough information to distinguish between the three compounds.
The largest peak shown on the mass spectrum is at m/z = 43, which could be due to a CH_3CO^+ fragment from butan-2-one, a $CH_3CHCH_3^+$ fragment from 2-methylpropanal or a combination of $CH_3CH_2CH_2^+$ and CH_2CHO^+ fragments from butanal.
Identifying the compound:
The result of the experiment to reflux compound X with the oxidising agent acidified potassium dichromate(VI) shows that compound X cannot be oxidised, as an oxidation reaction would have produced a different organic compound with different mass and infrared spectra.
Aldehydes can be easily oxidised to carboxylic acids, but ketones are not easily oxidised.
Therefore compound X must be butanone.

Module 5 : Physical Chemistry and Transition Elements

Pages 71-74: Rates and Equilibrium — 1

1   B *[1 mark]*
Tripling [A] makes the rate 3^2 = 9 times faster. Tripling [B] makes the rate 3 times faster. So the overall rate of reaction is 9 × 3 = 27 times faster.

2   B *[1 mark]*
X is a reactant so [X] must decrease with time as it is used up in the reaction. The gradient of graph 2 stays the same as [X] decreases, showing the rate doesn't change with concentration of X i.e. the reaction is order O with respect to X.

3   D *[1 mark]*
$N_2O_{4(g)} \rightleftharpoons 2NO_{2(g)}$

$K_p = \dfrac{(p_{NO_2})^2}{p_{N_2O_4}}$

$(p_{NO_2})^2 = K_p \times p_{N_2O_4}$

$\quad = (6.03 \times 10^3) \times (1.78 \times 10^3) = 1.07334 \times 10^7$

$p_{NO_2} = \sqrt{1.07334 \times 10^7} = 3.28 \times 10^3$ *atm (3 s.f.)*

4   C *[1 mark]*
Logarithmic form of Arrhenius equation: $\ln k = \ln A - \dfrac{E_a}{RT}$
Rearrange to make T the subject:

$\dfrac{E_a}{RT} = \ln A - \ln k$

$\dfrac{1}{T} = \dfrac{R(\ln A - \ln k)}{E_a}$

$T = \dfrac{E_a}{R(\ln A - \ln k)}$

$T = \dfrac{254\ 400}{8.314\,(\ln(4.00 \times 10^{14}) - \ln(1.37 \times 10^{-4}))} = 720\ K\ (3\ s.f.)$

5 a)

Concentration of $Na_2S_2O_{3(aq)}$ / mol dm^{-3}	Time taken / s	Rate of reaction / × 10^{-3} s^{-1}
0	0	0
0.200	404	**2.48**
0.400	199	**5.03**
0.600	137	**7.30**
0.800	103	**9.71**

[2 marks for all 4 values correct, otherwise 1 mark for 2 values correct.]

b i)

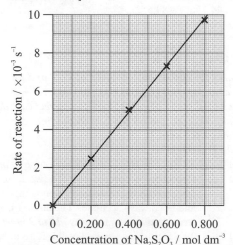

[3 marks — 1 mark for appropriate axes and scales, 1 mark for all points correctly plotted, 1 mark for appropriate straight line of best fit going through the origin.]

ii) The graph is a straight line through the origin *[1 mark]*. This suggests that the reaction is first order with respect to sodium thiosulfate *[1 mark]*.

On a rate-concentration graph, like this one, a first order reaction is shown by a straight line through the origin. On a concentration-time graph a first order reaction would be a curve.

c)   Rate = $k[Na_2S_2O_3]$ *[1 mark]*

6 a)

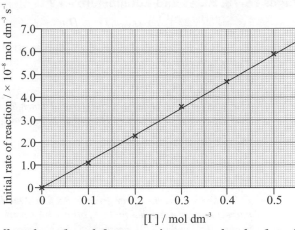

[3 marks — 1 mark for appropriate axes and scales, 1 mark for all points correctly plotted, 1 mark for appropriate straight line of best fit going through the origin.]

b)   This is a first order reaction, so k = gradient
E.g. gradient = change in y ÷ change in x
$\quad = (5.5 \times 10^{-8} - 0) \div (0.47 - 0)$
$\quad = 1.1702... \times 10^{-7}$
units = (mol dm^{-3} s^{-1}) ÷ (mol dm^{-3}) = s^{-1}
$k = 1.2 \times 10^{-7}$ s^{-1} (2 s.f.)
[2 marks — 1 mark for correctly calculating gradient of line of best fit, 1 mark for correct units.]

The gradient you calculate doesn't have to match this value exactly — as long as it's correct for the line of best fit you drew, you still get the marks.

7 a)   When [E] increases by a factor of 1.5 and [F] stays constant, the rate also increases by a factor of 1.5. So the reaction is first order with respect to E *[1 mark]*. When [F] increases by a factor of 1.5 and [E] stays constant the rate also increases by a factor of 1.5. So the reaction is first order with respect to F *[1 mark]*.

b)   Rate = $k[E][F]$ *[1 mark]*

c)   Second order *[1 mark]*.

d) $k = \dfrac{\text{Rate}}{[E][F]}$

$k = \dfrac{8.00 \times 10^{-4}}{0.0800 \times 0.0600} = 0.1666...$

Units of $k = \dfrac{\text{mol dm}^{-3}\ \text{s}^{-1}}{\text{mol dm}^{-3} \times \text{mol dm}^{-3}} = \text{mol}^{-1}\ \text{dm}^3\ \text{s}^{-1}$

$k = 0.167$ mol^{-1} dm^3 s^{-1} (3 s.f.)
[4 marks for correct answer given to 3 s.f. or 3 marks for correct answer not given to 3 s.f., otherwise 1 mark for rearranging the rate equation, 1 mark for correct units.]

e)   Rate = $0.1666... \times (0.200 \times 0.500)$
$= 0.0167$ mol dm^{-3} s^{-1} (3 s.f.) *[1 mark]*

If your value of k from part (d) was incorrect but you carried out the correct calculation using it, you still get the mark here.

Pages 75-78: Rates and Equilibrium — 2

1 a) $K_p = \dfrac{p(H_2) \times p(CO)}{p(H_2O)}$ *[1 mark]*

b) H_2 and CO are produced in equal amounts so $p(H_2) = p(CO)$
$71.6 + (2 \times p(H_2)) = 111$
$2 \times p(H_2) = 39.4$
$p(H_2) = 19.7$ kPa
[2 marks for correct answer, otherwise 1 mark for stating that the partial pressures of H_2 and CO are equal.]

c) $K_p = \dfrac{19.7 \times 19.7}{71.6} = 5.4202...$

units $= \dfrac{kPa \times kPa}{kPa} = kPa$

$K_p = 5.42$ kPa (3 s.f.)
[3 marks for correct answer given to 3 s.f. or 2 marks for correct answer not given to 3 s.f., otherwise 1 mark for units.]

If you calculated $p(H_2)$ and $p(CO)$ incorrectly in b), you can still get all the marks for c), as long as your answer is correct for the values of $p(H_2)$ and $p(CO)$ you used.

2 a) E.g.

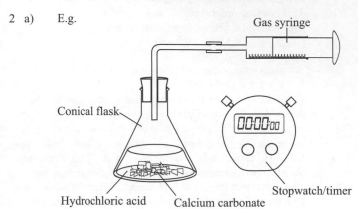

Gas syringe
Conical flask
Hydrochloric acid   Calcium carbonate
Stopwatch/timer

[3 marks — 1 mark for showing calcium carbonate and hydrochloric acid in a flask, 1 mark for showing a suitable method of collecting and measuring all of the gas produced, 1 mark for showing a timing device.]

You would also get the marks if you showed the gas being collected in a measuring cylinder over water instead of in a gas syringe. Don't worry about your diagram being super artistic — as long as it's clear and fully labelled, you'll get the marks.

b) i) E.g.

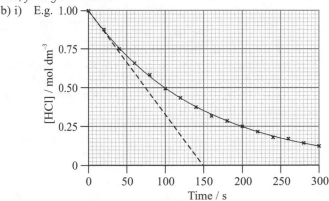

gradient = change in y ÷ change in x
= $(0.025 - 0.700) ÷ (145 - 45)$
= -6.75×10^{-3} mol dm^{-3} s^{-1}
Rate = 6.75×10^{-3} mol dm^{-3} s^{-1}
[2 marks — 1 mark for sensible tangent drawn at t = 0 s, 1 mark for calculating rate from gradient of tangent drawn.]

Your answer probably won't be exactly the same as ours here, but any answer close to it that's been correctly calculated from a sensible tangent gets full marks.

ii) The rate of reaction decreases *[1 mark]* as the concentration of the hydrochloric acid decreases *[1 mark]*.

c) i) The half-life of a reaction is the time taken for the concentration of one of the reactants to decrease by half *[1 mark]*.

ii) E.g.

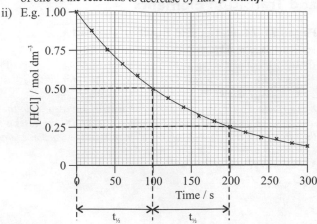

Half-life from 1.00 mol dm^{-3} to 0.50 mol dm^{-3} = 99 s
Half-life from 0.50 mol dm^{-3} to 0.25 mol dm^{-3} = 99 s
The constant half-life shows that the order of reaction with respect to HCl is first order.
half-life = any answer in range 97-102 s
order of reaction = first order
[3 marks — 1 mark for determining at least two half-lives from graph, 1 mark for half-life in correct range, 1 mark for deducing that the reaction is first order.]

iii) E.g. $k = \dfrac{\ln 2}{t_{\frac{1}{2}}} = \dfrac{\ln 2}{99 \text{ s}} = 7.001... \times 10^{-3}$ s^{-1}
$k = 7.0 \times 10^{-3}$ s^{-1} (2 s.f.)
[3 marks for correct answer using half-life calculated in ii), otherwise 1 mark for correct formula, 1 mark for correct units.]

3 a) i) $K_p = \dfrac{p(NH_3)^2}{p(N_2) \times p(H_2)^3}$ *[1 mark]*

ii) Total moles of gas = $15.0 + 30.0 + 22.0 = 67.0$
Partial pressure = mole fraction × total pressure

$p(N_2) = \dfrac{15}{67} \times 200 = 44.776...$ atm

$p(H_2) = \dfrac{30}{67} \times 200 = 89.552...$ atm

$p(NH_3) = \dfrac{22}{67} \times 200 = 65.671...$ atm

$K_p = \dfrac{65.671...^2}{44.776... \times 89.552...^3} = 1.3411... \times 10^{-4}$

Units of $K_p = \dfrac{atm^2}{atm \times atm^3} = atm^{-2}$

$K_p = 1.34 \times 10^{-4}$ atm^{-2} (3 s.f.)
[6 marks for correct answer given to 3 s.f. or 5 marks for correct answer not given to 3 s.f., otherwise 1 mark for correct total moles of gas, 1 mark for correct calculation of partial pressures, 1 mark for substituting into expression for K_p, 1 mark for units.]

iii) How to grade your answer:

Level 0: There is no relevant information. *[No marks]*

Level 1: One factor is covered well OR two factors are covered but the reasoning given is incomplete and not always accurate. The answer is not structured in a logical way. *[1 to 2 marks]*

Level 2: Two factors are covered well OR all three factors are covered but the reasoning given is incomplete and not always accurate. The answer is structured in a reasonably logical way. *[3 to 4 marks]*

Level 3: All three factors are covered in a way that is well-reasoned, detailed and accurate. The answer is coherent and is structured in a logical way. *[5 to 6 marks]*

Indicative scientific content may include:

Increasing the pressure

Increasing the total pressure increases the partial pressures of all the gases in the system.

There are fewer moles of products/on the right than of reactants/on the left.

So equilibrium shifts towards the products/to the right to oppose the increase in pressure.

This causes the partial pressure of ammonia to increase, but because the partial pressures of hydrogen and nitrogen have also increased, K_p stays the same.

Increasing the temperature

Negative ΔH means the forward reaction is exothermic.

So when the temperature is increased, the equilibrium shifts towards the reactants/to the left/in the endothermic direction to absorb excess heat.

Less product is formed.

The partial pressure of ammonia decreases and the partial pressures of nitrogen and hydrogen increase, so K_p decreases.

Adding a catalyst

The catalyst affects the rates of the forward and back reactions equally so there is no change in the equilibrium position.

The ratio of products to reactants remains the same and so there is no change in K_p.

b) i) $K_p = \dfrac{p(SO_3)^2}{p(O_2) \times p(SO_2)^2}$

$p(SO_2)^2 = \dfrac{p(SO_3)^2}{p(O_2) \times K_p} = \dfrac{96^2}{40 \times 0.056} = 4114.2...$

$p(SO_2)^2 = \sqrt{4114.2...} = 64.14... = \mathbf{64\ kPa\ (2\ s.f.)}$

[3 marks for correct answer, otherwise 1 mark for correct expression for K_p, 1 mark for rearranging to find $p(SO_2)^2$.]

ii) Total pressure = $64 + 40 + 96 = \mathbf{200\ kPa\ (2\ s.f.)}$ *[1 mark]*

Pages 79-82: Rates and Equilibrium — 3

1 a) i) E.g.

Expt.	Vol 1.0 mol dm^{-3} CH$_3$COCH$_3$ / cm^3	Vol 0.004 mol dm^{-3} I$_2$ / cm^3	Vol 1.0 mol dm^{-3} HCl / cm^3	Vol H$_2$O / cm^3	Time / s
1	10	4	10	26	210
2	**20**	**4**	**10**	**16**	**105**

[3 marks — 1 mark for changing volume of CH$_3$COCH$_3$ and keeping volumes of I$_2$ and HCl the same, 1 mark for adding water to give a total volume of 50 cm^3, 1 mark for correct time in relation to volume of CH$_3$COCH$_3$ given.]

Other answers you could have given include halving the volume of propanone to 5 cm^3 and doubling the reaction time to 420 s, or tripling the volume to 30 cm^3 and dividing the reaction time by 3 to give 70 s.

ii) Rate = k[CH$_3$COCH$_3$][HCl] *[1 mark]*

iii) E.g. $k = \dfrac{\text{Rate}}{[\text{CH}_3\text{COCH}_3]\,[\text{HCl}]}$

$[\text{CH}_3\text{COCH}_3] = \dfrac{10}{50} \times 1.0\ \text{mol dm}^{-3} = 0.20\ \text{mol dm}^{-3}$

$[\text{HCl}] = [\text{CH}_3\text{COCH}_3] = 0.20\ \text{mol dm}^{-3}$

$k = \dfrac{1.5 \times 10^{-6}}{0.20 \times 0.20} = 3.75 \times 10^{-5}$

Units of $k = \dfrac{\text{mol dm}^{-3}\ \text{s}^{-1}}{\text{mol dm}^{-3} \times \text{mol dm}^{-3}} = \text{mol}^{-1}\ \text{dm}^3\ \text{s}^{-1}$

$k = \mathbf{3.8 \times 10^{-5}\ mol^{-1}\ dm^3\ s^{-1}\ (2\ s.f.)}$

[5 marks for correct answer given to 2 s.f. or 4 marks for correct answer not given to 2 s.f., otherwise 1 mark for rearranging the rate equation, 1 mark for calculating concentrations, 1 mark for correct units.]

iv) The rate equation contains propanone and HCl and the proposed step involves propanone and H$^+$ ions from HCl *[1 mark]*. The reaction is first order with respect to propanone and HCl, and only one molecule of each appears in this rate-determining step *[1 mark]*.

b) i)

Time / s	0	20	40	60	80
Absorbance / arbitrary units	0.58	0.46	0.36	0.25	0.14
[I$_2$] / $\times$ 10^{-3} mol dm^{-3}	4.0	**3.2**	**2.5**	**1.7**	**0.95**

[2 marks for all four concentrations correct, otherwise 1 mark for two concentrations correct.]

ii) The graph would be a straight line (with a negative gradient) *[1 mark]*, because the reaction is zero order with respect to iodine *[1 mark]*.

2 a) i) Plot a graph of $\ln k$ against $\dfrac{1}{T}$ *[1 mark]*. Calculate the gradient of the graph's line of best fit *[1 mark]*. The activation energy for the reaction can be calculated by multiplying the value of the gradient by $-R$ *[1 mark]*.

ii) An increase in temperature would mean significantly more reactant particles had an energy equal to or greater than the activation energy *[1 mark]*. They would also move faster and be more likely to collide *[1 mark]*. As a result the rate of reaction would increase whilst the concentrations of the reactants stayed the same *[1 mark]*. So the rate constant would increase (exponentially) *[1 mark]*.

b) E.g. $\ln k = \dfrac{-E_a}{RT} + \ln A$

$\ln A = \ln k + \dfrac{E_a}{RT}$

$\ln A = \ln(1.54 \times 10^{-6}) + \dfrac{44\,900}{8.314 \times 298} = 4.73...$

$A = e^{4.73...} = 114.30... = \mathbf{114\ mol^{-1}\ dm^3\ s^{-1}\ (3\ s.f.)}$

[2 marks for correct answer, otherwise 1 mark for correctly substituting the numbers into the equation.]

You could also have used the other form of the Arrhenius equation ($k = Ae^{\frac{-E_a}{RT}}$) to get to the answer here.

3 a) i) $K_c = \dfrac{[CH_3COOC_3H_7][H_2O]}{[C_3H_7OH][CH_3COOH]}$ *[1 mark]*

   ii) How to grade your answer:

Level 0:   There is no relevant working. *[No marks]*

Level 1:   Only one stage of the calculation is present and correct OR two stages of the calculation are present, but with mistakes made in the working OR attempts have been made at parts of the calculations but with errors present and no logical method followed. *[1-2 marks]*

Level 2:   Only two stages of the calculation are present and correct OR all three stages are present but with mistakes made in the working. The steps of the calculation may not follow a completely logical order. *[3-4 marks]*

Level 3:   All three stages of the calculation are present and fully correct. The calculation steps are laid out in a logical order. *[5-6 marks]*

Indicative scientific content may include:

Stage 1: Find the number of moles of ethanoic acid present at the start of the reaction

number of moles = concentration × volume

moles of CH_3COOH = 17.4 mol dm^{-3} × $\dfrac{5.00}{1000}$ dm^3

                = 0.0870 moles

Stage 2: Find the number of moles of ethanoic acid present at equilibrium using the sodium hydroxide titration

number of moles = concentration × volume

moles of NaOH = 0.200 mol dm^{-3} × $\dfrac{42.6}{1000}$ dm^3

            = 8.52 × 10^{-3} moles

The equation for the reaction of CH_3COOH with NaOH is:

$CH_3COOH + NaOH \rightarrow CH_3COONa + H_2O$

1 mole of CH_3COOH reacts with 1 mole of NaOH, so in the titration 8.52 × 10^{-3} moles of CH_3COOH must have reacted with 8.52 × 10^{-3} moles of NaOH.

There were 8.52 × 10^{-3} moles of CH_3COOH in 25 cm^3 of solution, so there must have been (8.52 × 10^{-3}) × 10 = 0.0852 moles of CH_3COOH in 250 cm^3 of solution.

Stage 3: Find the number of moles and the concentration of propyl ethanoate at equilibrium

At the start of the reaction, the mixture contained 0.0870 moles of CH_3COOH. At equilibrium it contained 0.0852 moles of CH_3COOH. Therefore, 0.0870 − 0.0852 = 1.8 × 10^{-3} moles of CH_3COOH reacted. According to the reaction equation, 1 mole of CH_3COOH reacts to produce 1 mole of $CH_3COOC_3H_7$. So if 1.8 × 10^{-3} moles of CH_3COOH has reacted, 1.8 × 10^{-3} moles of $CH_3COOC_3H_7$ has been produced.

concentration = number of moles ÷ volume

volume of equilibrium mixture = 5.00 + 5.00 = 10.0 cm^3

concentration of $CH_3COOC_3H_7$ = (1.8 × 10^{-3}) ÷ $\dfrac{10.0}{1000}$

                    = 0.18 mol dm^{-3}

It doesn't matter which order you do stages 1 and 2 in in this calculation — either is logical.

b) i) The rate-determining step is the slowest step in a reaction mechanism *[1 mark]*.

   ii) Mechanism B is the correct mechanism, because e.g. the rate equation shows there must be one molecule of C_3H_7Br and one OH$^-$ ion in the rate-determining step *[1 mark]*.

Pages 83-85: pH — 1

1   C *[1 mark]*

2   A *[1 mark]*

$pK_a = -log_{10}K_a$

      $= -log_{10}(2.24 \times 10^{-5})$

      $= 4.649...$

      $= 4.65$ (3 s.f)

3   D *[1 mark]*

$K_w = [H^+][OH^-]$

$[H^+] = \dfrac{K_w}{[OH^-]}$

[LiOH] = 0.500 mol dm^{-3} and lithium hydroxide is a strong base, therefore [OH$^-$] = 0.500 mol dm^{-3}.

$[H^+] = \dfrac{1.00 \times 10^{-14}}{0.500}$

    $= 2.00 \times 10^{-14}$ mol dm^{-3}

$pH = -log_{10}(2.00 \times 10^{-14})$

    $= 13.698...$

    $= 13.7$ (3 s.f.)

4   C *[1 mark]*

5 a)   proton acceptor *[1 mark]*

   b) A strong acid would have a higher K_a value *[1 mark]*. This is because strong acids dissociate/ionise fully in water *[1 mark]*. Weak acids only partially dissociate/ionise in water (to set up an equilibrium) *[1 mark]*.

   c) i) $HCl + H_2O \rightarrow H_3O^+ + Cl^-$ / $HCl \rightarrow H^+ + Cl^-$ *[1 mark]*

      ii) $pH = -log_{10}[H^+]$

         $[H^+] = 0.0500$ mol dm^{-3}

         $pH = -log_{10}(0.0500)$

            $= 1.301...$

            $= 1.30$ (3 s.f.) *[1 mark]*

   d) i) E.g. place the bulb of the pH meter into distilled water and allow the reading to settle *[1 mark]*. Adjust the reading on the pH meter so that it reads 7.0 *[1 mark]*. Repeat these steps with a standard/buffer solution of pH 4 and pH 10 *[1 mark]*, making sure to rinse the probe with distilled water between each reading *[1 mark]*.

      ii) Percentage uncertainty = $\dfrac{uncertainty}{reading} \times 100$

                $= \dfrac{0.05}{2.7} \times 100$

                $= 1.851...$

                $= 2\%$ (1 s.f.) *[1 mark]*

     iii) $H_2SO_4 \rightleftharpoons H^+ + HSO_4^-$ / $H_2SO_4 + H_2O \rightleftharpoons H_3O^+ + HSO_4^-$ *[1 mark]*

You'd also get the mark if you showed the ionisation using a non-reversible arrow ($\rightarrow$).

     iv) Conjugate acid: H_2SO_4 / H_3O^+

         Conjugate base: HSO_4^- / H_2O *[1 mark]*

You'd only get the mark in part (iv) if the species you gave for the conjugate acid-base pair were also in the equation you gave in part (iii). For example, you wouldn't get the mark if you gave H_3O^+ and H_2O as the acid-base pair in part (iv), if your answer to part (iii) was $H_2SO_4 \rightarrow H^+ + HSO_4^-$.

6 a) $CH_3CH_2COOH + H_2O \rightleftharpoons CH_3CH_2COO^- + H_3O^+$ / $CH_3CH_2COOH \rightleftharpoons CH_3CH_2COO^- + H^+$ *[1 mark]*

Again, you'd get the mark if you showed the ionisation using a non-reversible arrow ($\rightarrow$).

   b) $K_a = \dfrac{[H^+][CH_3CH_2COO^-]}{[CH_3CH_2COOH]}$ *[1 mark]*

c) M_r of $CH_3CH_2COOH = (12.0 \times 3) + (1.0 \times 6) + (16.0 \times 2)$
$$= 74.0$$
number of moles = mass $\div M_r$
number of moles of $CH_3CH_2COOH = 12.0 \div 74.0$
$$= 0.16216... \text{ mol}$$
$[CH_3CH_2COOH]$ = number of moles $\div$ volume
$$= 0.16216... \text{ mol} \div \frac{150}{1000} \text{ dm}^3$$
$$= 1.081081... \text{ mol dm}^{-3}$$
As propanoic acid is a weak acid it can be assumed that $[H^+] = [CH_3CH_2COO^-]$.
Therefore it is possible to use the expression:
$$K_a = \frac{[H^+]^2}{[CH_3CH_2COOH]}$$
$[H^+]^2 = K_a \times [CH_3CH_2COOH]$
$[H^+] = \sqrt{K_a \times [CH_3CH_2COOH]}$
$$= \sqrt{1.34 \times 10^{-5} \text{ mol dm}^{-3} \times 1.081081... \text{ mol dm}^{-3}}$$
$$= 3.8061... \times 10^{-3} \text{ mol dm}^{-3}$$
pH $= -\log_{10}[H^+]$
$$= -\log_{10}(3.8061... \times 10^{-3})$$
$$= 2.4195...$$
$$= \mathbf{2.42 \ (3 \ s.f.)}$$

[5 marks for correct answer, otherwise 1 mark for calculating moles of propanoic acid, 1 mark for calculating concentration of propanoic acid, 1 mark for rearranging K_a expression to find $[H^+]$, 1 mark for calculating $[H^+]$]

d) Hydrofluoric acid has a larger K_a value than propanoic acid and so is a stronger acid *[1 mark]*. Hydrofluoric acid dissociates more in solution than propanoic acid *[1 mark]*. Therefore, the difference between $[HA]_{undissociated}$ and $[HA]_{equilibrium}$ becomes larger and the assumption that $[HA]_{undissociated} = [HA]_{equilibrium}$ becomes less accurate *[1 mark]*.

Pages 86-89: pH — 2

1 a) $K_w = [H^+][OH^-]$ *[1 mark]*
   b) The equilibrium shifting to the right means that the concentrations of H^+ and OH^- ions increase *[1 mark]* and so the value of K_w increases too *[1 mark]*.
   c) $[H^+] = \dfrac{K_w}{[OH^-]}$
   $$[H^+] = \frac{1.00 \times 10^{-14} \text{ mol}^2 \text{ dm}^{-6}}{0.800 \text{ mol dm}^{-3}}$$
   $$= 1.25 \times 10^{-14} \text{ mol dm}^{-3}$$
   pH $= -\log_{10}[H^+]$
   pH $= -\log_{10}(1.25 \times 10^{-14} \text{ mol dm}^{-3})$
   $$= 13.903...$$
   $$= \mathbf{13.9 \ (3 \ s.f.)}$$
   [3 marks for correct answer, otherwise 1 mark for rearranging equation to find $[H^+]$, 1 mark for calculating $[H^+]$]
   d) $[H^+] = 10^{-pH}$
   $$= 10^{-12.19}$$
   $$= 6.456... \times 10^{-13} \text{ mol dm}^{-3}$$
   $K_w = [H^+][OH^-]$
   $$= (6.456... \times 10^{-13} \text{ mol dm}^{-3}) \times (0.800 \text{ mol dm}^{-3})$$
   $$= 5.165... \times 10^{-13} \text{ mol}^2 \text{ dm}^{-6}$$
   $$= \mathbf{5.17 \times 10^{-13} \ mol^2 \ dm^{-6} \ (3 \ s.f.)}$$
   [2 marks for correct answer, otherwise 1 mark for calculating $[H^+]$]
   e) i) purple *[1 mark]*
      ii) In acidic solution at the start of the titration, there will be a high concentration of H^+ ions and so the position of equilibrium will lie to the left and the solution will appear orange *[1 mark]*. As the potassium hydroxide/alkali is added, the concentration of H^+ ions will decrease as the OH^- ions from the potassium hydroxide/alkali react with the H^+ ions *[1 mark]*. This causes the position of equilibrium to shift to the right, and the solution will appear purple *[1 mark]*.

2 a) $CH_3CH_2COONa \rightarrow Na^+ + CH_3CH_2COO^-$ *[1 mark]*
   b) $[CH_3CH_2COOH] = 0.050 \text{ mol dm}^{-3} \times \dfrac{25}{125}$
   $$= 0.010 \text{ mol dm}^{-3}$$
   $[CH_3CH_2COONa] = 0.125 \text{ mol dm}^{-3} \times \dfrac{100}{125}$
   $$= 0.10 \text{ mol dm}^{-3}$$
   $$K_a = \frac{[H^+][CH_3CH_2COO^-]}{[CH_3CH_2COOH]}$$
   $$[H^+] = \frac{K_a \times [CH_3CH_2COOH]}{[CH_3CH_2COO^-]}$$
   $$= \frac{(1.34 \times 10^{-5} \text{ mol dm}^{-3}) \times 0.010 \text{ mol dm}^{-3}}{0.10 \text{ mol dm}^{-3}}$$
   $$= 1.34 \times 10^{-6} \text{ mol dm}^{-3}$$
   pH $= -\log_{10}[H^+]$
   $$= -\log_{10}(1.34 \times 10^{-6})$$
   $$= 5.8728...$$
   $$= \mathbf{5.9 \ (2 \ s.f.)}$$
   [5 marks for correct answer, otherwise 1 mark for calculating $[CH_3CH_2COOH]$, 1 mark for calculating $[CH_3CH_2COONa]$, 1 mark for substituting the correct values into the K_a expression to find $[H^+]$, 1 mark for calculating $[H^+]$]
   c) The pH of the solution does not change/only changes slightly *[1 mark]*. Adding a small amount of acid increases the concentration of H^+ ions in the solution *[1 mark]*. The equilibrium of the buffer solution shifts to the left as the extra H^+ ions combine with the $CH_3CH_2COO^-$ ions to produce CH_3CH_2COOH *[1 mark]*, so there is no overall increase in the concentration of H^+ ions/the H^+ ion concentration is reduced to close to its original value *[1 mark]*.
   d) Conjugate acid: H_2CO_3
   Conjugate base: HCO_3^- *[1 mark]*

3 a) i) E.g. the equivalence point of a titration is shown on the pH curve as the vertical portion of the curve *[1 mark]*. An indicator can be used if the pH range over which it changes colour falls within the pH range covered by this vertical portion of the curve *[1 mark]*.

   ii) Indicator: methyl orange
   Colour change: red to yellow
   [1 mark]

   iii) E.g. In a weak acid/weak base titration there is no sharp pH change at the equivalence point so any colour change would only occur very gradually *[1 mark]*, making it very difficult to accurately identify the equivalence point *[1 mark]*.

b) $CH_3CH_2CH_2COOH + NaOH \rightarrow CH_3CH_2CH_2COONa + H_2O$
   [1 mark]

c) i) From the reaction equation, there is a 1:1 ratio of acid reacting with base, so 25.0 cm^3 of 0.0500 mol dm^{-3} NaOH neutralises 25.0 cm^3 of 0.0500 mol dm^{-3} butanoic acid.

   So initial moles of acid $= 0.0500 \times \dfrac{25.0}{1000} = 0.00125$ mol
   So moles of acid at half-neutralisation point
   $= 0.00125 \div 2 = 6.25 \times 10^{-4}$ mol
   Volume of reaction mixture at half-neutralisation point
   $= 25.0 + 12.5 = 37.5$ cm^3
   So concentration of acid at half-neutralisation point
   $= (6.25 \times 10^{-4}) \div \dfrac{37.5}{1000}$
   $= 0.01666...$ mol dm^{-3}
   $= 0.0167$ mol dm^{-3} (3 s.f.)
   At the half-neutralisation point, moles of salt produced = moles of acid reacted = moles of acid remaining
   So concentration of salt = concentration of acid
   $= 0.0167$ mol dm^{-3} (3 s.f.)
   [6 marks for correct answers given to 3 s.f. or 5 marks for correct answers not given to 3 s.f., otherwise 1 mark for stating and using the 1:1 reaction ratio between acid and base, 1 mark for calculating moles of acid at half-neutralisation point, 1 mark for calculating volume at half-neutralisation point, 1 mark for calculating concentration of acid at half-neutralisation point]

   ii) $K_a = \dfrac{[H^+][CH_3CH_2CH_2COO^-]}{[CH_3CH_2CH_2COOH]}$ *[1 mark]*

   iii) $[H^+] = 10^{-pH}$
   $= 10^{-4.80}$
   $= 1.5848... \times 10^{-5}$ mol dm^{-3}
   $K_a = \dfrac{(1.5848... \times 10^{-5}) \times 0.01666...}{0.01666...}$
   $= 1.58 \times 10^{-5}$ mol dm^{-3} (3 s.f.)
   [2 marks — 1 mark for correct calculation of $[H^+]$, 1 mark for correct use of expression to calculate K_a]

Pages 90-92: Energy — 1

1   A *[1 mark]*
Under standard conditions, any solutions must have a concentration of 1 mol dm^{-3}.

2   D *[1 mark]*
$\Delta G = \Delta H - T\Delta S$, so if ΔS is positive and T is high enough, $T\Delta S$ will be greater than ΔH and ΔG will be negative, making the reaction feasible.

3   C *[1 mark]*
Al is the only substance with a more negative E° than hydrogen, and so the only one which will be oxidised in a reaction with hydrogen ions.

4   A *[1 mark]*

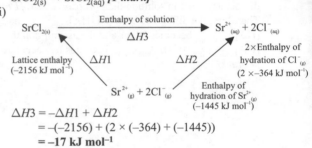

$\Delta H2 = \Delta H1 + \Delta H3$
$= -2056 + -36$
$= -2092$ kJ mol^{-1}
Enthalpy of hydration of $Ba^{2+}_{(g)} = \Delta H2 - 2 \times$ Enthalpy of hydration of $Cl^-_{(g)}$
$= -2092 - (2 \times -364)$
$= -1364$ kJ mol^{-1}

5 a) i) The enthalpy change when 1 mole of a solute is dissolved *[1 mark]*.

   ii) $SrCl_{2(s)} \rightarrow Sr^{2+}_{(aq)} + 2Cl^-_{(aq)}$ *[1 mark]*
   OR
   $SrCl_{2(s)} \rightarrow SrCl_{2(aq)}$ *[1 mark]*

   iii)

   $\Delta H3 = -\Delta H1 + \Delta H2$
   $= -(-2156) + (2 \times (-364) + (-1445))$
   $= -17$ kJ mol^{-1}
   [2 marks for correct answer, otherwise 1 mark for correct cycle or equation]

b) i) Dissolving rubidium chloride increases its entropy *[1 mark]*. ΔS is positive and large enough to overcome the effect of ΔH also being positive, so ΔG is negative and the reaction is feasible *[1 mark]*. The activation energy is also low enough for the reaction to happen spontaneously *[1 mark]*.

   ii) Strontium ions are smaller than rubidium ions and have a higher charge/greater charge density *[1 mark]*. Therefore water molecules are more strongly attracted to the strontium ions and more energy is released when bonds between them are made *[1 mark]*.

6 a) Negative, since there are 3 moles of reactants and only 2 moles of product *[1 mark]*. Fewer molecules means fewer possible arrangements of molecules, and so lower entropy *[1 mark]*.

b) i) $\Delta S = S_{products} - S_{reactants}$
   $= (2 \times 240.0) - (2 \times 210.8 + 205.3)$
   $= -146.9$ J K^{-1} mol^{-1}
   [2 marks for correct answer, otherwise 1 mark for correct equation for ΔS]

   ii) E.g. The reaction is only feasible below a certain temperature *[1 mark]*. Reactions are feasible when $\Delta G = \Delta H - T\Delta S$ is negative so only reactions where ΔH is negative and ΔS is positive are feasible at all temperatures *[1 mark]*.
   OR
   $T = \dfrac{\Delta H}{\Delta S} = \dfrac{-114\,000}{-146.9} = 776$ K (3 s.f.) *[1 mark]*
   The reaction is only feasible at temperatures of 776 K or lower, as at these temperatures ΔG is zero or lower *[1 mark]*.

c) Molecules in a liquid are less free to move around than molecules in a gas *[1 mark]*, so there is less disorder/there are fewer ways of arranging the molecules and the entropy decreases *[1 mark]*.

Pages 93-96: Energy — 2

1 a)

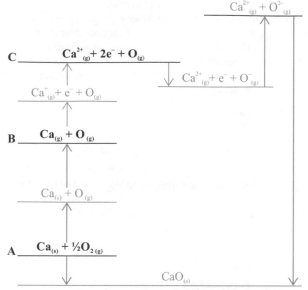

[1 mark for each correct line]

b) Enthalpy of atomisation of oxygen = Enthalpy of formation of calcium oxide − Lattice enthalpy of calcium oxide − Second electron affinity of oxygen − First electron affinity of oxygen − Second ionisation energy of calcium − First ionisation energy of calcium − Enthalpy of atomisation of calcium = $-635 - (-3513) - (+844) - (-142) - (+1150) - (+590) - (+193)$
= **+243 kJ mol^{-1}**

[2 marks for correct answer, otherwise 1 mark for correct expression for enthalpy of atomisation of oxygen.]

2 E.g.
Moles of $Cr_2O_7^{2-}$ = $\frac{23.85}{1000} \times 0.0200$
= 4.77×10^{-4} mol
From reaction equation, Fe^{2+} and $Cr_2O_7^{2-}$ react in 6:1 ratio, so
Moles of Fe^{2+} in 25.0 cm^3 = $6 \times (4.77 \times 10^{-4})$
= 0.002862 mol
Moles of Fe^{2+} in 250 cm^3 = 0.02862 mol
Mass of iron = 0.02862×55.8
= 1.596996 g
Percentage of iron = $\frac{1.596996}{2.00} \times 100$
= 79.8498 = **79.8% (3 s.f.)**

[6 marks for correct answer given to 3 s.f. or 5 marks for correct answer not given to 3 s.f., otherwise 1 mark for calculating moles of $Cr_2O_7^{2-}$, 1 mark for calculating moles of Fe^{2+} in 25 cm^3, 1 mark for calculating moles of Fe^{2+} in 250 cm^3 or calculating mass of iron in 25 cm^3, 1 mark for calculating mass of iron in 250 cm^3.]

3 a) material: e.g. platinum metal *[1 mark]*
reasons: It conducts electricity *[1 mark]*. It is inert so will not react with any of the ions in solution *[1 mark]*.

b)

Half-cells	Reaction equation
A and C	$Zn_{(s)} + 2H^+_{(aq)} \rightarrow Zn^{2+}_{(aq)} + H_{2(g)}$
B and D	$Fe_{(s)} + Cu^{2+}_{(aq)} \rightarrow Fe^{2+}_{(aq)} + Cu_{(s)}$
E and F	$2Fe^{3+}_{(aq)} + 2I^-_{(aq)} \rightarrow 2Fe^{2+}_{(aq)} + I_{2(aq)}$
B and G	$5Fe_{(s)} + 2MnO_4^-{}_{(aq)} + 16H^+_{(aq)}$ $\rightarrow 5Fe^{2+}_{(aq)} + 2Mn^{2+}_{(aq)} + 8H_2O_{(l)}$

[1 mark for each line correct]

c) $E^{\ominus}_{cell} = E^{\ominus}_{reduced} - E^{\ominus}_{oxidised}$
= $+1.51 - (-0.44)$
= **+1.95 V** *[1 mark]*

d) i)

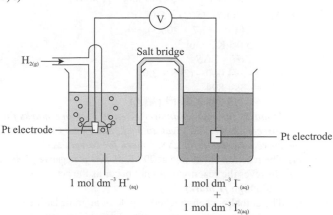

Temperature: 298 K / 25 °C
[4 marks — 1 mark for each correctly labelled half-cell, 1 mark for salt bridge, voltmeter and wires, 1 mark for correct temperature.]
The size that you've drawn your platinum electrodes doesn't matter. As long as you've labelled them correctly, you'll get the marks.

ii) The salt bridge completes the circuit by allowing ions to move between the half-cells *[1 mark]* but prevents the two solutions from mixing together *[1 mark]*.

4 Moles of MnO_4^- = $\frac{19.10}{1000} \times 0.0200$
= 3.82×10^{-4} mol
From reaction equation, $C_2O_4^{2-}$ and MnO_4^- react in 5:2 ratio, so
Moles of $C_2O_4^{2-}$ in 25.0 cm^3 = $\frac{5}{2} \times (3.82 \times 10^{-4})$
= 9.55×10^{-4} mol
Moles of $C_2O_4^{2-}$ in 250 cm^3 = 9.55×10^{-3} mol
Relative formula mass of hydrated acid = $\frac{\text{mass of acid}}{\text{number of moles}}$
= $\frac{1.20}{9.55 \times 10^{-3}}$
= 125.654...
Formula mass of $C_2O_4H_2$ = $(2 \times 12.0) + (4 \times 16.0) + (2 \times 1.0)$
= 90.0
So formula mass of xH_2O = 125.654... − 90.0
= 35.654...
Formula mass of H_2O = $(2 \times 1.0) + 16.0$
= 18.0
$\frac{35.654...}{18.0}$ = 1.9808... = 2 (nearest whole number)
therefore **$x = 2$**

[6 marks for correct answer, otherwise 1 mark for calculating moles of MnO_4^-, 1 mark for calculating moles of $C_2O_4^{2-}$ in 25 cm^3, 1 mark for calculating moles of $C_2O_4^{2-}$ in 250 cm^3, 1 mark for calculating relative formula mass of acid, 1 mark for calculating formula mass of xH_2O]

You could also work out x like this:
Mass of 9.55×10^{-3} moles of $C_2O_4H_2$ = $(9.55 \times 10^{-3}) \times 90.0$
= 0.8595
Mass of H_2O in $C_2O_4H_2.xH_2O$ = 1.20 − 0.8595 = 0.3405 g
Moles of H_2O in 0.3405 g = 0.3405 ÷ 18.0 = 0.0189...
Ratio of H_2O to $C_2O_4H_2$ = 0.0189... ÷ 9.55×10^{-3} ≈ 2
If you've done the question this way and not by calculating the formula mass of acid and the formula mass of x.H_2O, you get 1 mark for calculating the masses of $C_2O_4H_2$ and H_2O present and 1 mark for calculating the number of moles of H_2O.

Pages 97-100: Energy — 3

1 a) Carbon is a solid and oxygen is a gas *[1 mark]*. Solids have a more ordered structure/gases are more disordered *[1 mark]*.

b) i) $\Delta_r H = \Delta_f H(CO_2) = -394 \text{ kJ mol}^{-1}$ *[1 mark]*

ii) $\Delta S = S(CO_2) - (S(C) + S(O_2))$
$= 214.0 - (5.7 + 205.3)$
$= 3.0 \text{ J K}^{-1} \text{ mol}^{-1}$
$\Delta G = \Delta H - T\Delta S$
$= -394\,000 - (298 \times 3.0)$
$= -394\,894$
$= \mathbf{-395\,000 \text{ J mol}^{-1} \text{ (3 s.f.)}}$
[4 marks for correct answer given to 3 s.f. or 3 marks for correct answer not given to 3 s.f., otherwise 1 mark for correct equation for ΔS, 1 mark for correct ΔS]

iii) The reaction is feasible at 298 K as ΔG is negative *[1 mark]*. However the reaction does not occur as the activation energy is too high *[1 mark]*.

2 a) i) The enthalpy change when 1 mole of an ionic lattice is formed from its gaseous atoms *[1 mark]*.

ii) Lithium and fluoride ions have smaller ionic radii than sodium and chloride ions *[1 mark]*. So in lithium fluoride the ions have a higher charge density and sit closer together in the lattice *[1 mark]*, meaning the attractions between the ions are stronger *[1 mark]*.

b) E.g.

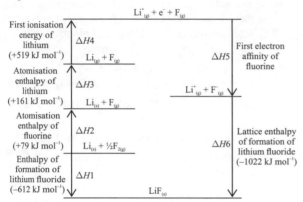

[3 marks — 1 mark for enthalpy changes shown in a correct order, 1 mark for species shown correctly on each line, 1 mark for arrows all shown correctly.]
$\Delta H5 = -\Delta H4 - \Delta H3 - \Delta H2 + \Delta H1 - \Delta H6$
$\Delta H5 = -(+519) - (+161) - (+79) + (-612) - (-1022)$
$= \mathbf{-349 \text{ kJ mol}^{-1}}$
[2 marks for correct answer, otherwise 1 mark for attempting correct calculation]

It's also acceptable to label the enthalpy changes on your cycle with symbols (e.g. $\Delta_{IE1}H$) instead of words.

3 a) i)

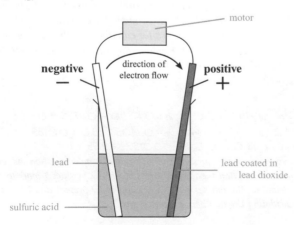

[1 mark for correctly labelled electrodes, 1 mark for arrow correctly showing electron flow]

ii) $Pb + PbO_2 + 2SO_4^{2-} + 4H^+ \rightarrow 2PbSO_4 + 2H_2O$ *[1 mark]*

iii) Oxidising agent: lead dioxide/PbO_2 *[1 mark]*
Reducing agent: lead/Pb *[1 mark]*

b) i) cell voltage $= E^\ominus_{\text{reduced}} - E^\ominus_{\text{oxidised}}$
$= 1.69 - (-0.36)$
$= \mathbf{2.05 \text{ V}}$ *[1 mark]*

ii) The cell voltage was calculated using standard electrode potentials *[1 mark]*. In everyday use, conditions are unlikely to be standard and so the electrode potentials will not have their standard values *[1 mark]*.

c) Advantage: Any one from: e.g. electrochemical cells do not produce CO_2 emissions. / Electrochemical cells are more efficient (as less energy is wasted as heat) *[1 mark]*. Disadvantage: Any one from: e.g. the fuel for electrochemical cells may be bulky/need to be compressed/difficult to obtain *[1 mark]*.

4 E.g. Moles of $X^{2+} = \frac{25.00}{1000} \times 0.160$
$= 0.004 \text{ mol}$
Moles of $MnO_4^- = \frac{26.7}{1000} \times 0.0300$
$= 8.01 \times 10^{-4} \text{ mol}$
Moles of e^- accepted by $MnO_4^- = 5 \times (8.01 \times 10^{-4})$
$= 0.004005$
Moles of e^- per mole of $X = \frac{0.004005}{0.004}$
$= 1.00125$
$= 1 \text{ (nearest whole number)}$
So $X^{2+} \rightarrow X^{3+} + e^-$
Oxidation state $= \mathbf{+3}$
[5 marks for correct answer, otherwise 1 mark for calculating moles of X^{2+}, 1 mark for calculating moles of MnO_4^-, 1 mark for calculating moles of e^-, 1 mark for calculating moles of e^- per mole of X.]

Another way you could do this question is by working out the ratio of X^{2+} to MnO_4^- in the full reaction equation, i.e. $(4.00 \times 10^{-3}) \div (8.01 \times 10^{-4}) \approx 5$, then writing out the full equation:
$$5X^{2+} + MnO_4^- + 8H^+ \rightarrow 5X^{3+} + Mn^{2+} + 4H_2O$$
You know from the half-equation given that each MnO_4^- needs $5e^-$, and so each X^{2+} must donate e^-, making the product X^{3+}, with an oxidation state of +3. If you've done the question this way, you get a mark for writing out the full equation, and a mark for recognising that each X^{2+} donates e^-.

Pages 101-104: Energy — 4

1 a) i) $\Delta_r H = -\Delta_f H(Al_2O_3) + 3 \times \Delta_f H(CO)$
$= -(-1675.7) + (3 \times -110.5)$
$= +1344.2 \text{ kJ mol}^{-1}$
$\Delta S = (3 \times S(CO) + 2 \times S(Al)) - (3 \times S(C) + S(Al_2O_3))$
$= (3 \times 197.6 + 2 \times 28.3) - (3 \times 5.7 + 50.9)$
$= +581.4 \text{ J K}^{-1} \text{ mol}^{-1}$
$277 \,°C = 550 \text{ K}$
$\Delta G = \Delta H - T\Delta S$
$= 1\,344\,200 - (550 \times 581.4)$
$= 1\,024\,430 \text{ J mol}^{-1}$
$= \mathbf{1\,020\,000 \text{ J mol}^{-1} \text{ (3 s.f.)}}$
[6 marks for correct answer given to 3 s.f. or 5 marks for correct answer not given to 3 s.f., otherwise 1 mark for correct expression for $\Delta_r H$, 1 mark for correct value for $\Delta_r H$, 1 mark for correct expression for ΔS, 1 mark for correct value for ΔS]

ii) ΔG is positive, therefore the reaction is not feasible at this temperature *[1 mark]*.

b) $\Delta G = 0$ therefore $T = \frac{\Delta H}{\Delta S}$
$T = \frac{1\,344\,200}{581.4} = 2312.005... = \mathbf{2310 \text{ K} \text{ (3 s.f.)}}$
[2 marks for correct answer, otherwise 1 mark for correct equation for T]

You can still get both marks in b) if your values from a)i) are incorrect, as long as you use the values you got in a)i) and your calculation is correct.

c) E.g. temperatures that high are too expensive/the activation energy is too high even though the reaction is feasible at high temperatures/the reaction proceeds too slowly *[1 mark]*.

2 a) Mn is the strongest reducing agent *[1 mark]*, as it has the most negative standard electrode potential (and so is most likely to be oxidised) *[1 mark]*.

b) i) The $O_{2(g)}/2H_2O_{(l)}$ half-cell has a more positive standard electrode potential than the $Ag^+_{(aq)}/Ag_{(s)}$ half-cell *[1 mark]*. Therefore the O_2 should be reduced to H_2O, whilst the Ag is oxidised to Ag^+ *[1 mark]*.

ii) Any pair from: E.g. the activation energy for the reaction between Ag and O_2 may be too high for the reaction to occur under standard conditions *[1 mark]* so a catalyst could be used to reduce the activation energy needed/the temperature could be increased to give the energy needed to reach the activation energy *[1 mark]*. / The rate of reaction may be too slow under standard conditions *[1 mark]* so temperature/concentration could be increased to increase the rate of reaction *[1 mark]*.

c) An increase in the concentration of Fe^{2+} ions would cause the electrode potential of the Fe^{2+}/Fe half-cell to become more positive/the position of the half-cell equilibrium to shift to the right *[1 mark]*. The cell potential will then become more positive/increase overall *[1 mark]*.

3 a) i) An oxidising agent gains electrons *[1 mark]*.

ii) +1 *[1 mark]*

b) $2I^-_{(aq)} + ClO^-_{(aq)} + 2H^+_{(aq)} \rightarrow I_{2(aq)} + Cl^-_{(aq)} + H_2O_{(l)}$ *[1 mark]*
You didn't need to include state symbols in your equation to get the mark.

c) i) E.g. to avoid going past the end-point of the titration *[1 mark]*.

ii) When the iodine has been used up this blue-black complex cannot be formed and the solution turns colourless *[1 mark]*.

iii) $2S_2O_3^{2-}_{(aq)} \rightarrow S_4O_6^{2-}_{(aq)} + 2e^-$ *[1 mark]*

d) i) How to grade your answer:

Level 0: There is no relevant working. *[No marks]*

Level 1: Only one stage of the calculation is present and fully correct OR two stages of the calculation are present but with mistakes in the working out OR attempts have been made at parts of the calculation but with errors present and no logical method followed. The final answer is given to an incorrect number of significant figures. *[1-2 marks]*

Level 2: Only two stages of the calculation are present OR all three stages are present but with mistakes made in the working out. The steps of the calculations may not follow a logical order or may not be explained fully. The final answer is given to an incorrect number of significant figures. *[3-4 marks]*

Level 3: All three stages of the calculation are present and fully correct. The calculation steps are completed and explained in a logical manner. The final answer is given to three significant figures. *[5-6 marks]*

Indicative scientific content may include:

Calculation of average titre and number of moles of sodium thiosulfate used
average titre $= (22.50 + 22.55 + 22.55) \div 3 = 22.533...$
number of moles of thiosulfate
$\quad = $ concentration $\times$ volume of average titre
$\quad = 0.250$ mol dm$^{-3} \times \dfrac{22.53...}{1000}$ dm^3
$\quad = 5.6333... \times 10^{-3}$ moles

Calculating the number of moles of iodine which reacted with the thiosulfate
From the titration reaction equation, 2 moles of thiosulfate react with 1 mole of iodine.
Therefore number of moles of iodine that reacted
$\quad = 5.6333... \times 10^{-3} \div 2$
$\quad = 2.8166... \times 10^{-3}$ moles
Therefore $2.8166... \times 10^{-3}$ moles of iodine were produced by the oxidation with 25.0 cm^3 of the diluted bleach solution.

Calculating the number of moles of chlorate ions in the original 25.0 cm^3 sample of bleach
From the equation for the reaction between the chlorate and iodide ions, the number of moles of iodine reduced in the titration is equal to the number of moles of chlorate ions which reacted.
So there were $2.8166... \times 10^{-3}$ mol ClO^- in 25.0 cm^3 of diluted bleach.
So moles of ClO^- in original 25.0 cm^3 sample of undiluted bleach = moles of ClO^- in 250 cm^3 of diluted bleach = $(2.8166... \times 10^{-3}) \times 10 = 2.8166... \times 10^{-2}$ mol.
Concentration = number of moles $\div$ volume
$\quad = (2.8166... \times 10^{-2}) \div \dfrac{25.0}{1000}$
$\quad = 1.1266...$
$\quad = $ **1.13 mol dm^{-3} (3 s.f.)**

If you calculated the average titre incorrectly (e.g. by including the rough titre value in your average) you won't get credit for the first stage, but as long as you've used the correct methods for the second and third stages you can still receive credit for these.

ii) Two burette readings were used to determine the total titre, and so the total uncertainty is $0.05 + 0.05 = 0.10$ cm^3

percentage uncertainty $= \dfrac{\text{uncertainty}}{\text{measurement}} \times 100$
$\quad = (0.10 \div 22.55) \times 100$
$\quad = 0.4434...$
$\quad = $ **0.44% (2 s.f.)**

[2 marks for correct answer, otherwise 1 mark for using correct equation for percentage uncertainty]

Pages 105-108: Transition Elements — 1

1   B *[1 mark]*

2   C *[1 mark]*

Cu has a full 3d subshell — $1s^2$ $2s^2$ $2p^6$ $3s^2$ $3p^6$ $3d^{10}$ $4s^1$ — it's more stable that way.

3   C *[1 mark]*

If the ammonia weren't in excess, a blue precipitate of $[Cu(OH)_2(H_2O)_4]$ would form instead.

4   B *[1 mark]*

5 a) Cobalt has the electron configuration $1s^2$ $2s^2$ $2p^6$ $3s^2$ $3p^6$ $3d^7$ $4s^2$ *[1 mark]*, and so has a partially filled d-subshell when it forms stable ions, which is the definition of a transition metal *[1 mark]*. Zinc has the electron configuration $1s^2$ $2s^2$ $2p^6$ $3s^2$ $3p^6$ $3d^{10}$ $4s^2$ *[1 mark]* and only forms Zn^{2+} ions (by losing its 4s electrons), so has a full d-subshell as an ion *[1 mark]*.

  b) i) coordinate/dative (covalent) bonding *[1 mark]*

     ii) A ligand is an ion or molecule that donates a pair of electrons to a central transition metal ion to form a coordinate bond *[1 mark]*.

  c) i)

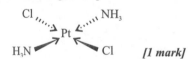

       [2 marks — 1 mark for tetrahedral shape, 1 mark for bond angle]

     ii) $[CoCl_4]^{2-} + 6H_2O \rightleftharpoons [Co(H_2O)_6]^{2+} + 4Cl^-$ *[1 mark]*

You can write the equilibrium going in either direction for the mark.

     iii) Water molecules are neutral, so have a charge of 0, whereas Cl^- ions have a charge of –1, so the overall charge must change *[1 mark]*.

     iv) e.g. ammonia/NH_3 *[1 mark]*

6 a) i) e.g. sodium hydroxide/NaOH *[1 mark]*

You could write any other source of OH^- ions, such as potassium hydroxide/KOH here.

     ii) ammonia/NH_3 *[1 mark]*

  b) (dark) green *[1 mark]*

  c) oxidation/redox *[1 mark]*

  d) i) The oxidation number of chromium decreases *[1 mark]* from +6 in $Cr_2O_7^{2-}$ to +3 in $Cr(H_2O)_6^{3+}$ *[1 mark]*.

     ii) e.g. acidified zinc / Zn/H^+ *[1 mark]*

7 a) i) chloride/Cl^- *[1 mark]*

     ii)

[1 mark]

You don't need to show the 3D structure here — if you've just shown normal arrows for the bonds that's fine too.

     iii) E.g.

cis   trans

[3 marks — 1 mark for cis isomer with NH_3 ligands adjacent, 1 mark for trans isomer with NH_3 ligands opposite one another, 1 mark for correct labelling.]

     iv) $Pt(NH_3)_2Cl_2 + NH_2CH_2CH_2NH_2 \rightarrow$ $Pt(NH_2CH_2CH_2NH_2)Cl_2 + 2NH_3$ *[1 mark]*

  b) i) Any two from: e.g. vanadium(V) oxide/V_2O_5 in the reaction of SO_2 with O_2 to produce SO_3 / copper sulfate/$CuSO_4$ in the reactions of zinc with acids / manganese(IV) oxide/MnO_2 in the decomposition of H_2O_2. *[2 marks — 1 mark for each correct example.]*

     ii) advantage: E.g. transition metal catalysts speed up the rate of reaction so lower operating temperatures/pressures can be used, therefore reducing energy usage *[1 mark]*.
disadvantage: E.g. many transition metals are toxic and pose a health risk *[1 mark]*.

Pages 109-110: Transition Elements — 2

1 a) $1s^2$ $2s^2$ $2p^6$ $3s^2$ $3p^6$ $3d^5$ *[1 mark]*

  b) i) $2Fe^{2+} + H_2O_2 + 2H^+ \rightarrow 2Fe^{3+} + 2H_2O$ *[1 mark]*

     ii) The reaction mixture turns from (pale) green to yellow *[1 mark]*.

     iii) iron(II) ions/Fe^{2+} *[1 mark]*

  c) $[Fe(H_2O)_6]^{2+}$: A green precipitate will be formed *[1 mark]* with the formula $Fe(OH)_2(H_2O)_4$/$Fe(OH)_2$ *[1 mark]*. $[Fe(H_2O)_6]^{3+}$: An orange/brown precipitate will be formed *[1 mark]*, with the formula $Fe(OH)_3(H_2O)_3$/$Fe(OH)_3$ *[1 mark]*.

  d) i) $[Fe(H_2O)_6]^{3+} + 3C_2O_4^{2-} \rightarrow [Fe(C_2O_4)_3]^{3-} + 6H_2O$ *[1 mark]*

     ii) Two of the lone pairs on two oxygen atoms in the ethanedioate ion form two coordinate bonds with a metal ion *[1 mark]*.

  e) i) Fe^{2+}/iron(II) *[1 mark]*

     ii) Oxygen forms a coordinate bond to the Fe^{2+}/central metal ion, forming oxyhaemoglobin *[1 mark]*. Where the oxygen is needed in the body, the oxygen molecule is exchanged for a water molecule which bonds to the Fe^{2+}/metal ion and the haemoglobin returns to the lungs *[1 mark]*.

2 a) $Mn(H_2O)_6^{2+}$: pink *[1 mark]*
$CuCl_4^{2-}$: yellow *[1 mark]*

  b) i) **A**: Fe^{2+} *[1 mark]*
$[Fe(H_2O)_6]^{2+}_{(aq)} + 2OH^-_{(aq)} \rightarrow Fe(OH)_2(H_2O)_{4(s)} + 2H_2O_{(l)}$/ $Fe^{2+}_{(aq)} + 2OH^-_{(aq)} \rightarrow Fe(OH)_{2(s)} + 2H_2O_{(l)}$ *[1 mark]*
B: NH_4^+ *[1 mark]*
$NH_4^+_{(aq)} + OH^-_{(aq)} \rightarrow NH_{3(g)} + H_2O_{(l)}$ *[1 mark]*
X: SO_4^{2-} *[1 mark]*
$Ba^{2+}_{(aq)} + SO_4^{2-}_{(aq)} \rightarrow BaSO_{4(s)}$ *[1 mark]*

You don't need to include state symbols in your equations to get the marks here.

     ii) formula: $Fe(NH_4)_2(SO_4)_2.6H_2O$ *[1 mark]*
colour of solution: (pale) green *[1 mark]*

The solution is pale green due to the presence of the Fe^{2+} ion.

Module 6 : Organic Chemistry and Analysis

Pages 111-113: Aromatic Compounds and Carbonyls — 1

1   C *[1 mark]*
The structure shown has a carboxylic acid functional group and a ketone functional group. Na_2CO_3 reacts with carboxylic acids to produce CO_2. Tollens' reagent and acidified $K_2Cr_2O_7$ reagent will both oxidise aldehydes, but do not react with ketones.

2   B *[1 mark]*
The bonds in the benzene ring are all 140 pm long (between the length of a single bond and a double bond). But the bonds from the benzene ring to the methyl groups are just standard single bonds with a length of 154 pm.

3   B *[1 mark]*

4 a)   E.g.

[1 mark for showing the polarities of the C=O, C–O and O–H bonds correctly, 1 mark for a correct hydrogen bond.]
The hydrogen bond should be shown as a dashed line going between <u>either</u> the H of the –COOH group and the O of the H_2O <u>or</u> the O of the C=O bond and the H of the H_2O.

  b) $CH_3COOH \xrightarrow{Mg} (CH_3COO)_2Mg + H_2$ *[1 mark]*

        $CH_3COOH \xrightarrow{CaO} (CH_3COO)_2Ca + H_2O$ *[1 mark]*

        $CH_3COOH \xrightarrow{NaOH} CH_3COONa + H_2O$ *[1 mark]*

  c) i) $CH_3COOH + SOCl_2 \rightarrow CH_3COCl + SO_2 + HCl$ *[1 mark]*
    ii) water/H_2O *[1 mark]*
   iii) **Ester**
        $C_3H_7COCl + C_2H_5OH \rightarrow C_3H_7COOC_2H_5 + HCl$ *[1 mark]*
        Amide
        $C_2H_5COCl + NH_3 \rightarrow C_2H_5CONH_2 + HCl$ /
        $C_2H_5COCl + 2NH_3 \rightarrow C_2H_5CONH_2 + NH_4Cl$ *[1 mark]*
        Substituted amide
        $CH_3COCl + C_2H_5NH_2 \rightarrow CH_3CONHC_2H_5 + HCl$ /
        $CH_3COCl + 2C_2H_5NH_2 \rightarrow CH_3CONHC_2H_5 + C_2H_5NH_3Cl$
        [1 mark]
   iv) ethyl butanoate *[1 mark]*

5 a)   E.g. electrophilic addition reactions would destroy the stable delocalised ring of electrons *[1 mark]*.
  b)   How to grade your answer:

Level 0:	There is no relevant information. *[No marks]*
Level 1:	The answer covers two areas out of structure and bonding, reactivity and evidence from enthalpy of hydrogenation data. The answer has little or no structure. The information given is basic and lacking in detail. It may not all be relevant. *[1 to 2 marks]*
Level 2:	The answer covers all three areas of structure and bonding, reactivity and evidence from enthalpy of hydrogenation data. The answer has some structure. Most of the information given is relevant and there is some detail involved. *[3 to 4 marks]*
Level 3:	The answer covers all three areas of structure and bonding, reactivity and evidence from enthalpy of hydrogenation data. The answer has a clear and logical structure. The information given is relevant and detailed. *[5 to 6 marks]*

Indicative scientific content may include:
<u>Structure and bonding</u>
Cyclohexa-1,3,5-triene contains alternating single and double carbon-carbon bonds, which would have different bond lengths.
In benzene, each carbon atom forms single covalent bonds to the carbons on either side of it.
Because of this, all the carbon-carbon bonds lengths in benzene are the same.
The unpaired electron on each carbon atom is in a p-orbital that sticks out above and below the plane of the ring.
The p-orbitals on each carbon atom combine to form a ring of delocalised electrons.
<u>Reactivity</u>
You would expect cyclohexa-1,3,5-triene to readily undergo electrophilic addition reactions like other alkenes.
Benzene is less reactive/more stable than you would expect cyclohexa-1,3,5-triene to be.
Benzene undergoes electrophilic substitution reactions.
This is because the delocalised electron ring makes benzene very stable. It will only willingly undergo reactions which do not destroy the delocalised electron ring.
<u>Evidence from enthalpy of hydrogenation data</u>
Cyclohexene has one double bond, so you would expect the enthalpy of hydrogenation of cyclohexa-1,3,5-triene to be three times that of cyclohexene.
When cyclohexene is hydrogenated, the enthalpy change is -120 kJ mol^{-1}. So if cyclohexa-1,3,5-triene was hydrogenated, you would expect the enthalpy change to be -360 kJ mol^{-1}.
The enthalpy change of hydrogenation of benzene is -208 kJ mol^{-1}, which is much less exothermic than expected.
Energy is put in to break bonds and released when bonds are made. So more energy is needed to break the bonds in benzene than would be expected to be needed to break the bonds in cyclohexa-1,3,5-triene.

Pages 114-117: Aromatic Compounds and Carbonyls — 2

1 a)   Displayed formula:

        Name: propanal *[1 mark]*
  b) i) $CH_3CH_2CHO + [O] \rightarrow CH_3CH_2COOH$ *[1 mark]*
    ii) E.g. add sodium carbonate to product **B** *[1 mark]*. **B** is a carboxylic acid so effervescence/fizzing should be observed as CO_2 is given off *[1 mark]*.
  c)   Determine the melting point of the crystalline product **C** *[1 mark]* and compare it with known melting points of carbonyl compound derivatives to confirm the identity of compound **A** *[1 mark]*.
  d) i) Displayed formula:

        Name: propanone *[1 mark]*
    ii) There would be no reaction/colour change *[1 mark]*.

2 a)   Reaction 1: e.g. chloroethane/C_2H_5Cl *[1 mark]*
        Reaction 2: e.g. ethanoyl chloride/CH_3COCl *[1 mark]*
        Reaction 3: chlorine/Cl_2 *[1 mark]*
You could also use bromoethane in reaction 1 or ethanoyl bromide in reaction 2.
  b) i) e.g. aluminium chloride/$AlCl_3$ / iron(III) chloride/$FeCl_3$ / iron/Fe *[1 mark]*
Aluminium(III) bromide or iron(III) bromide would also be fine to use.
    ii) The halogen carrier acts as a catalyst *[1 mark]*. It accepts a lone pair of electrons from a halogen atom on the electrophile, increasing the strength of the electrophile *[1 mark]*.

c) E.g.

[4 marks — 1 mark for curly arrow from benzene ring
to Cl$^{\delta+}$ and correct polarity on Cl–Cl bond, 1 mark for
curly arrow from Cl–Cl bond to AlCl$_3$, 1 mark for correct
intermediate shown and 1 mark for curly arrow from
C–H bond to benzene ring]

*It doesn't matter whether you've shown AlCl$_3$ or a different halogen carrier
in your mechanism here.*

3 a) i) $(CH_3CO)_2O + CH_3CH_2CH_2OH \rightarrow$
$CH_3COOCH_2CH_2CH_3 + CH_3COOH$ *[1 mark]*

*It's also fine to show propan-1-ol as C_3H_7OH and the ester as
$CH_3COOC_3H_7$ in this equation.*

ii)   propyl ethanoate *[1 mark]*

b) i) $(CH_3)_2CHCOOH + CH_3OH \rightleftharpoons (CH_3)_2CHCOOCH_3 + H_2O$
*[2 marks — 1 mark for correct reactants and 1 mark for
correct products]*

You also get the marks if you wrote this equation as:
$CH_3CH(CH_3)COOH + CH_3OH \rightleftharpoons CH_3CH(CH_3)COOCH_3 + H_2O$

ii)   E.g. the reaction is reversible *[1 mark]*, therefore an
equilibrium mixture is produced / some carboxylic acid is
produced by the backwards reaction/hydrolysis of the ester
[1 mark].

c) i)

[2 marks — 1 mark for correct structure for ester,
1 mark for rest of equation correct.]

ii)   E.g. use a large volume of water *[1 mark]*.

iii)

[1 mark]

*This works just the same as the hydrolysis of a straight chain ester,
except that the one product must contain both a carboxylic acid
functional group and an alcohol functional group.*

4 a) i)   Reaction 1:

[1 mark]

Reaction 2:

[1 mark]

Reaction 3:

[1 mark]

*You still get the mark if you've drawn the product of reaction 3 as the
carboxylic acid (i.e. RCOOH) or the carboxylate ion (i.e. RCOO$^-$).*

ii)   Tollens' reagent/ammoniacal silver nitrate *[1 mark]*.

b) i)   nucleophilic addition *[1 mark]*

ii)

[5 marks — 1 mark for correct polarity of C=O bond,
1 mark for curly arrow from H$^-$ to C$^{\delta+}$ in CHO group,
1 mark for curly arrow from C=O bond to O$^{\delta-}$ in CHO
group, 1 mark for curly arrow from O$^-$ to H$^{\delta+}$ in water
molecule and 1 mark for curly arrow from O–H bond to
O$^{\delta-}$ within the water molecule.]

Pages 118-119: Aromatic Compounds
and Carbonyls — 3

1 a) $HNO_3 + H_2SO_4 \rightarrow H_2NO_3^+ + HSO_4^-$
$H_2NO_3^+ \rightarrow NO_2^+ + H_2O$

[4 marks — 1 mark for correct equations to form NO$_2^+$,
1 mark for curly arrow from benzene ring to NO$_2^+$, 1 mark
for curly arrow from C–H bond to positively charged ring,
1 mark for structure of product.]

b) i)

[2 marks — 1 mark for correct structure of organic product,
1 mark for rest of equation correct.]

ii)

[2 marks — 1 mark for correct structure of organic product,
1 mark for rest of equation correct.]

iii) Using phenol, nitration occurs with dilute nitric acid rather
than the concentrated HNO_3/H_2SO_4 mixture needed for
benzene to react *[1 mark]*.

c)

*A correct mirror image or rotation of this is fine too. If you label the carbon
with the NO$_2$ joined to it 1, the SO$_3$H group must be at position 3 or 5
(because an NO$_2$ group in a benzene ring is 3- and 5- directing).*

2 a)   2-methylphenol *[1 mark]*
  b) i)   In **X**, a lone pair on the O atom is partially delocalised into the benzene ring *[1 mark]*. This increases the electron density of the ring, making **X** more attractive to electrophiles *[1 mark]*. In **Y**, the OH group is not directly attached to the benzene ring, and so this partial delocalisation does not happen *[1 mark]*.
  ii)   The delocalisation of the lone pair on the O atom into the benzene ring reduces the electron density on the O atom *[1 mark]*. This reduces the attraction between the O atom and the H atom/stabilises the ion, meaning the H can be lost *[1 mark]*.
  c)   Sodium hydroxide: A reaction does occur.

[2 marks — 1 mark for correct structure of the organic product, 1 mark for rest of equation correct.]
Sodium carbonate:
There is no reaction as arene **X** is only weakly acidic *[1 mark]*.

Pages 120-122: Nitrogen Compounds, Polymers and Synthesis — 1

1   A *[1 mark]*
2   D *[1 mark]*
An addition reaction converts the starting alkene into a bromoalkane. Then nucleophilic substitution of the bromine with a cyanide ion occurs, followed by reduction of the nitrile group to give a primary amine.
3   C *[1 mark]*
4   C *[1 mark]*
The shortest possible reaction pathways for converting haloalkanes to carboxylic acids involve more than one step. (E.g. you could convert a haloalkane to a primary alcohol, then oxidise it to get a carboxylic acid.)
5 a) $RCH(NH_2)COOH$ *[1 mark]*
  b)

[1 mark]
  c)   The carboxylic acid/COOH group can donate a proton to an alkali *[1 mark]*. The lone pair on the nitrogen atom of the amino/NH_2 group can form a dative covalent/coordinate bond with/accept a proton donated by an acid *[1 mark]*.
6 a) i)   condensation (polymerisation) *[1 mark]*
  ii)

[1 mark]

[1 mark]
You still get the mark here if you've drawn COOH groups instead of COO^-Na^+ groups.
  b) i)

[1 mark]
You don't need to include brackets or n in your repeat unit, but it's fine if you have.
  ii)   water/H_2O *[1 mark]*
  iii)   Product 1:

[1 mark]
Name of product 1: hexanedioic acid/hexane-1,6,-dioic acid
[1 mark]

Product 2:

[1 mark]
Name of product 2: hexane-1,6-diamine/1,6-diaminohexane
[1 mark]

It doesn't matter which product you've shown as product 1 and which product you've shown as product 2 here. And if you've shown the amine groups protonated (i.e. as NH_3^+ rather than NH_2), you'll still get the mark.

Pages 123-125: Nitrogen Compounds, Polymers and Synthesis — 2

1 a) E.g. a pair of optical isomers are molecules that are non-superimposable mirror images of one another *[1 mark]*.

b) i)

A **B**

[1 mark for both chiral centres in compound A correct, 1 mark for chiral centre in compound B correct]

ii) E.g. the chiral centres are the carbon atoms in each compound which have four different groups (or atoms) attached *[1 mark]*.

c) E.g.

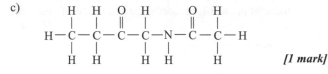

[1 mark for mirror images shown as 3D tetrahedral molecules with correct groups attached to central C atom.]

2 a) i) The lone pair of electrons on the nitrogen atom can accept/ form a dative covalent/coordinate bond with a proton so amines can act as a base *[1 mark]*. Amines can act as nucleophiles as the lone pair of electron on the nitrogen atom can be donated *[1 mark]*.

ii) $CH_3CH_2CH_2CH_2NH_2 + HCl \rightarrow CH_3CH_2CH_2CH_2NH_3^+Cl^-$
[1 mark]

It's ok if you didn't show the charges here — you still get the mark.

b) i)

[1 mark]

ii) The secondary amine has a lone pair of electrons so can act as a nucleophile and react with other bromomethane molecules *[1 mark]*.

c)

[1 mark]

3 a) Name of mechanism: nucleophilic addition
Mechanism:

[5 marks — 1 mark for correct name of mechanism, 1 mark for curly arrow from lone pair or negative charge on cyanide atom to the δ^+ carbon atom of C=O bond, 1 mark for correct dipole on C=O bond and curly arrow from C=O bond to oxygen atom, 1 mark for correct structure of intermediate with negative charge on the O atom and a curly arrow from a lone pair or negative charge on the O atom to an H^+ ion, 1 mark for correct structure of product]

b) i) sodium cyanide/potassium cyanide in ethanol *[1 mark]*

ii)

[3 marks — 1 mark for curly arrow from lone pair or negative charge on cyanide atom to the δ^+ carbon atom of C–Br bond, 1 mark for correct dipole on C–Br bond and curly arrow from C–Br bond to bromine atom, 1 mark for correct products.]

c) i) E.g. hydrogen/H_2 with a nickel/Ni catalyst. / Lithium aluminium hydride/$LiAlH_4$ followed by dilute acid/$H^+_{(aq)}$. / Sodium metal/Na and ethanol.
[2 marks — 1 mark for a suitable reducing agent, 1 mark for suitable reagents and conditions.]

ii) $CH_3CN + 4[H] \rightarrow CH_3CH_2NH_2$ *[1 mark]*

d) i)

[1 mark]

2-hydroxypentanoic acid *[1 mark]*

It's also fine if you drew the skeletal instead of the displayed formula here.

ii) ammonium chloride *[1 mark]*

Pages 126-129: Nitrogen Compounds, Polymers and Synthesis — 3

1 a) Compound **H**:

NO$_2$

OH *[1 mark]*

Compound **I**:

NH$_2$

Br *[1 mark]*

Reagents: Br$_2$/bromine water *[1 mark]*

You won't lose the mark if you also gave a halogen carrier and a haloalkane as reagents here, but it isn't necessary to use a halogen carrier for this reaction. The −NH$_2$ group donates electron density to the ring in a similar way to the −OH group in phenol. This means that compound I is reactive enough to react with bromine (water) without the need for a catalyst.

b) i) (Friedel-Crafts) acylation / electrophilic substitution *[1 mark]*

ii)

H H O
| | ‖
H−C−C−C
| | \Cl
H H

[1 mark]

Name: propanoyl chloride *[1 mark]*

c) The yield of compound **J** would decrease. The amine group and the bromomethyl group are both 2-, 4-, 6-directing, so compound **J** is the major product when bromination is the second step *[1 mark]*. The nitro group is 3-, 5-directing, so will compete with the directing effect of the bromomethyl group if bromination is carried out first *[1 mark]*.

2 a) How to grade your answer:

Level 0: There is no relevant information. *[No marks]*

Level 1: The answer covers only one technique and its suitability OR covers both techniques but with no comments on suitability. The answer has no clear structure. The information given is basic and lacking in detail. It may not all be relevant. *[1 to 2 marks]*

Level 2: The answer covers both techniques and their suitability. The answer has some structure. Most of the information given is relevant and there is some detail involved. *[3 to 4 marks]*

Level 3: The answer covers both techniques and their suitability in detail. The answer has a clear and logical structure. The information given is relevant and detailed. *[5 to 6 marks]*

Indicative scientific content may include:

Preparation of crude aspirin using reflux

Place anti-bumping granules in a round-bottomed flask.
Add the reaction mixture of 2-hydroxybenzoic acid and ethanoic anhydride to the flask along with a small amount of acid catalyst.
Place a (Liebig) condenser vertically in the neck of the flask and run water through it.
The reaction mixture is heated under reflux using an electric hot plate / heating mantle / water bath.
Your answer may also include: a fully labelled diagram showing the correctly labelled condenser, flask, anti-bumping granules, heat source and reaction mixture including acid catalyst.

Separation of the crude aspirin using vacuum filtration

Allow the reflux mixture to cool.
Solid crystals of aspirin form.
Filter the solid crystals out from the reaction mixture using vacuum filtration.
Carry out the vacuum filtration using a Büchner funnel with a piece of damp filter paper placed inside.
Place the Büchner funnel in the neck of a Büchner flask connected to a vacuum system.
Pour the reaction mixture into the funnel.
The liquid passes quickly into the flask leaving the dry crystals behind.
Your answer may also include: a fully labelled diagram showing a Büchner flask connected to a vacuum, a bung in the neck of the Büchner flask, a Büchner funnel inserted through the bung and filter paper inside the Büchner funnel.

Suitability of techniques

Refluxing allows the reaction mixture to be heated (to speed up the reaction) without losing any of the volatile organic reagents to evaporation before they get a chance to react.
Vacuum filtration is suitable because aspirin is insoluble in the cooled reaction mixture.
It quickly separates the aspirin crystals from the liquid.
It also dries the crystals.

b) i) E.g. The minimum amount of solvent is used so that the solution that forms is saturated, meaning the maximum possible amount of crystals will form on cooling. / The minimum amount of solvent is used to minimise the amount of impurities that dissolve in it *[1 mark]*.

ii) The solvent used must be one in which the aspirin is very soluble when it is hot but nearly insoluble when it is cold *[1 mark]*. If the aspirin is too soluble in the cold solvent, crystals will not form on cooling as most of the aspirin will stay in solution *[1 mark]*.

iii) The solvent must be ice-cold to prevent the crystals from dissolving again *[1 mark]*. The solvent removes any soluble impuritites from the crystals *[1 mark]*.

c) E.g. impure substances melt at temperatures below the data book value for the melting point. / Impure substances melt over a wider range of temperatures *[1 mark]*.

3 a) i) acyl chloride *[1 mark]*
hydroxyl/(secondary) alcohol *[1 mark]*

ii)

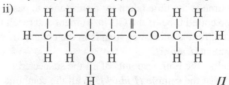

[1 mark]

b) i) Stage 1: electrophilic addition / hydrogenation *[1 mark]*
Stage 2: (free) radical substitution *[1 mark]*

ii) chloroethane *[1 mark]*

iii) Type of reaction: nucleophilic substitution *[1 mark]*.
Reagents and conditions: ethanolic ammonia *[1 mark]* and heat *[1 mark]*.
Name of primary amine: ethylamine *[1 mark]*.

iv) Ethene could be converted to chloroethane/compound **L** in one stage rather than two *[1 mark]* by reacting it with hydrogen chloride/HCl (at room temperature) *[1 mark]*.

Pages 130-131: Analysis — 1

1   B *[1 mark]*

B has 4 different carbon environments, so it will have 4 peaks in its ^{13}C NMR spectrum, whereas A has 7, C has 5, and D has 9.

2   C *[1 mark]*

Tollens' reagent only gives a positive result if an aldehyde is present, and the molecule shown does not contain any aldehyde groups. However it does contain a halogen atom, bromine, which reacts with the aqueous silver nitrate in ethanol, and a primary −OH group, which is oxidised by the acidified sodium dichromate. So tests using these reagents produce positive results.

3   B *[1 mark]*

The H signal is a quartet, as there are 3 H atoms attached to an adjacent carbon.

4 a)   glycine *[1 mark]*

The amino acid which is most strongly adsorbed to the solid coating will be carried the shortest distance up the plate by the solvent, and so will have the smallest R_f value.

b) i) R_f value $= \dfrac{\text{distance travelled by spot}}{\text{distance travelled by solvent}}$ *[1 mark]*

ii) R_f value $= \dfrac{0.9 \text{ cm}}{5.0 \text{ cm}} = \mathbf{0.18}$ *[1 mark]*

c) i)   E.g. there is a spot with the same R_f value in both samples. The R_f value for these spots is:

R_f value $= \dfrac{2.5 \text{ cm}}{5.0 \text{ cm}} = 0.50$

Tyrosine also has an R_f value of 0.50 when run in the same solvent, so the amino acid present in both samples is likely to be tyrosine.
[2 marks — 1 mark for correct R_f value, 1 mark for identification as tyrosine]

ii)   E.g. the scientist could run a TLC plate with samples of mixtures X and Y, alongside a sample of pure tyrosine *[1 mark]*. The pure tyrosine sample should be aligned with the two tyrosine spots from the mixtures *[1 mark]*. / The scientist could run a TLC plate with samples of mixtures X and Y using a different solvent *[1 mark]*. The R_f values of the two tyrosine spots from the mixtures should be the same as the R_f value for pure tyrosine in this new solvent *[1 mark]*.

Pages 132-134: Analysis — 2

1 a)   The relative amounts of each substance detected *[1 mark]*.

b) i)   Retention time is the time taken for a substance to pass through the coiled tube of the GC instrument and reach the detector / the time a substance spends in the column of the GC instrument *[1 mark]*.

ii)   50 °C is below the boiling points of all the suspected components of the sample *[1 mark]*, so all the components would remain condensed as liquids inside the GC instrument and not be able to pass through it *[1 mark]*.

iii)   the solvent *[1 mark]*

c) i)   Identity of impurity: phenol, as its retention time matches that of the impurity peak *[1 mark]*.
Source of impurity: the solution of hexan-1-ol used to make up the mixture, as there is less hexan-1-ol than expected for an equimolar mixture *[1 mark]*.

ii)   E.g. run the same chromatogram with some added phenol *[1 mark]*. The size of the impurity peak should increase *[1 mark]*.

iii)   Make standard solutions of phenol, using the same solvent as in the original chromatogram, above and below the expected concentration of the impurity *[1 mark]*. Inject each standard solution into the GC instrument under the same conditions as the original chromatogram and record the result *[1 mark]*. Calculate the area under the peak of each response for each phenol standard solution *[1 mark]*. Plot the area values on a graph of area against concentration and join the points to create an external calibration curve *[1 mark]*. Use the area of the impurity peak in the original chromatogram to read its concentration off the calibration curve *[1 mark]*.

2 a) i)   How to grade your answer:

Level 0:   There is no relevant information. *[No marks]*

Level 1:   The answer provides some analysis of the splitting patterns and/or chemical shifts, leading to an attempt to identify the ester. The answer has no clear structure. The information given is basic and lacking in detail. It may not all be relevant. *[1 to 2 marks]*

Level 2:   The answer provides analysis of both the splitting patterns and chemical shifts, leading to a correct identification of the ester, with some justification. The answer has some structure. Most of the information given is relevant and there is some detail involved. *[3 to 4 marks]*

Level 3:   The answer provides detailed analysis of both the splitting patterns and chemical shifts, leading to a correct and fully justified identification of the ester. The answer has a clear and logical structure. The information given is relevant and detailed. *[5 to 6 marks]*

Indicative scientific content may include:

Analysis of splitting

The spectrum has a triplet and a quartet, which must be caused by the CH_2CH_3 group of the ester.

The triplet is caused by the CH_3 of the CH_2CH_3 group, as there are two H atoms on the adjacent C atom.

The quartet is caused by the CH_2 of the CH_2CH_3 group, as there are three H atoms on the adjacent C atom.

The spectrum has a singlet, which must be caused by the CH_3 group in the ester that has no adjacent H atoms.

Analysis of chemical shifts

The triplet is at $\delta \approx 1.1$ ppm, so it must be caused by the H atoms in an RCH_3 group.

The singlet is at $\delta \approx 2.1$ ppm, so it must be caused by the H atoms in an $RC=OCH$ group.

The quartet is at $\delta \approx 4.1$ ppm, so it must be caused by the H atoms in an $RC=OOCH$ group.

Identification of ester

The spectrum is produced by ester A.

The singlet is caused by the H atoms of the $RC=OCH$ group, so the C of the ester group must be adjacent to only CH_3.

The quartet is caused by the H atoms of the $RC=OOCH$ group, so the O of the ester group must be adjacent to CH_2.

ii)

[1 mark]

b)

Peak number	δ / ppm	
	A	B
1	15	10
2	23	28
3	60	52
4	**160 - 220**	**160 - 220**

[1 mark for both chemical shifts in correct range]
Peak 4 is caused by a C atom in an $RC=O$ group in both ester A and ester **B** *[1 mark]*.

Pages 135-138: Analysis — 3

1 a) The broad peak at 3400 cm^{-1} suggests an –OH group is present *[1 mark]*. The peak at 1700 cm^{-1} suggests a C=O group is present *[1 mark]*.

b) i) Compound **C** does not contain an aldehyde functional group *[1 mark]*.

ii) Add 2,4-DNP to compound **C** and watch for the formation of a bright orange precipitate to confirm the presence of the C=O (ketone) *[1 mark]*. Add acidified dichromate to compound **C** and watch for colour change from orange to green to confirm the presence of an –OH group, provided **C** is a primary or secondary alcohol *[1 mark]*.

c) i) Divide by the A_r of each element:
C: $55 \div 12.0 = 4.583...$
H: $9 \div 1.0 = 9$
O: $36 \div 16.0 = 2.25$
Divide through by the smallest number:
C: $4.583... \div 2.25 = 2.037...$
H: $9 \div 2.25 = 4$
O: $2.25 \div 2.25 = 1$
Simplest whole-number ratio of C:H:O = 2:4:1
Empirical formula = **C_2H_4O**
[2 marks for correct answer, otherwise 1 mark for dividing by the A_r of each element]

ii) From the mass spectrum, the M_r of compound **C** is 88.
Mass of empirical formula
$$= (2 \times 12.0) + (4 \times 1.0) + 16.0 = 44$$
Number of empirical units in compound = $88 \div 44 = 2$
Molecular formula = $2 \times (C_2H_4O) = C_4H_8O_2$ *[1 mark]*

iii) $m/z = 29$: $CH_3CH_2^+$ / CHO^+ *[1 mark]*
$m/z = 31$: CH_2OH^+ *[1 mark]*
$m/z = 57$: $CH_3CH_2CO^+$ *[1 mark]*

It's also fine if you wrote the molecular formulae of the fragment ions (e.g. $C_2H_5^+$).

d)

[1 mark]
Name: 1-hydroxybutan-2-one *[1 mark]*

2 a) i)

[1 mark]
E.g. all 12 hydrogen atoms in TMS are in the same chemical environment *[1 mark]*, so TMS produces a single, intense peak (to the right of most other absorption peaks) *[1 mark]*.

ii) E.g. CCl_4/$CDCl_3$/C_6D_6 *[1 mark]*. Chosen solvent does not contain any ^1H atoms that would produce additional peaks *[1 mark]*.

b) How to grade your answer:
Level 0: There is no relevant information. *[No marks]*
Level 1: The answer provides some analysis of the carbon-13 and/or proton NMR spectrum, leading to an attempt to deduce the structure of the compound. The answer is not set out in a logical order. The information given is basic and lacking in detail. It may not all be relevant. *[1 to 2 marks]*
Level 2: The answer provides analysis of both the carbon-13 and proton NMR structure, leading to a mostly correct deduction of the structure of the compound. The answer is set out in a mostly logical order. Most of the information given is relevant and there is some detail involved. *[3 to 4 marks]*
Level 3: The answer provides detailed analysis of both the carbon-13 and proton NMR spectra, leading to a correct deduction of the structure of the compound. The answer is set out in a logical order. The information given is relevant and detailed. *[5 to 6 marks]*

Indicative scientific content may include:
Analysis of carbon-13 NMR spectrum
There are 3 peaks in the carbon-13 spectrum, indicating 3 carbon environments.
The peak at $\delta \approx 14$ ppm is caused by a C–C bond.
The peak at $\delta \approx 56$ ppm is caused by a C–O bond.
The peak at $\delta \approx 172$ ppm is caused by a C=O bond.
Analysis of proton NMR spectrum
There are 3 peaks in the proton spectrum, indicating 3 hydrogen environments.
The peak at $\delta \approx 1.3$ ppm is produced by the H atoms in an HC–R group.
It is a doublet, so there must be one hydrogen atom on the adjacent carbon atom.
The doublet has an integration ratio of 3, so there must be three H atoms in this environment.
The peak at $\delta \approx 2.8$ ppm is produced by the H atoms in an HCC=O group.
It is a quartet, so there must be three H atoms on the adjacent carbon atom. Therefore there is a CH_3 group in the structure. The quartet has an integration ratio of 1, so there must be one H atom in this environment.
The peak at $\delta \approx 11.7$ ppm is produced by H atoms in a C=OOH group.
It has an integration ratio of 2, so there must be 2 H atoms in this environment.
Deduction of structure
There are two H atoms in C=OOH groups, so there must be two C=OOH groups in the structure.
At least one C=OOH group must be part of an HCC=OOH group to give rise to the quartet in the proton NMR spectrum. So there is a central carbon with two C=OOH groups, a CH_3 group and and H atom bonded to it.
The structure is:

c) i) E.g.

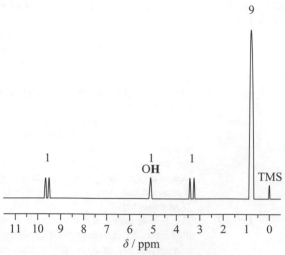

[5 marks — 1 mark for a signal in the range 0.5-1.9 ppm, 1 mark for a signal in the range 3-4.3 ppm, 1 mark for a signal in the range 9-10 ppm, 1 mark for showing the signals at 3-4.3 ppm and 9-10 ppm as doublets, 1 mark for correct relative peak areas]

ii) Add D_2O to the sample solution and run a further proton NMR spectrum *[1 mark]*. The OH signal disappears/ decreases as the deuterium, which does not produce an NMR signal, replaces the hydrogen in the OH group *[1 mark]*.

3 Compound **F** is a carbonyl compound which cannot be oxidised, which suggests that it is a ketone *[1 mark]*.
It has 3 peaks in its proton spectrum, indicating 3 different hydrogen environments *[1 mark]*.
The quartet is at $\delta = 2.4$ ppm, so must be caused by H atoms in an RC=OCH group, which are adjacent to 3 other H atoms *[1 mark]*.
The triplet is at $\delta = 1.1$ ppm, so it must be caused by the H atoms in an RCH_3 group, which are adjacent to 2 other H atoms *[1 mark]*.
The quartet and triplet together suggest a CH_2CH_3 group *[1 mark]*.
The singlet with $\delta = 0.9$ ppm must be caused by the H atoms in an RCH_3 group with no adjacent H atoms *[1 mark]*.
The relative area ratio of 2 : 3 : 9 suggests that the singlet represents three equivalent CH_3 groups (whilst the quartet and the triplet represent a CH_2 and a CH_3 respectively) *[1 mark]*.
Structure of compound **F**:

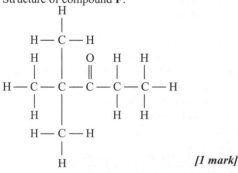

[1 mark]

Mixed Questions

Pages 139-141: Mixed Questions — 1

1 D *[1 mark]*
2 B *[1 mark]*
3 C *[1 mark]*
Hydrogen almost always has an oxidation number of −1 in metal hydrides.
4 C *[1 mark]*
When 2-bromopentan-3-ol is heated with aqueous sodium hydroxide, its bromine atom may be substituted for an —OH group, giving pentane-2,3-diol.
5 a) $Ca \rightarrow Ca^{2+} + 2e^-$ *[1 mark]*
  b) +1 *[1 mark]*
Oxygen has an oxidation number of −2, and the sum of the oxidation numbers in a molecule of water is zero. Therefore, each hydrogen atom must have an oxidation number of +1.
  c) If n is the number of moles of H_2 that occupy 100 cm³
   Then $n = (pV) \div (RT)$
   $= ((100 \times 10^3) \times (100 \times 10^{-6})) \div (8.314 \times 298)$
   $= 0.00403...$ mol
   The balanced equation for the reaction is:
   $Ca + 2H_2O \rightarrow Ca(OH)_2 + H_2$
   So 1 mole of H_2 is produced from 1 mole of Ca, meaning moles of Ca = 0.00403... mol
   Maximum mass of Ca = $0.00403... \times 40.1 = 0.1618...$ g
   $= 0.1618...$ g × 1000
   $= 161.85...$ mg = **162 mg (3 s.f.)**
   [5 marks for correct answer, otherwise 1 mark for correctly rearranging the ideal gas equation, 1 mark for correct number of moles of H_2, 1 mark for correctly balanced reaction equation, 1 mark for mass of Ca in grams.]
  d) E.g. some of the gas produced may have been lost from the conical flask before the gas syringe was attached. / The reaction was stopped before it could go to completion *[1 mark]*.
  e) Barium would produce the gas in the shortest amount of time *[1 mark]*. This is because the ionisation energy is lower/the outer electron is more easily lost from barium than strontium or calcium, so barium is more reactive. / This is because barium is below calcium and strontium in Group 2, and reactivity increases going down the group *[1 mark]*.
6 a) $1s^2\ 2s^2\ 2p^6\ 3s^2\ 3p^1$ *[1 mark]*
  b) Aluminium oxidation number: +3
   Chlorine oxidation number: −1
   [1 mark]
  c) Aluminium has a giant metallic lattice structure and chlorine is a simple covalent substance *[1 mark]*. In aluminium there are strong electrostatic attractions between the metal ions and the sea of positive electrons *[1 mark]*. In chlorine there are weak intermolecular forces between the molecules *[1 mark]*. Aluminium has a much higher melting point because the forces that need to be overcome in aluminium are much stronger than in chlorine, so more energy is required to break the forces in aluminium *[1 mark]*.
  d) Moles of Al = $(2.00 \times 1000) \div 27.0 = 74.074...$
   From the balanced equation, 2 moles of Al reacts to form 2 moles of $AlCl_3$. So 74.074... moles of Al will react to form 74.074... moles of $AlCl_3$.
   Theoretical yield = $74.074... \times 133.5 = 9888.8...$ g
   Percentage yield = $((7.14 \times 1000) \div 9888.8...) \times 100$
   $= 72.202...$
   $= $ **72.2 % (3 s.f.)**
   [3 marks for correct answer, otherwise 1 mark for moles of Al, 1 mark for theoretical yield.]
  e) $K_c = \dfrac{[Al_2Cl_6]}{[AlCl_3]^2}$ *[1 mark]*

f) i) 109.5° *[1 mark]*
 ii)

[2 marks — 1 mark for showing the correct structure, 1 mark for showing 3D bonds.]

You don't need to show the dative covalent bonds as arrows to get the marks here, but it's generally a good idea to do so.

Pages 142-145: Mixed Questions — 2

1 a) i) $CH_3CHC(CH_3)CH_2CH_3$ *[1 mark]*
 ii)

[1 mark]

Make sure you remember what you're looking for with different types of isomerism. In E/Z isomerism, it's the positions of the <u>highest priority</u> groups attached to each carbon atom of the double bond that are important. In this case that's $-CH_3$ on the left hand carbon and $-CH_2CH_3$ on the right hand carbon. They're on opposite sides of the double bond so this is the E isomer. In cis-trans isomerism, it's the positions of groups that are <u>the same</u> which matter — their priorities don't come into it. So this molecule is also a cis isomer, because both of its $-CH_3$ groups are on the same side.

b) i) How to grade your answer:
Level 0: There is no relevant information. *[No marks]*
Level 1: One stage is covered well OR two stages are covered but they are incomplete and not always accurate. The answer is not in a logical order. *[1 to 2 marks]*
Level 2: Two stages are covered well OR all 3 stages are covered but they are incomplete and not always accurate. The answer is mostly in a logical order. *[3 to 4 marks]*
Level 3: All 3 stages are covered and are complete and accurate. The answer is coherent and is in a logical order. *[5 to 6 marks]*

Indicative scientific content may include:
<u>Shapes and polarities</u>
Carbon dioxide contains 2 polar C=O bonds.
The molecule is symmetrical/linear, so the charges are evenly spread across the molecule.
This leads to the charges cancelling each other out so a molecule of carbon dioxide has no permanent dipole.
Water contains 2 polar O–H bonds.
The molecule is asymmetrical/bent, so the charges are unevenly spread across the molecule.
This leads to a permanent dipole.
<u>Intermolecular forces</u>
Carbon dioxide is non-polar, so the only intermolecular forces acting between molecules are induced dipole-dipole/London forces.
Water also has induced dipole-dipole/London forces acting between molecules.
There are also permanent dipole-dipole forces between water molecules.
These are weak electrostatic forces of attraction between the δ+ and δ– charges on neighbouring molecules.
Water can also undergo hydrogen bonding, as it contains two O–H bonds.
<u>Physical states</u>
The induced dipole-dipole/London forces between carbon dioxide molecules are very weak.
So, not a lot of energy is required to break them and at room temperature carbon dioxide is a gas.
Water molecules have stronger intermolecular forces than carbon dioxide molecules.
Permanent dipole-dipole forces and hydrogen bonds require a lot more energy to break than induced dipole-dipole/London forces.
So water is a liquid at room temperature.

ii) $C_6H_{12} + 9O_2 \rightarrow 6CO_2 + 6H_2O$ *[1 mark]*
iii) $\Delta_f H [C_6H_{12}] = \Sigma \Delta_c H$ reactants $- \Sigma \Delta_c H$ products
$= ((6 \times -393.5) + (6 \times -285.8)) - (-4003.4)$
$= -4075.8 + 4003.4 =$ **−72.4 kJ mol⁻¹**
[3 marks for correct answer, otherwise 1 mark for stating the formula and 1 mark for correctly substituting in the enthalpies of combustion.]

You'd get the mark if you drew a Hess's law diagram here, instead of stating the formula.

c) i)

[4 marks — 1 mark for arrow from C=C to $H^{\delta+}$, 1 mark for arrow from H–I bond to $I^{\delta-}$, 1 mark for arrow from I^- to C^+, 1 mark for correct structure of product.]

ii) phosphoric acid/H_3PO_4 *[1 mark]*
iii) Hexan-2-ol contains an –OH group, so can undergo hydrogen bonding *[1 mark]*. So, more energy is required to break the intermolecular forces in hexan-2-ol than in hex-1-ene and allow it to vaporise *[1 mark]*.

2 a) i) Shape: trigonal planar *[1 mark]*
Bond angle: 120° *[1 mark]*
 ii) One of the double-bond carbons has two identical groups attached to it *[1 mark]*.
b) Any one from: the double bond has a high electron density, making it likely to be attacked by electrophiles. / The π-bond has a (relatively) low bond enthalpy and so is easily broken *[1 mark]*.
c) i)

[1 mark]

ii) E.g. burning PVC produces toxic hydrogen chloride/HCl, which must be safely removed *[1 mark]*.
d) i) $Cl\cdot + C_2H_3Cl \rightarrow C_2H_3Cl_2\cdot$ *[1 mark]*
$C_2H_3Cl_2\cdot + C_2H_3Cl \rightarrow C_4H_6Cl_3\cdot$ *[1 mark]*
 ii) E.g. the more chlorine there is in the mixture, the shorter the polymer chains will be *[1 mark]*. This is because there will be more radicals in the mixture, so termination steps are more likely to occur *[1 mark]*.

3 a) 2,2-dimethylpropan-1-ol *[1 mark]*
b) There will be a small peak at m/z = 89/M+1 *[1 mark]*. / There will be small peaks with m/z values 1 higher than those expected for the various fragment ions *[1 mark]*.
c) i)

[1 mark]

ii) The greater the number of alkyl groups attached to the charged/central carbon in a carbocation, the more stable it is *[1 mark]*. The carbocation/fragment that is responsible for the peak at 57 m/z is a tertiary carbocation/has three alkyl groups attached, so will be relatively stable *[1 mark]*.

Pages 146-147: Mixed Questions — 3

1   B *[1 mark]*

2   D *[1 mark]*

3   C *[1 mark]*

Moles of H_3PO_4 = 1.2 × (30 ÷ 1000) = 0.036 moles
The balanced equation for the reaction is
$2H_3PO_4 + 3Ca(OH)_2 \rightarrow Ca_3(PO_4)_2 + 6H_2O$, so the number of moles of
$Ca(OH)_2$ required to neutralise 0.036 moles of H_3PO_4 is
3 × (0.036 ÷ 2) = 0.054 moles.
M_r of $Ca(OH)_2$ = 40.1 + (2 × (16.0 + 1.0)) = 74.1
Mass of $Ca(OH)_2$ = 74.1 × 0.054 = 4.0014 g = 4.0 g (2 s.f.)

4   B *[1 mark]*

5 a) i) An electrophile is an electron pair acceptor *[1 mark]*.

     ii) $CH_3CH_2Cl + AlCl_3 \rightarrow CH_3CH_2^+ + AlCl_4^-$ *[1 mark]*

     iii)

+ HCl + AlCl₃

[4 marks — 1 mark for curly arrow from benzene ring to C^+, 1 mark for correct intermediate shown, 1 mark for curly arrow from C–H bond to benzene ring, 1 mark for correct products shown]

  b) The reaction is endothermic/has a positive $\Delta_r H$, and so at a high temperature/600 °C equilibrium will shift towards the products to oppose the change, increasing the yield of styrene *[1 mark]*. There are more moles of gas on the product side of the equation than on the reactant side, and so at a low pressure equilibrium will shift towards the products to oppose the change, increasing the yield of styrene *[1 mark]*.

Pages 148-150: Mixed Questions — 4

1 a) $2MnO_4^- + 16H^+ + 10Cl^- \rightarrow 2Mn^{2+} + 8H_2O + 5Cl_2$ *[1 mark]*

  b) $E^{\ominus} = E^{\ominus}_{reduced} - E^{\ominus}_{oxidised}$
       = +1.51 − (+1.36)
       = **+0.15 V** *[1 mark]*

  c) Moles of MnO_4^- = 0.230 × (18.7 ÷ 1000)
                  = 4.301 × 10⁻³ moles
From the balanced equation, 2 moles of MnO_4^- react with 10 moles of Cl^-, therefore 4.301 × 10⁻³ moles of MnO_4^- will react with 4.301 × 10⁻³ × (10 ÷ 2) = 0.021505 moles of Cl^-.
Number of Cl^- ions in 35 cm³ = 0.021505 × 6.02 × 10²³
                           = 1.294601 × 10²²
Number of Cl^- ions in 150 cm³ = 1.294601 × 10²² × (150 ÷ 35)
                           = 5.54829 × 10²²
                          = **5.55 × 10²² ions (3 s.f.)**

[4 marks for correct answer, otherwise 1 mark for moles of MnO_4^-, 1 mark for moles of Cl^- in 35 cm³, 1 mark for number of ions of Cl^- in 35 cm³ or moles of Cl^- in 150 cm³]

  d) i) Two burette readings must have been used to determine the total volume added, and so the total uncertainty is 0.05 + 0.05 = 0.10 cm³
percentage uncertainty = $\dfrac{\text{uncertainty}}{\text{measurement}} \times 100$
                        = (0.10 ÷ 18.7) × 100
                        = 0.5347...
                        = **0.53% (2 s.f.)**

[2 marks for correct answer, otherwise 1 mark for using correct equation for percentage uncertainty]

     ii) The uncertainty of the equipment has stayed the same, but the magnitude of the reading has increased *[1 mark]*. This will cause the ratio of the uncertainty to the reading to decrease, reducing the percentage error *[1 mark]*.

2 a) i) E.g. one of the products of the breakdown of urea catalysed by urease is ammonia *[1 mark]*, which is basic *[1 mark]*.

     ii) $k = Ae^{\frac{-E_a}{RT}}$
         $\ln k = \ln A - \dfrac{E_a}{RT}$
         $\dfrac{E_a}{RT} = \ln A - \ln k$
         $E_a = RT \times (\ln A - \ln k)$
         E_a = 8.314 × 298 × ($\ln(7.089 \times 10^3) - \ln(1.46 \times 10^{-7})$)
           = 60963.03... J mol⁻¹
           = 60.96303... kJ mol⁻¹
           = **61.0 kJ mol⁻¹ (3 s.f.)**

[2 marks for correct answer, otherwise 1 mark for rearranging equation to find E_a]

  b) i) 4 *[1 mark]*

The aromatic ring contains 3 different proton environments, and the protons in the –NH_2 groups are all equivalent. So there are 4 proton environments in the molecule (and 4 signals would appear in the NMR spectrum).

     ii) 8 *[1 mark]*

Each of the oxygen and nitrogen atoms can form hydrogen bonds, as well as the four hydrogen atoms in the two amine groups.

     iii) O–P bond *[1 mark]*

The products of the reaction are an alcohol (phenol) and an acid (diamidophosphoric acid).

  c) i)

[1 mark]

     ii)

[1 mark]

d) i) E.g. lysine would be more soluble, as it has an amine group attached to its side-chain *[1 mark]* which can form hydrogen bonds with water/which makes the side-chain polar *[1 mark]*.

ii) Any two from: e.g. the students could have used different solvents. / They could have used TLC plates with different compositions. / They could have carried out their experiments at different temperatures. *[2 marks — 1 mark for each correct reason.]*

Pages 151-153: Mixed Questions — 5

1 a) i)

[1 mark]

ii) +3 *[1 mark]*
Each ethane-1,2-diamine ligand is neutral. As the complex has a 3+ charge, the oxidation number of cobalt must therefore be +3.

iii) 6 *[1 mark]*

iv) E.g. the entropy would decrease, as three en/ethane-1,2-diamine ligands would be substituted for six H_2O/water ligands *[1 mark]*. A decrease in entropy would cause the free energy to increase *[1 mark]*.

b) i) $C_{10}H_{16}N_2O_8$ *[1 mark]*
It's fine if you put the elements in a different order here, e.g. $C_{10}O_8H_{16}N_2$.

ii) e.g. chloroethanoic acid/bromoethanoic acid *[1 mark]*
The lone pair on a nitrogen atom in ethane-1,2-diamine would attack the carbon in the carbon-halogen bond present in the reagant. This would keep occurring, until all the H−N bonds in ethane-1,2-diamine had been replaced with C−N bonds.

iii) E.g. NaOH *[1 mark]*. This would react with the carboxylic acid groups in EDTA, so they would become deprotonated, and therefore charged *[1 mark]*. This would lead to stronger forces of attraction between the EDTA ions and the water molecules and the solubility of EDTA would increase *[1 mark]*.
You didn't have to write NaOH here. You get the mark for any base.

2 a) i) $K_a = \dfrac{[H^+][C_6H_5COO^-]}{[C_6H_5COOH]}$
As benzoic acid is a weak acid, it can be assumed that $[H^+] = [C_6H_5COO^-]$.
Therefore it is possible to use the expression:
$K_a = \dfrac{[H^+]^2}{[C_6H_5COOH]}$
$[H^+]^2 = K_a \times [C_6H_5COOH]$
$[H^+] = \sqrt{K_a \times [C_6H_5COOH]}$
$\quad = \sqrt{6.3 \times 10^{-5} \text{ mol dm}^{-3} \times 0.025 \text{ mol dm}^{-3}}$
$\quad = 1.254... \times 10^{-3} \text{ mol dm}^{-3}$
$pH = -\log_{10}[H^+]$
$\quad = -\log_{10}(1.254... \times 10^{-3})$
$\quad = 2.901...$
$\quad = \mathbf{2.9 \ (2 \ s.f.)}$
[3 marks for correct answer, otherwise 1 mark for a correct expression for K_a, 1 mark for calculating $[H^+]$]

ii) $C_6H_5COOH + OH^- \rightarrow C_6H_5COO^- + H_2O$ /
$H^+ + OH^- \rightarrow H_2O$ *[1 mark]*

iii) $[H^+]$ at end of reaction $= 10^{-12.2} = 6.309... \times 10^{-13} \text{ mol dm}^{-3}$
$K_w = [H^+][OH^-] = 1.00 \times 10^{-14} \text{ mol dm}^{-3}$
$[OH^-] = K_w \div [H^+] = 1.00 \times 10^{-14} \div 6.309... \times 10^{-13}$
$\quad\quad\quad\quad = 0.0158... \text{ mol dm}^{-3}$
Number of excess moles of NaOH added
= concentration × volume
= 0.0158... × (750 ÷ 1000)
= 0.0118... moles
Moles of benzoic acid present in original solution
= concentration × volume
= 0.025 × (750 ÷ 1000)
= 0.01875 moles
Moles of benzoic acid
= moles of NaOH present before excess was added
Therefore the total number of moles of NaOH added to the solution = 0.0118... + 0.01875
$\quad\quad\quad\quad = 0.0306...$ moles
Mass of NaOH = moles × M_r
$\quad\quad\quad\quad = 0.0306... \times (23.0 + 16.0 + 1.0)$
$\quad\quad\quad\quad = 1.225...$ g
$\quad\quad\quad\quad = \mathbf{1.2 \ g \ (2 \ s.f.)}$
[7 marks for correct answer given to 2 s.f. or 6 marks for correct answer not given to 2 s.f., otherwise 1 mark for calculating $[H^+]$, 1 mark for calculating $[OH^-]$, 1 mark for calculating the number of excess moles of NaOH, 1 mark for calculating the number of moles of benzoic acid, 1 mark for finding the total number of moles of NaOH added to the solution.]

b) i) Step 1: warm (below 55 °C) *[1 mark]* with concentrated nitric and sulfuric acids *[1 mark]*.
Step 2: reflux *[1 mark]* with tin metal and hydrochloric acid *[1 mark]*, followed by the addition of e.g. NaOH *[1 mark]*.
You didn't have to write NaOH here. You get the mark for any alkali.

ii) Number of peaks in proton spectrum: 4 *[1 mark]*
Number of peaks in carbon-13 spectrum: 5 *[1 mark]*

iii)

[1 mark]

Data Sheet

Constants, Equations and Conversions

Molar gas volume = 24.0 $dm^3\,mol^{-1}$ at RTP (room temperature and pressure)

Avogadro constant, N_A = $6.02 \times 10^{23}\,mol^{-1}$

Specific heat capacity of water, c = 4.18 $J\,g^{-1}\,K^{-1}$

Ionic product of water, K_w = $1.00 \times 10^{-14}\,mol^2\,dm^{-6}$ (at 298 K)

1 tonne = 10^6 g

Gas constant, R = 8.314 $J\,mol^{-1}\,K^{-1}$

Arrhenius equation: $k = Ae^{-E_a/RT}$ or $\ln k = -E_a/RT + \ln A$

Infrared Absorptions in Organic Molecules

Bond	Location	Wavenumber / cm^{-1}
C–C	alkanes alkyl chains	750 - 1100
C–X	haloalkanes (X = Cl, Br or I)	500 - 800
C–F	fluoroalkanes	1000 - 1350
C–O	alcohols esters carboxylic acids	1000 - 1300
C=C	alkenes	1620 - 1680
C=O	aldehydes ketones carboxylic acids esters amides acyl chlorides acid anhydrides	1630 - 1820
aromatic C=C	arenes	several peaks in range 1450 - 1650
C≡N	nitriles	2220 - 2260
C–H	alkyl groups alkenes arenes	2850 - 3100
O–H	carboxylic acids	2500 - 3300 (broad)
N–H	amines amides	3300 - 3500
O–H	alcohols phenols	3200 - 3600

¹³C and ¹H NMR Chemical Shifts

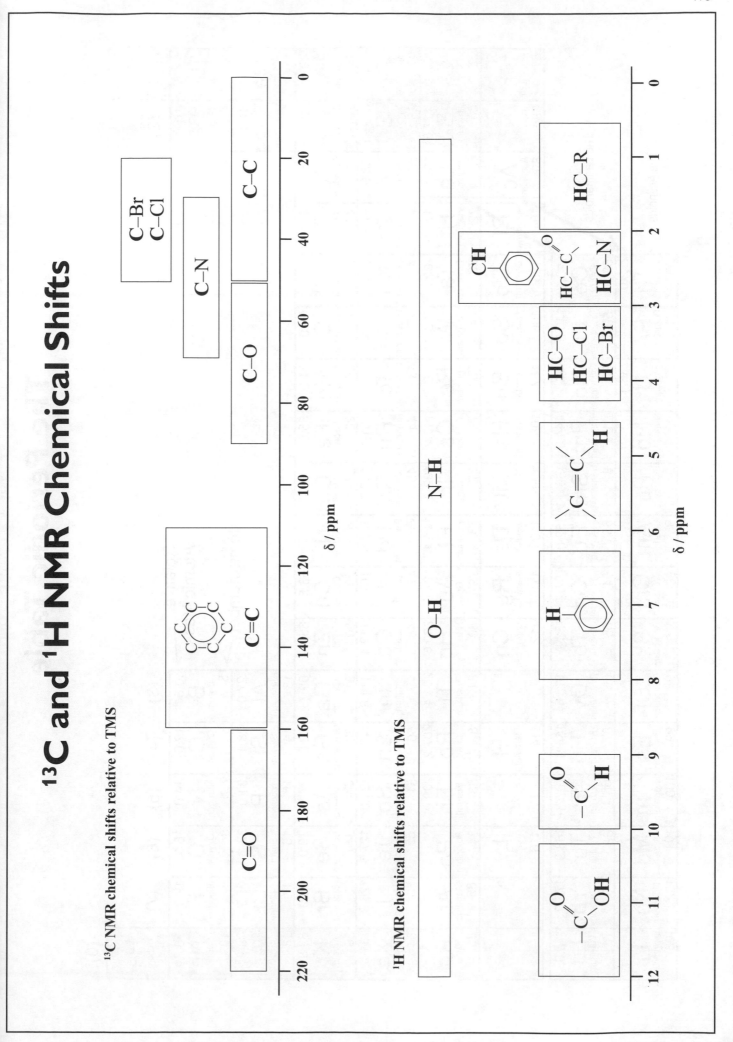

¹³C NMR chemical shifts relative to TMS

¹H NMR chemical shifts relative to TMS

The Periodic Table

Relative Atomic Mass
Atomic number

(1)	(2)												(3)	(4)	(5)	(6)	(7)	(0)
1.0 **H** Hydrogen 1																		4.0 **He** Helium 2
6.9 **Li** Lithium 3	9.0 **Be** Beryllium 4												10.8 **B** Boron 5	12.0 **C** Carbon 6	14.0 **N** Nitrogen 7	16.0 **O** Oxygen 8	19.0 **F** Fluorine 9	20.2 **Ne** Neon 10
23.0 **Na** Sodium 11	24.3 **Mg** Magnesium 12												27.0 **Al** Aluminium 13	28.1 **Si** Silicon 14	31.0 **P** Phosphorus 15	32.1 **S** Sulfur 16	35.5 **Cl** Chlorine 17	39.9 **Ar** Argon 18
39.1 **K** Potassium 19	40.1 **Ca** Calcium 20	45.0 **Sc** Scandium 21	47.9 **Ti** Titanium 22	50.9 **V** Vanadium 23	52.0 **Cr** Chromium 24	54.9 **Mn** Manganese 25	55.8 **Fe** Iron 26	58.9 **Co** Cobalt 27	58.7 **Ni** Nickel 28	63.5 **Cu** Copper 29	65.4 **Zn** Zinc 30		69.7 **Ga** Gallium 31	72.6 **Ge** Germanium 32	74.9 **As** Arsenic 33	79.0 **Se** Selenium 34	79.9 **Br** Bromine 35	83.8 **Kr** Krypton 36
85.5 **Rb** Rubidium 37	87.6 **Sr** Strontium 38	88.9 **Y** Yttrium 39	91.2 **Zr** Zirconium 40	92.9 **Nb** Niobium 41	95.9 **Mo** Molybdenum 42	**Tc** Technetium 43	101.1 **Ru** Ruthenium 44	102.9 **Rh** Rhodium 45	106.4 **Pd** Palladium 46	107.9 **Ag** Silver 47	112.4 **Cd** Cadmium 48		114.8 **In** Indium 49	118.7 **Sn** Tin 50	121.8 **Sb** Antimony 51	127.6 **Te** Tellurium 52	126.9 **I** Iodine 53	131.3 **Xe** Xenon 54
132.9 **Cs** Caesium 55	137.3 **Ba** Barium 56	138.9 **La** Lanthanum 57	178.5 **Hf** Hafnium 72	180.9 **Ta** Tantalum 73	183.8 **W** Tungsten 74	186.2 **Re** Rhenium 75	190.2 **Os** Osmium 76	192.2 **Ir** Iridium 77	195.1 **Pt** Platinum 78	197.0 **Au** Gold 79	200.6 **Hg** Mercury 80		204.4 **Tl** Thallium 81	207.2 **Pb** Lead 82	209.0 **Bi** Bismuth 83	**Po** Polonium 84	**At** Astatine 85	**Rn** Radon 86
Fr Francium 87	**Ra** Radium 88	**Ac** Actinium 89	**Rf** Rutherfordium 104	**Db** Dubnium 105	**Sg** Seaborgium 106	**Bh** Bohrium 107	**Hs** Hassium 108	**Mt** Meitnerium 109	**Ds** Darmstadtium 110	**Rg** Roentgenium 111	**Cn** Copernicium 112		**Fl** Flerovium 114		**Lv** Livermorium 116			

The Lanthanoids

140.1 **Ce** Cerium 58	140.9 **Pr** Praseodymium 59	144.2 **Nd** Neodymium 60	**Pm** Promethium 61	150.4 **Sm** Samarium 62	152.0 **Eu** Europium 63	157.2 **Gd** Gadolinium 64	158.9 **Tb** Terbium 65	162.5 **Dy** Dysprosium 66	164.9 **Ho** Holmium 67	167.3 **Er** Erbium 68	168.9 **Tm** Thulium 69	173.0 **Yb** Ytterbium 70	175.0 **Lu** Lutetium 71

The Actinoids

232.0 **Th** Thorium 90	**Pa** Protactinium 91	238.1 **U** Uranium 92	**Np** Neptunium 93	**Pu** Plutonium 94	**Am** Americium 95	**Cm** Curium 96	**Bk** Berkelium 97	**Cf** Californium 98	**Es** Einsteinium 99	**Fm** Fermium 100	**Md** Mendelevium 101	**No** Nobelium 102	**Lr** Lawrencium 103